KS3 Maths Progress

Confidence • Fluency • Problem-solving • Progression

THREE

Series editors:

Dr Naomi Norman • Katherine Pate

ALWAYS LEARNING

PEARSON

Published by Pearson Education Limited, Edinburgh Gate, Harlow, Essex, CM20 2JE.

www.pearsonschoolsandfecolleges.co.uk

Text © Pearson Education Limited 2014
Typeset by Tech-Set Ltd, Gateshead
Original illustrations © Pearson Education Limited 2014
Cover illustration by Robert Samuel Hanson
Index by Wendy Simpson

The rights of Nick Asker, Jack Barraclough, Sharon Bolger, Lynn Byrd, Andrew Edmondson, Catherine Murphy, Mary Pardoe, Harry Smith and Angela Wheeler to be identified as authors of this work have been asserted by them in accordance with the Copyright, Designs and Patents Act 1988.

First published 2014

17 16 15 14
10 9 8 7 6 5 4 3 2 1

British Library Cataloguing in Publication Data
A catalogue record for this book is available from the British Library
ISBN 978 1 447 96238 0

Printed in Italy by Lego S.p.A

Acknowledgements
The publisher would like to thank the following for their kind permission to reproduce their photographs:

123RF.com: Boris Rabtsevich 175, kavram 147, Rainer Plendl 48, Somsak Sudthangtum 76; **Fotolia.com:** Brian Jackson 105, Christian Müller 53, Christian Schwier 51, Marek 81, ollirg 79, Željko Radojko 56; **Getty Images:** Bentley Archive / Popperfoto 225, picturegarden 34; **Imagemore Co., Ltd:** 59; **Pearson Education Ltd:** Martin Sookias 145; **Photolibrary.com:** 124; **Press Association Images:** Chris Ison / EMPICS Sport 32; **Science Photo Library Ltd:** David Nunuk 1, James King-Holmes 3; **Shutterstock.com:** Creativa 155, EML 211, FERNANDO BLANCO CALZADA 12, Franz Pfluegl 30, Galyna Andrushko 209, haveseen 199, imredesiuk 7, Joakim Lloyd Raboff 206, konstantinks 197, l i g h t p o e t 229, luiggi33 85, Marcio Jose Bastos Silva 168, mikeledray 100, Nataliavand 27, Noel Powell 203, ramcreations 227, RyFlip 73, Sebastian Kaulitzki 181, Tyler Olson 83; **Veer / Corbis:** Alliance 172, Andrey Armyagov 129, Avraham Kushnirov 107, herreid 121, iofoto 5, Lisafx 150, michaeljung 169, Mikhail Dudarev 152, Monkey Business Images 102, Nadezhda Bolotina 10, Philip Lange 126

All other images © Pearson Education

We are grateful to the following for permission to reproduce copyright material:
Age of British adults and internet use (p78) from 'Internet Access - Households and Individuals', Office for National Statistics licensed under the Open Government license v.2.0; Meteor impact craters (p87), Earth Impact Database, Planetary and Space Science Centre, University of New Brunswick, Canada; UK house prices (p89), Land Registry (Crown Copyright), licensed under the Open Government license v.2.0; One-way Channel swim times (p93), Channel Swimming Association Ltd; Distance travelled by human-powered flying machines (p94), International Bognor Birdman – The First Birdman in the World; UK General Election voters (p96), House of Commons Research Papers 01/37, 01/54, 05/33 & 10/36, licensed under the Open Parliament license.

Every effort has been made to contact copyright holders of material reproduced in this book. Any omissions will be rectified in subsequent printings if notice is given to the publishers.

CONTENTS

Unit 4 Collecting and analysing data

Unit 5 Multiplicative reasoning

Unit 6 Non-linear graphs

Unit 7 Accuracy and measures

Unit 8 Graphical solutions

Unit 9 Trigonometry

Unit 10 Mathematical reasoning

KS3 Maths Progress

Confidence • Fluency • Problem-solving • Progression

Pedagogy at the heart – This new course is built around a unique pedagogy that's been created by leading mathematics educational researchers and Key Stage 3 teachers. The result is an innovative learning structure based around 10 key principles designed to nurture confidence and raise achievement.

Pedagogy – our 10 key principles

- Fluency
- Mathematical Reasoning
- Multiplicative Reasoning
- Problem Solving
- Progression
- Concrete-Pictorial - Abstract (CPA)
- Relevance
- Modelling
- Reflection (metacognition)
- Linking

Progression to Key Stage 4 – In line with the 2014 National Curriculum, there is a strong focus on fluency, problem-solving and progression to help prepare your students' progress through their studies.

Stretch, challenge and support – Catering for students of all abilities, these Student Books are structured to deliver engaging and accessible content across three differentiated tiers, each offering a wealth of worked examples and questions, supported by key points, literacy and strategy hints, and clearly defined objectives.

Within each unit:

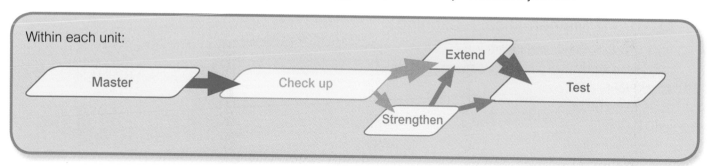

Differentiated for students of all abilities:

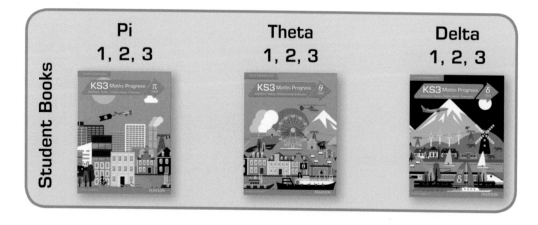

Progress with confidence!

This innovative Key Stage 3 Maths course embeds a modern pedagogical approach around our trusted suite of digital and print resources, to create confident and numerate students ready to progress further.

Help at the front-of-class – **ActiveTeach Presentation** is our tried and tested service that makes all of the Student Books available for display on a whiteboard. The books are supplemented with a range of videos and animations that present mathematical concepts along a concrete - pictorial - abstract pathway, allowing your class to progress their conceptual understanding at the right speed.

Learning beyond the classroom – Focussing on online homework, **ActiveCourse** offers students unprecedented extra practice (with automarking) and a chance to reflect on their learning with the confidence-checker. Powerful reporting tools can be used to track student progression and confidence levels.

Easy to plan, teach and assess – Downloadable **Teacher Guides** provide assistance with planning through the Schemes of Work. Lesson plans link both front-of-class **ActiveTeach Presentation** and **ActiveCourse** and provide help with reporting, functionality and progression. Both **Teacher Guides** and **ActiveTeach Presentation** contain the **answers** to the Student Book exercises.

Teacher Guides include **Class Progression Charts** and **Student Progression Charts** to support formative and summative assessment through the course.

Practice to progress – KS3 Maths Progress has an extensive range of practice across a range of topics and abilities. From the **Student Books** to write-in **Progression Workbooks** through to **ActiveCourse**, there is plenty of practice available in a variety of formats whether for in the classroom or for learning at home independently.

> **For more information, visit**
> **www.pearsonschools.co.uk/ks3mathsprogress**

Welcome to KS3 Maths Progress student books!

Confidence • Fluency • Problem-solving • Progression

Starting a new course is exciting! We believe you will have fun with maths, at the same time nurturing your confidence and raising your achievement.

Here's how:

At the end of the *Master* lessons, take a *Check up* test to help you decide to *Strengthen*, or *Extend* your learning. You may be able to mark this test yourself.

Choose only the topics in *Strengthen* that you need a bit more practice with. You'll find more hints here to lead you through specific questions. Then move on to *Extend*.

Extend helps you to apply the maths you know to some different situations. *Strengthen* and *Extend* both include *Enrichment* or *Investigations*.

When you have finished the whole unit, a *Unit test* helps you see how much progress you are making.

Clear *Objectives,* showing what you will cover in each lesson, are followed by a *Confidence* panel to boost your understanding and engage your interest.

Have a look at *Why Learn This?* This shows you how maths is useful in everyday life.

Improve your *Fluency* – practise answering questions using maths you already know.

The first questions are *Warm up*. Here you can show what you already know about this topic or related ones…

…before moving on to further questions, with *Worked examples* and *Hints* for help when you need it.

Your teacher has access to Answers in either ActiveTeach Presentation or the Teacher Guides.

Topic links show you how the maths in a lesson is connected to other mathematical topics. Use the *Subject links* to find out where you might use the maths you have learned here in your other lessons, such as science, geography and computing .

Explore a real-life problem by discussing and having a go. By the end of the lesson you'll have gained the skills you need to start finding a solution to the question using maths.

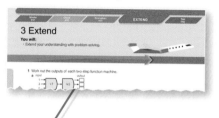

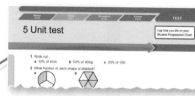

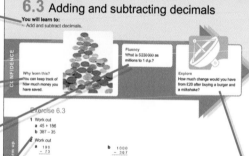

STEM and Finance lessons

Context lessons expand on *Real, STEM* and *Finance* maths. Finance questions are related to money. STEM stands for Science, Technology, Engineering and Maths. You can find out how charities use maths in their fundraising, how engineers monitor water flow in rivers, and why diamonds sparkle (among other things!)

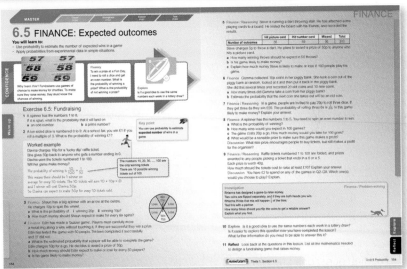

Some questions are tagged as *Finance* or *STEM*. These questions show how the real world relies on maths. Follow these up with whole lessons that focus on how maths is used in the fields of finance, science and technology.

As well as hints that help you with specific questions, you'll find *Literacy hints* (to explain some unfamiliar terms) and *Strategy hints* (to help with working out).

You can improve your ability to use maths in everyday situations by tackling *Modelling, Reasoning, Problem-solving* and *Real* questions. *Discussions* prompt you to explain your reasoning or explore new ideas with a partner.

At the end of each lesson, you get a chance to *Reflect* on how confident you feel about the topic.

Your teacher may give you a Student Progression Chart to help you see your progression through the units.

Further support

You can easily access extra resources that tie in to each lesson – look for the ActiveLearn icon on the lesson pages for ActiveCourse online homework links. These are clearly mapped to lessons and provide fun, interactive exercises linked to helpful worked examples and videos.

The Progression Workbooks, full of extra practice for key questions will help you reinforce your learning and track your own progress.

Enjoy!

1 Powers and roots

MASTER

Check
P15

Strengthen
P17

Extend
P21

Test
P25

1.1 Reciprocals

You will learn to:
- Find the reciprocal of a number
- Work with reciprocals.

CONFIDENCE

Why learn this?
Builders of telescopes use reciprocals to work out the shapes of lenses they need.

Fluency
- How many eighths are in 1 whole?
- Which is larger, $\frac{1}{9}$ or $\frac{1}{10}$?
- What do you multiply $\frac{1}{3}$ by to get 1 whole?

Explore
Will a sequence of reciprocals ever have a 0 term?

Exercise 1.1

Warm up

1 Which of these calculations has the biggest answer?

A $4 \times \frac{1}{3}$

B $5 \times \frac{1}{5}$

C $5 \times \frac{5}{16}$

D $8 \times \frac{1}{9}$

2 Work out

a $\frac{2}{5} \times \frac{2}{3}$

b $\frac{5}{7} \times \frac{1}{6}$

c $\frac{11}{16} \times \frac{9}{11}$

d $\frac{9}{20} \times \frac{5}{18}$

3 Write down the **reciprocal** of

a $\frac{2}{3}$

b 4

c $\frac{1}{7}$

d 8

e 11

4 Write down the reciprocal of

a $1\frac{1}{2}$

b $2\frac{2}{3}$

c $5\frac{1}{5}$

d $3\frac{11}{13}$

5 Use the reciprocal to work out

a $9 \div \frac{1}{3}$

b $6 \div \frac{2}{3}$

c $\frac{1}{5} \div \frac{2}{3}$

d $8 \div 1\frac{3}{5}$

e $7 \div 2\frac{2}{7}$

f $25 \div \frac{10}{11}$

> **Key point**
>
> The **reciprocal** of a fraction is the 'upside down' or inverse of that fraction.
> The reciprocal of $\frac{2}{5} = \frac{1}{\frac{2}{5}} = \frac{1 \times 5}{\frac{2}{5} \times 5} = \frac{5}{2}$

> **Q3b hint**
>
> $4 = \frac{4}{1}$

> **Q4 Strategy hint**
>
> Write mixed numbers as improper fractions first.

> **Q5 hint**
>
> To divide by a fraction, multiply by the reciprocal.

Topic links: Calculating with fractions

Subject links: Science (Q7)

Investigation

1 Work out

    a $\frac{2}{3} \times \frac{3}{2}$ **b** $\frac{3}{4} \times \frac{4}{3}$ **c** $\frac{1}{3} \times 3$ **d** $\frac{2}{9} \times \frac{9}{2}$

2 Copy and complete.

$$\frac{a}{b} \times \square = 1$$

    Discussion Is your statement from part **2** correct for $\frac{4}{5} \times 1\frac{1}{4} = 1$?

    The $\boxed{\frac{1}{x}}$ or $\boxed{x^{-1}}$ button on your calculator works out the reciprocal of a number.

3 **a** Use this button to find the reciprocal of 8.

    b Use the button again to find the reciprocal of your answer to part **a**.

4 Repeat part **3** for different numbers.
    What do you notice?

5 Copy and complete.
    If a number is greater than 1, its reciprocal is … than 1.
    If a number is less than 1, its reciprocal is … than 1.
    The reciprocal of 1 is …

6 Copy and complete.

    a $\frac{1}{7} \times \square = 1$

    b $\frac{5}{4} \times \square = 1$

    c $3\frac{1}{2} \times \square = 1$

    d $\frac{5}{7} \times \square = 1$

    e A number multiplied by its … always equals …

7 STEM In this electrical circuit, the resistors
A and B are connected in parallel.
The combined resistance is R where

$$\frac{1}{R} = \frac{1}{A} + \frac{1}{B}$$

Work out the combined resistance when

    a $A = 2$ ohms and $B = 4$ ohms

    b $A = 5$ ohms and $B = 3$ ohms

    c $A = \frac{2}{5}$ ohms and $B = \frac{2}{7}$ ohms

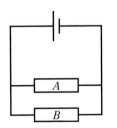

> **Q7 Literacy hint**
> Resistance is measured in ohms (Ω).

Discussion What is the combined resistance when A and B are
the same?

8 Explore Will a sequence of reciprocals ever have a 0 term?
Choose some sensible numbers to help you explore this situation.
Then use what you've learned in this lesson to help you answer
the question.

9 Reflect The reciprocal of a fraction is sometimes called the
'multiplicative inverse'.
What does 'multiplicative' mean?
What does 'inverse' mean?
Use what you have learned in this lesson to explain why the reciprocal
of a fraction is its multiplicative inverse.

> **Strategy hint**
> Use examples to help your
> explanation.

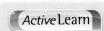

1.2 Indices

You will learn to:
- Use negative indices
- Work out powers of fractions.

Why learn this?
Carbon dating uses negative indices to describe the decay of carbon-14.

Fluency
- Work out $3^3 - 4^2$
- Which is larger: $\frac{1}{2} \times \frac{1}{2}$ or $\frac{1}{3} \times \frac{1}{3}$?
- Work out -15×-3

Explore
Does raising a number to a power always make the number bigger?

Exercise 1.2

1 Write as a single power.

a $3^4 \times 3^5$ b $7^9 \div 7^5$

c $4^{13} \div 4^{10}$ d $(2^4)^3$

e $(11^7)^3$ f $(5^5)^5$

g 8×2^6 h $3^5 \times 81$

i $5^{10} \div 125$

> **Q1 hint**
>
> To multiply powers, add the indices.
> To divide powers, subtract the indices.
> To work out the power of a power, multiply the indices.

Investigation

Reasoning

1 Copy and complete the sequence of powers. Write your numbers as integers or fractions of 10.

2 Repeat part **1** for powers of 2.

3 Copy and complete.

a $10^{-2} = \dfrac{1}{10^{\square}}$ b $2^{-3} = \dfrac{1}{2^{\square}}$

c $2^{-5} = \dfrac{1}{2^{\square}}$ d The reciprocal of 10^4 is $\square$

4 Copy and complete the rules.

$2^{-n} = \dfrac{1}{2^{\square}}$

$10^{-n} = \dfrac{1}{10^{\square}}$

5 Write down the value of 5^{-2} as a decimal. Check your answer with a calculator.

Discussion What is the value of any number raised to the power 0?

$10^5 = 100\,000$
$10^4 = 10\,000$ $\div 10$ $\div 10$
$10^3 =$
$10^2 =$
$10^1 =$
$10^0 =$
$10^{-1} =$
$10^{-2} =$
$10^{-3} =$
$10^{-4} =$
$10^{-5} =$

---

2 Copy and complete.

a $3^{-2} = \square$ b $\dfrac{1}{3} = 3^{\square}$

c $6^{\square} = \dfrac{1}{36}$ d $\square^{-2} = \dfrac{1}{169}$

e $4^{-3} = \square$ f $\dfrac{1}{81} = 3^{\square} = 9^{\square}$

g $\dfrac{1}{64} = 8^{\square} = 4^{\square} = 2^{\square}$ h $5^{-1} = \square$

> **Key point**
>
> A number raised to a negative power is the same as the reciprocal of that number to the power.

Topic links: Calculations with fractions, Laws of indices

3 Write each calculation as a single power.

  a $10^5 \times 10^{-2}$ **b** $4^3 \times 4^{-1}$

  c $11^{-2} \times 11^{-5}$ **d** $7^2 \div 7^{-5}$

  e $6^{-2} \div 6^4$ **f** $8^{-7} \div 8^{-3}$

  g $(9^{-2})^5$ **h** $(12^{-4})^{-2}$

Q3 hint

The laws of indices still apply with negative numbers.

4 Write each calculation as

  i a single power

  ii an integer or a fraction.

  a $3^2 \times 3^{-1} \times 3^{-4}$ **b** $4^2 \times 4^{-1} \div 4^{-2}$

  c $5^{-3} \div 5 \div 5^{-2}$ **d** $\dfrac{2^{-3} \times 2^{-5}}{2^{-4}}$

5 Write each calculation as a fraction.

  a $\dfrac{1}{3} \times \dfrac{1}{3}$ **b** $\left(\dfrac{3}{4}\right)^2$

  c $\left(\dfrac{3}{5}\right)^3$ **d** $\left(\dfrac{2}{3}\right)^4$

Q5 hint

The brackets show that the whole fraction (the numerator and denominator) is squared.

6 Write each number as a fraction raised to a power.

  a $\dfrac{16}{100}$ **b** $\dfrac{9}{49}$

  c $\dfrac{25}{64}$ **d** $\dfrac{8}{64}$

  e $\dfrac{16}{625}$ **f** $\dfrac{1}{27}$

7 **Problem-solving** Jamal eats half a cheesecake, his brother eats half of what is left and his sister eats half of what is then left. How much cheesecake remains?

  Write your answer

  a as a fraction

  b as a fraction raised to a power.

8 **Explore** Does raising a number to a power always make the number bigger?

  Choose some sensible numbers to help you explore this situation.

  Then use what you've learned in this lesson to help you answer the question.

9 **Reflect** Rhiannon says, 'Mathematics is often about spotting patterns'. Do you agree? Explain.

  When else have you used pattern spotting in maths?

Q9 hint

Look back at this lesson and the previous lesson. Can you find any questions where you were spotting a pattern?

Explore

Reflect

1.3 Standard form

You will learn to:
- Write numbers using standard form
- Order numbers written in standard form.

CONFIDENCE

Why learn this?
Scientists describing the universe need to write down very large numbers in a way that is easy to read.

Fluency
Multiply 3.05 by
- 10
- 1000
- 0.1

Work out $10^3 \times 0.15$

Explore
What units are used to measure distances in the universe?

Exercise 1.3

Warm up

1 Work out
  a 2.5×100
  b 7.3×0.01
  c 4.06×10^{-1}
  d 9.55×10^{-3}

2 Copy and complete.
  a $23.4 \times 10^3 = \square$
  b $2.35 \times 10^{\square} = 235$
  c $34 \times 10^{\square} = 34\,000$
  d $0.067 \times 10^2 = \square$

3 Which of these numbers are written in **standard form**?
  a 2.8×10^3
  b 7×10^5
  c 0.2×10^2
  d 27×10^{-5}
  e 3.3×10
  f 5.022×10^{-6}

4 These numbers are written in standard form.
  Write them as ordinary numbers.
  a 7×10^2
  b 2.5×10^{-5}
  c 5.4×10^6
  d 3.04×10^{-3}

> **Key point**
>
>
>
> A number written in **standard form** is a number between 1 and 10 multiplied by a power of 10. 4.2×10^6 is written in standard form. Using algebra, standard form is $A \times 10^n$ where $1 \leqslant A < 10$ and n is an integer.

> **Q4 hint**
>
> $7 \times 10^2 = 7 \times 100 = \square$

Worked example

Write each number using standard form.
  a $41\,000$

  b $0.003\,94$

> 4.1 lies between 1 and 10. Multiply by the power of 10 needed to give the original number 4.1000

$41\,000 = 4.1 \times 10^4$

> 3.94 lies between 1 and 10.
> Multiply by the power of 10 needed to give the original number.
> The number is less than 1 so the power of 10 is negative.
> This is the same as dividing by a power of 10. 0.00394

$0.003\,94 = 3.94 \times 10^{-3}$

Topic links: Powers, Laws of indices, Priority of operations

Subject links: Science (Explore, Q6, Q8–10)

5 Write each number in standard form.
   a 23500   b 315   c 12000000
   d 0.04   e 0.00035   f 0.0000000901

Q5 Literacy hint

Standard form is sometimes called **standard index form**.

6 STEM The distance light travels in a year is called a light-year.
   a Write each of the distances in the table in standard form.

Object	Distance from Earth (light-years)
Centre of our galaxy	26000
Andromeda (a neighbouring galaxy)	2500000
Betelgeuse (a star of Orion)	600

   b The Triangulum Galaxy is the furthest galaxy you can see without a telescope.
      It is 3×10^6 light-years away. Is it closer to Earth than Betelgeuse?

7 Put these sets of numbers in order, from smallest to largest.
   a 9.87×10^2 8.65×10^4 1.9×10^3 3.59×10^2 1.95×10^4
   b 5.3×10^{-3} 4.8×10^{-2} 3.99×10^{-5} 8.05×10^{-6} 8.76×10^{-3}
   c 3.22×10^{-2} 3.02×10^2 3.2×10^{-3} 3.22×10^2 3.22×10^{-3}

Q7 hint

Write each number in full to help you order them.

8 STEM / Problem-solving The table shows the mass of the planets in our Solar System.
   a Rewrite each mass in standard form (some already are).

Planet	Mass (kg)
Earth	5.97×10^{24} kg
Jupiter	1899×10^{24} kg
Mars	0.642×10^{24} kg
Mercury	0.33×10^{24} kg
Neptune	102×10^{24} kg
Saturn	568.5×10^{24} kg
Uranus	86.8×10^{24} kg
Venus	4.87×10^{24} kg

   b Approximately how many times heavier is Earth than Mars?
   c Which planet is approximately 1000 times heavier than Mars?

9 STEM Write these atoms in order of the size of their nucleus, largest first.

Atom	Size of nucleus (m)
gold	1.4×10^{-14}
helium	3.8×10^{-15}
aluminum	7.2×10^{-15}

10 STEM Write the following measurements as ordinary numbers
      i in metres   ii in millimetres.
   a The diameter of the core in an optical fibre: 6.25×10^{-5} m
   b The line width on a microprocessor: 1.8×10^{-7} m

Q10 hint

There are 1000 mm in 1 metre, so multiply by $10^{\square}$.

11 Explore What units are used to measure distances in the universe?
   Is it easier to explore this question now you have completed the lesson?
   What further information do you need to be able to answer this?

12 Reflect Look back at your answer to Q7. You could answer this using ordinary numbers or standard form. Which method did you choose? Explain your choice.

Explore

Reflect

1.4 STEM: Calculating with standard form

You will learn to:
* Calculate with numbers written in standard form.

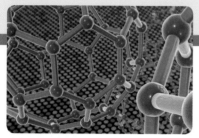

CONFIDENCE

Why learn this?
Scientists exploring nanotechnology need to describe very small numbers in a way that is easy to read.

Fluency
Write as a single power of 10
* $10^4 \times 10^3$
* 10×10^{-5}
* $(10^2)^{-3}$
* $10^2 \times 10^3 \times 10^3$

Explore
What is the smallest organism you can see?

Exercise 1.4: Orders of magnitude

Warm up

1 Write each number in standard form.

  a 59 000   **b** 0.0601

  c 0.000 000 072   **d** 5323

2 Write as a single power of 10

  a $10^{-3} \times 10^2$ **b** $10^{-3} \times 10^{-2}$

  c $10^3 \div 10^{-1}$ **d** $10^{-1} \div 10^2$

Worked example

Write $(2.7 \times 10^3) \times (4 \times 10^2)$ in standard form.

$(2.7 \times 10^3) \times (4 \times 10^2) = 2.7 \times 4 \times 10^3 \times 10^2$

$\qquad\qquad\qquad\qquad\qquad\quad = 10.8 \times 10^5$

$\qquad\qquad\qquad\qquad\qquad\quad = 1.08 \times 10 \times 10^5$

$\qquad\qquad\qquad\qquad\qquad\quad = 1.08 \times 10^6$

> Rearrange so that the numbers are together and the powers of 10 are together.

> Calculate the product of the numbers and use laws of indices to simplify the powers of 10.

> Rewrite the answer in standard form, if necessary. $10.8 = 1.08 \times 10^1$

3 Work out each calculation. Give your answer in standard form.

  a $(1.2 \times 10^2) \times (3 \times 10^3)$ **b** $(1.5 \times 10^5) \times (5 \times 10^3)$

  c $(4 \times 10^4) \times (6.25 \times 10)$ **d** $(1.2 \times 10^3)^2$

4 Work out each calculation. Give your answer in standard form.

  a $\dfrac{6 \times 10^8}{3 \times 10^2}$ **b** $\dfrac{8 \times 10^5}{2 \times 10^3}$

  c $\dfrac{1.2 \times 10^6}{3 \times 10}$ **d** $\dfrac{2 \times 10^5}{1.25 \times 10^4}$

> **Q4 hint**
> Divide the number parts. Use the laws of indices to divide the powers of 10.

Topic links: Ratio, Enlargement   **Subject links:** Science (Q6–14, Q18)

5 Use a calculator to work out

   a $(9.6 \times 10^7) \times (6.41 \times 10^3)$ **b** $\dfrac{1.342 \times 10^{11}}{6.1 \times 10^5}$

   Discussion Which buttons do you use on your calculator? Is the answer in standard form?

6 **STEM** Light travels at 299 792 458 metres per second (m/s).

   a Write down the speed of light in km/s, correct to 1 significant figure

     i as an ordinary number   **ii** using standard form.

   The distance from the Sun to the Earth is 1.496×10^8 km.

   b Use your answer to part **a** to work out how long it takes light to travel from the Sun to the Earth. Give your answer to the nearest minute.

7 **STEM / Problem-solving** Sound travels at 3.4×10^2 m/s. What is the ratio of the speed of light to the speed of sound? Give your answer in the form $n:1$, to 2 d.p.

Q7 hint

Use the speed of light given in Q6.

8 **STEM / Reasoning** A human hair has a diameter of approximately 1×10^{-1} mm. The human eye cannot easily see anything smaller than a human hair without a microscope.

   An optical microscope can enlarge an image to 1000 times the size of the object. Is it possible to see these organisms with a microscope?

   a polio virus 2×10^{-5} mm

   b human red blood cell 1×10^{-2} mm

   c staphylococcus 5×10^{-4} mm

Q8c Literacy hint

Staphylococcus is a bacteria that causes food poisoning.

9 **STEM / Modelling** The table gives the sizes of eggs from different animals.

Object	Approximate diameter (m)
Extinct elephant bird	2.5×10^{-1}
Ostrich	1.5×10^{-1}
Hummingbird	1×10^{-2}
Sea star	9×10^{-4}
Human	1.2×10^{-4}

   A model of an ostrich egg is built for an exhibition. Its diameter is 10 m. The same scale is used to build models of the other objects.

   a Work out the length of each model. Choose an appropriate unit of length for each answer.

   b Is this a good scale to use? Would you be able to hold each model in your hand?

10 **STEM** A 3D electron microscope magnifies objects 1 000 000 times. A water molecule has a diameter of 2×10^{-10} m. How large will it appear in the microscope? Give your answer in millimetres.

11 **STEM** Graphite is made up of layers of graphene sheets. Each sheet of graphene is one atom thick. There are 3×10^6 layers of graphene in 1 mm thickness of graphite. If you ignore the thickness of the layers, what is the gap between the layers? Give your answer in standard form.

Q11 hint

Layers of graphene are so thin, about 1.4×10^{-10} m thick, that they can be ignored in this calculation.

12 STEM Here are some wavelengths in the electromagnetic spectrum.

Gamma ray	1×10^{-12} m
Red light	6.8×10^{-7} m
Microwave	1.22×10^{-1} m
VHF radio wave	3 m
Low frequency radio wave	10 km

  a How many gamma ray wavelengths fit into the length of one red light wave?

  b How many times larger are low frequency radio waves than microwaves?

  c Which is longer: 10^2 VHF radio waves or 3×10^{10} red light rays?

13 STEM / Problem-solving The mass of a proton is about 2000 times larger than the mass of an electron.
Copy and complete this sentence, using standard form.
The mass of an electron = the mass of a proton $\times \, \square \times 10^{\square}$

14 Real / STEM Sunglasses are coated with very thin layers to cut out ultraviolet radiation. These layers are about 4×10^2 nm thick. Give the thickness in metres.

Literacy hint

1 nm = 1 nanometer = 10^{-9} m

15 Real Your fingernail grows about 1 nm per second. How much could your fingernail grow in 4 weeks? Give your answer in millimetres.

16 Work out each calculation. Give your answers in standard form.

  a $5.1 \times 10^8 + 1.45 \times 10^8$ **b** $9.05 \times 10^5 + 7.8 \times 10^5$

  c $6.75 \times 10^{-4} + 4.25 \times 10^{-4}$ **d** $3.9 \times 10^7 + 4.2 \times 10^6$

  e $5.6 \times 10^{-4} + 2.07 \times 10^{-3}$

Q16d hint

Both numbers need to have the same power of 10 before you add them.
$4.2 \times 10^6 = \square \times 10^7$

17 Work out

  a $9.6 \times 10^{-7} - 6.3 \times 10^{-7}$ **b** $8.88 \times 10^4 - 8.37 \times 10^4$

  c $5.33 \times 10^6 - 2.8 \times 10^5$ **d** $7.02 \times 10^{-3} - 6.1 \times 10^{-4}$

18 STEM The wavelengths in the visible light spectrum extend from 3.8×10^{-7} m to 7.5×10^{-7} m.
What is the range of wavelengths in the visible light spectrum?

19 Explore What is the smallest organism you can see?
Is it easier to explore this question now you have completed the lesson?
What further information do you need to be able to answer this?

20 Reflect The title of this lesson is 'Orders of magnitude'. Why do you think scientists find it useful to know about orders of magnitude?

1.5 Fractional indices

You will learn to:
- Calculate with fractional indices.

Why learn this?
Engineers use indices to work out the solutions to equations involving force.

Fluency
What are the first ten square numbers?
What are the first five cube numbers?

Explore
Will a fractional index ever give a negative answer?

Exercise 1.5

1 Write as a single power

   a $5^3 \times 5^8$ **b** $17^5 \div 17^2$ **c** $8^3 \div 8^{10}$

   d $(3^5)^2$ **e** $(10^3)^{-5}$

2 Work out

   a $\sqrt{121}$ **b** $\sqrt{64}$

   c $\sqrt[3]{64}$ **d** $\sqrt[3]{\frac{1}{8}}$

Investigation   **Problem solving / Reasoning**

1   **a**   Use the index laws to work out $4^{\frac{1}{2}} \times 4^{\frac{1}{2}}$

     b   Solve the equation $x^2 = 4$.

     c   Use your answers to parts **a** and **b** to work out $4^{\frac{1}{2}}$.

2   Repeat part **1** for $25^{\frac{1}{2}} \times 25^{\frac{1}{2}}$ and $x^2 = 25$ to work out $25^{\frac{1}{2}}$.

3   Complete the statement: A number to the power $\frac{1}{2}$ is the same as the _____ of the number.

4   **a**   Use the index laws to work out $27^{\frac{1}{3}} \times 27^{\frac{1}{3}} \times 27^{\frac{1}{3}}$

     b   Solve the equation $x^3 = 27$.

     c   Use your answers to parts **a** and **b** to work out $27^{\frac{1}{3}}$.

5   Repeat part **4** for $64^{\frac{1}{3}} \times 64^{\frac{1}{3}} \times 64^{\frac{1}{3}}$ and $x^3 = 64$ to work out $64^{\frac{1}{3}}$.

6   Complete the statement: A number to the power $\frac{1}{3}$ is the same as the _____ of the number.

---

3 Work out

   a $9^{\frac{1}{2}}$ **b** $121^{\frac{1}{2}}$ **c** $81^{\frac{1}{2}}$

   d $400^{\frac{1}{2}}$ **e** $\dfrac{1}{49^{\frac{1}{2}}}$ **f** $\left(\dfrac{4}{9}\right)^{\frac{1}{2}}$

4 Work out

   a $8^{\frac{1}{3}}$ **b** $125^{\frac{1}{3}}$

   c $1000^{\frac{1}{3}}$ **d** $\dfrac{1}{27^{\frac{1}{3}}}$

5 Copy and complete.

   a $169^{\frac{1}{\square}} = 13$

   b $\dfrac{1}{64^{\frac{1}{\square}}} = \dfrac{1}{4}$

   c $\dfrac{9}{25^{\frac{1}{2}}} = \square$

   d $\square^{\frac{1}{3}} = 5$

   e $\square^{\frac{1}{2}} = \dfrac{7}{8}$

   f $2500^{\frac{1}{\square}} = 50$

Worked example

Work out

   a $16^{\frac{3}{2}}$

   b $27^{-\frac{1}{3}}$

   a $16^{\frac{3}{2}} = \left(16^{\frac{1}{2}}\right)^{3}$

           $= 4^{3}$

           $= 64$

> Use the rule for powers of powers.
> It is easier to find the square root of 16 first and then cube it, than to work out $(16^{3})^{\frac{1}{2}}$

   b $27^{-\frac{1}{3}} = \dfrac{1}{27^{\frac{1}{3}}}$

> Use the rule for negative indices.

           $= \dfrac{1}{3}$

> Work out the cube root of 27.

6 Work out

   a $8^{\frac{2}{3}}$

   b $64^{\frac{2}{3}}$

   c $25^{\frac{3}{2}}$

   d $81^{\frac{3}{4}}$

   e $\left(\dfrac{1}{16}\right)^{\frac{3}{2}}$

   f $\left(\dfrac{9}{100}\right)^{\frac{3}{2}}$

7 Work out

   a $49^{-\frac{1}{2}}$

   b $64^{-\frac{1}{3}}$

   c $\left(\dfrac{1}{144}\right)^{-\frac{1}{2}}$

   d $\left(\dfrac{4}{81}\right)^{-\frac{1}{2}}$

   e $\left(\dfrac{1}{27}\right)^{-\frac{2}{3}}$

   f $\left(\dfrac{64}{125}\right)^{-\frac{1}{3}}$

8 **Explore** Will a fractional index ever give a negative answer?
Look back at the maths you have learnt in this lesson.
How can you use it to answer this question?

9 **Reflect** Look at your answers to Q7. Which parts of the question needed more than one step? How did you decide which step to do first?

1.6 Surds

You will learn to:

- Use surds
- Understand the difference between rational and irrational numbers.

Why learn this?
Using surds means you can give an accurate answer instead of a rounded answer.

Fluency
Work out

- 3^3
- 2^4
- $\sqrt{64}$
- $\sqrt[3]{64}$

Explore
When did mathematicians start using surd notation?

Exercise 1.6

1 Work out

  a $\sqrt{64}$ **b** $\sqrt{121}$

  c $\sqrt{\frac{1}{4}}$ **d** $\sqrt{\frac{4}{9}}$

2 Write each number as the product of its prime factors.

  a 32   **b** 50

  c 120   **d** 225

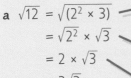

Worked example

Write each square root as a **surd** in its simplest form.

  a $\sqrt{12}$ **b** $\sqrt{15}$

  a $\sqrt{12} = \sqrt{(2^2 \times 3)}$

Write 12 as the product of its prime factors, so you can see any square numbers.

       $= \sqrt{2^2} \times \sqrt{3}$

The square root of a squared number is the number itself.

       $= 2 \times \sqrt{3}$

       $= 2\sqrt{3}$

$2 \times \sqrt{3}$ is written as $2\sqrt{3}$.

  b $\sqrt{15} = \sqrt{(3 \times 5)}$

       $= \sqrt{3} \times \sqrt{5}$

$\sqrt{3}$ and $\sqrt{5}$ cannot be simplified any further.

       $= \sqrt{3}\sqrt{5}$

Key point

A **surd** is a square root that cannot be simplified any further. It is written with the root symbol, for example $\sqrt{5}$.

3 Write these as surds in their simplest form.

  a $\sqrt{20}$ **b** $\sqrt{48}$

  c $\sqrt{100}$ **d** $\sqrt{3}\sqrt{6}$

  e $\sqrt{2}\sqrt{10}$ **f** $\sqrt{3}\sqrt{60}$

Q3d hint

$\sqrt{3}\sqrt{6} = \sqrt{3} \times (\sqrt{3} \times \sqrt{2})$

Warm up

4 Simplify

a $\sqrt{7} \times 3 \times \sqrt{7}$

b $2 \times \sqrt{20}$

c $\sqrt{9} - \sqrt{3}$

d $\sqrt{12} \times \sqrt{3}$

e $\sqrt{98} \div \sqrt{2}$

f $\dfrac{\sqrt{18}}{\sqrt{6}}$

5 Reasoning

a i Write 484 as a product of its prime factors.

ii Use your answer to work out $\sqrt{484}$.

b i Write 450 as a product of its prime factors.

ii Write $\sqrt{450}$ in its simplest form.

6 Problem-solving The area of the square ABCD is $3\,cm^2$.

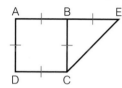

Q6 Strategy hint

Use Pythagoras' theorem.

Giving your answers in surd form, work out the length of

a BC

b CE.

7 Problem-solving Work out the length of the hypotenuse of this triangle.
Leave your answer in surd form.

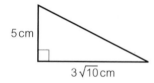

5 cm

$3\sqrt{10}$ cm

8 Problem-solving / Reasoning Show that the area of the triangle ABC is $9\sqrt{2}\,cm^2$.

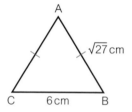

A

$\sqrt{27}$ cm

C   6 cm   B

9 Reasoning This equilateral triangle has sides of length $4x$.

a Show that the length AB is $2\sqrt{3}x$.

b Work out the area of the triangle in terms of x.

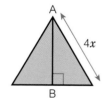

A

$4x$

B

Topic links: Pythagoras' theorem, Area of triangle, Prime factors

1 Write down $\sqrt{3}$ correct to
   a 1 decimal place
   b 2 decimal places
   c 5 decimal places.
2 Square each of your answers to part **1**. Why do they not equal 3?
The diagram shows a right-angled isosceles triangle.

5 cm

5 cm

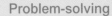

3 Work out the length of the diagonal, giving your answer
   a correct to 2 decimal places
   b correct to 2 significant figures
   c as a **surd**.
4 Which of your answers to part **3** is the most accurate? Explain why.
Discussion Is a surd a **rational** or an **irrational** number?

10 Write down whether each number is **terminating**, **recurring** or irrational.
   a $\frac{1}{2}$
   b $\frac{1}{3}$
   c 0.3^2
   d $\sqrt{9}$
   e $\sqrt{3}$
   f π
   g $\frac{1}{11}$
   h 3π

11 Which of these are rational numbers?
   a $\sqrt{196}$
   b $\sqrt{11}$
   c $\sqrt{\frac{1}{7}}$
   d $\sqrt{\frac{1}{100}}$
   e $\sqrt{2}$
   f $(0.\dot{3})^2$

12 **Explore** When did mathematicians start using surd notation? Is it easier to explore this question now you have completed the lesson?
What further information do you need to be able to answer this?

13 **Reflect** Look at Q9 part **a**. In this question you had to show your working to get an answer that was already given to you. Do you prefer this type of question to ones where you have to find the answer? Explain why or why not.

Explore

Reflect

Master
P1

CHECK

Strengthen
P17

Extend
P21

Test
P25

1 Check up

Log how you did on your
Student Progression Chart.

Standard form

1 Write each number in standard form.
   a 345
   c 34.5×10^3
   d 0.005×10^6

2 Write 0.007 231 in standard form.

3 Write these numbers in order, from smallest to largest.

   3.1×10^{-2} 3.2×10^{-3} 3.22×10^3 3.022×10^4 3.2×10^{-5}

4 Work out each calculation. Give your answers in standard form.
   a $(4.1 \times 10^{-6}) \times (2 \times 10^3)$
   b $\dfrac{6 \times 10^3}{1.5 \times 10^2}$

5 Work out each calculation. Give your answers
   i in standard form
   ii as an ordinary number.
   a $\dfrac{23.31 \times 10^5}{3.7 \times 10^7}$
   b $(7.09 \times 10^2) \times (6.3 \times 10^3)$

Reciprocals and indices

6 Write the reciprocal of
   a $\frac{3}{7}$
   b 6
   c $2\frac{1}{4}$

7 What is the reciprocal of $\frac{1}{7}$?

8 Write $\left(\frac{2}{5}\right)^3$ as a fraction.

9 Write $\frac{36}{49}$ as a power of a fraction.

10 Write as a single power.
   a $10^3 \times 10^{-4}$
   b $3^{-2} \div 3$
   c $(3^{-2})^3$
   d $7^{-5} \div 7^{-2}$

11 Copy and complete.

　a $49^{\frac{1}{2}} = \square$

　b $\square^{\frac{1}{3}} = 4$

　c $\left(\frac{1}{100}\right)^{\frac{1}{\square}} = \frac{1}{10}$

12 Work out

　a $125^{\frac{2}{3}}$

　b $\left(\frac{4}{25}\right)^{\frac{3}{2}}$

13 Work out

　a $16^{-\frac{1}{2}}$

　b $\left(\frac{1}{64}\right)^{-\frac{2}{3}}$

Surds

14 Simplify

　a $\sqrt{75}$

　b $\sqrt{10} \times \sqrt{40}$

15 Show that the area of the rectangle ABCD is $3\sqrt{5}\,\text{cm}^2$

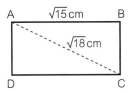

16 Choose the most accurate answer to $\sqrt{28}$.

　A 5.29 (to 3 s.f.)

　B 5.3 (to 1 d.p.)

　C 5.291 502 622

　D $2\sqrt{7}$

17 Which of these numbers are irrational?

　A $\frac{1}{3}$

　B $\sqrt{5}$

　C $\frac{3}{8}$

　D $6^{\frac{3}{2}}$

18 **How sure are you of your answers? Were you mostly**

　😣 **Just guessing**　😐 **Feeling doubtful**　🙂 **Confident**

　What next? Use your results to decide whether to strengthen or extend your learning.

Challenge

19 $64^{\frac{1}{2}} = 8$, $64^{\frac{1}{3}} = 4$, $64^{\frac{1}{6}} = 2$

　Find another number that has three different integer roots.

20 In how many different ways can you write $\frac{100}{1000}$?

> **Q20 hint**
>
> Use powers, roots and standard form.

Master
P1

Check
P15

STRENGTHEN

Extend
P21

Test
P25

1 Strengthen

You will:

• Strengthen your understanding with practice.

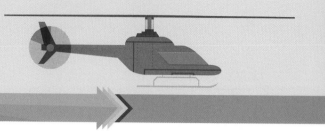

Standard form

1 Work out

   a 3.7×10^3

   c 8.1×10^2

   b 2.5×10^4

   d 5.4×10^7

2 Work out

   a 9.3×10^{-3}

   c 1.5×10^{-4}

   b 7.3×10^{-2}

   d 4.9×10^{-6}

3 A number written using standard form looks like this:

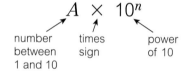

$$A \times 10^n$$

number between 1 and 10   times sign   power of 10

Write each number using standard form.

   a $3100 = 3.1 \times 10^{\square}$

   c $7\,150\,000$

   b $29\,000$

   d $69\,000\,000\,000$

4 Write each number using standard form.

   a $0.0064 = 6.4 \times 10^{\square}$

   c 0.000004

   b 0.072

   d $0.000\,000\,021$

5 Write the numbers in each list in order, from smallest to largest.

   a 1.8×10^5 3.7×10^{-2} 9.4×10^2 6.9×10^{-7}

   b 4×10^{-1} 4.2×10^{-2} 4.22×10^2 2.4×10^2 2.44×10^{-1}

6 Work out each calculation. Give your answers in standard form.

   a $(3 \times 10^4) \times (2.6 \times 10^5) = 3 \times 2.6 \times 10^4 \times 10^5 = \square \times 10^{\square}$

   b $(1.7 \times 10^5) \times (2 \times 10^3)$ **c** $(5 \times 10^2) \times (2.5 \times 10^8)$

   d $\dfrac{6.6 \times 10^6}{2.2 \times 10^3} = \dfrac{6.6}{2.2} \times \dfrac{10^6}{10^3} = \square \times 10^{\square}$

   e $\dfrac{7.8 \times 10^3}{3 \times 10^7}$ **f** $\dfrac{2 \times 10^9}{8 \times 10^5}$

 7 Work out each calculation. Give your answers in standard form.

   a $(6.41 \times 10^5) \times (1.8 \times 10^7)$ **b** $(3.7 \times 10^{-3}) \times (9.3 \times 10^{10})$

   c $\dfrac{55.8 \times 10^9}{6.2 \times 10^2}$ **d** $\dfrac{2.136 \times 10^3}{3.56 \times 10^8}$

Q1a hint

3.7 ⌒⌒⌒
3 7 0 0

3.7×10^3 means multiply 3.7 by 10 three times.

Q2a hint

⌒⌒⌒ 9.3
0 0 0 9 3

9.3×10^{-3} means divide 9.3 by 10 three times.

Q4a hint

⌒⌒⌒ 6.4   Divide by how many
0 0 0 6 4   10s to get 0.0064?

6.4 lies between 1 and 10.

Q5 hint

Look at the powers of 10 first.
If numbers have the same power of 10, sort them by the decimal number.

Q7a hint

Use the $\boxed{10^x}$ key on your calculator.

Reciprocals and indices

1 Write down the reciprocal of

    a $\frac{2}{5}$ **b** $\frac{3}{7}$ **c** 9

    d 20   **e** $\frac{1}{6}$ **f** $\frac{1}{15}$

Q1c hint

The reciprocal of a whole number is $\dfrac{1}{\text{number}}$.

2 a i Write $3\frac{1}{4}$ as an improper fraction.

    ii Use your answer to part **i** to write the reciprocal of $3\frac{1}{4}$.

   b Work out the reciprocals of

     i $4\frac{2}{3}$ **ii** $2\frac{3}{8}$

3 a Write the reciprocal of 4.

   b Write the reciprocal of your answer to part **a**.

   c Copy and complete

     The reciprocal of the reciprocal of a number is _____

4 Work out

    a $\left(\frac{1}{2}\right)^3$ **b** $\left(\frac{1}{5}\right)^2$ **c** $\left(\frac{2}{5}\right)^2$

    d $\left(\frac{1}{3}\right)^4$ **e** $\left(\frac{2}{3}\right)^3$

Q4a hint

$\left(\frac{1}{2}\right)^3 = \frac{1}{2} \times \frac{1}{2} \times \frac{1}{2} = \frac{1 \times 1 \times 1}{2 \times 2 \times 2}$

5 a i $3^2 \div 3^5 = 3^{\square}$

Q5a i hint

Which index rule can you use?

    ii $3^2 \div 3^5 = \dfrac{3^2}{3^5} = \dfrac{\cancel{3} \times \cancel{3}}{\cancel{3} \times \cancel{3} \times 3 \times 3 \times 3} = \dfrac{\square}{\square}$

    iii Use your answers to copy and complete: $3^{-3} = \dfrac{1}{3^{\square}}$

   b Copy and complete.

     i $7^{-2} = \dfrac{1}{7^{\square}}$ **ii** $4^{-5} = \dfrac{1}{4^{\square}}$ **iii** $\dfrac{1}{9^3} = 9^{\square}$ **iv** $\dfrac{1}{5^7} = 5^{\square}$

6 Write each calculation as a single power.

    a $7^2 \times 7^{-4} = 7^{2 + -4} = 7^{\square}$ **b** $3^{-1} \times 3^5 = 3^{\square + \square} = 3^{\square}$

    c $5^{-4} \times 5$ **d** $8^2 \div 8^6 = 8^{\square - \square} = 8^{\square}$

    e $4^{-3} \div 4^{-5}$ **f** $\dfrac{10^3}{10^7}$

    g $(5^{-2})^3 = 5^{-2 \times \square} = 5^{\square}$ **h** $(6^5)^{-4}$

Q6c hint

$5 = 5^1$

7 Which calculations in Q6 have answers that are less than 1?

Q7 hint

Write each answer as a fraction. Which fractions have a numerator smaller than the denominator?

8 Work out

    a $64^{\frac{1}{2}}$ **b** $81^{\frac{1}{2}}$

    c $\left(\dfrac{1}{100}\right)^{\frac{1}{2}}$ **d** $\left(\dfrac{25}{49}\right)^{\frac{1}{2}}$

Q8a hint

$64^{\frac{1}{2}}$ is the same as $\sqrt{64}$

9 a $8^{\frac{1}{3}}$ **b** $64^{\frac{1}{3}}$

    c $\left(\dfrac{1}{125}\right)^{\frac{1}{3}}$ **d** $\left(\dfrac{8}{27}\right)^{\frac{1}{3}}$

10 Work out

a $25^{\frac{3}{2}} = \left(25^{\frac{1}{2}}\right)^3 = \square^3 = \square$　　　　**b** $4^{\frac{3}{2}}$

c $27^{\frac{2}{3}} = \left(27^{\frac{1}{\square}}\right)^{\square} = \square$　　　　**d** $8^{\frac{2}{3}}$

e $\left(\frac{4}{9}\right)^{\frac{3}{2}} = \left(\sqrt{\frac{4}{9}}\right)^3 = \left(\frac{\square}{\square}\right)^3 = \frac{\square}{\square}$　　　　**f** $\left(\frac{27}{1000}\right)^{\frac{2}{3}}$

11 Work out

a $25^{-\frac{1}{2}}$　　　　**b** $100^{-\frac{1}{2}}$　　　　**c** $64^{-\frac{1}{3}}$

d $64^{-\frac{2}{3}}$　　　　**e** $27^{-\frac{2}{3}}$

Surds

1 Simplify

a $\sqrt{28} = \sqrt{(2^2 \times 7)} = \sqrt{(2^2)} \times \sqrt{7} = \square\sqrt{\square}$

b $\sqrt{75} = \sqrt{(\square \times \square^2)} = \square\sqrt{\square}$

c $\sqrt{45}$

d $\sqrt{180} = \sqrt{(2^2 \times 3^2 \times 5)} = \sqrt{(2^2)} \times \sqrt{(3^2)} \times \sqrt{5} = 2 \times 3 \times \sqrt{\square} = \square\sqrt{\square}$

e $\sqrt{200}$

f $\sqrt{35} = \sqrt{(5 \times 7)} = \sqrt{5}\sqrt{\square}$

g $\sqrt{21}$

2 Simplify

a $\sqrt{10} \times \sqrt{2}$

b $\sqrt{12} \times \sqrt{8}$

c $\sqrt{5} \times \sqrt{20}$

d $\dfrac{\sqrt{192}}{\sqrt{8}}$

e $\sqrt{84} \div \sqrt{6}$

3 Copy and complete the working to show that the area of rectangle ABCD is $2\sqrt{3}$ cm².

$BC^2 = AC^2 - \square^2$

$ = \left(\sqrt{8}\right)^2 - \left(\sqrt{6}\right)^2$

$ = \square - \square$

$BC = \sqrt{\square}$ cm

Area of rectangle ABCD $= AB \times \square$

$ = \sqrt{6} \times \square$

$ = \sqrt{\square}$

$ = \square\sqrt{\square}$ cm²

4 Decide whether each of these numbers is rational or irrational.

a $\frac{1}{4}$　　　　**b** $\frac{1}{3}$　　　　**c** 5

d 2π　　　　**e** $\sqrt{2}$　　　　**f** $\frac{2}{9}$

Q10 hint

The power $\frac{3}{2}$ is telling you to do two things:
– work out the square root $(\frac{1}{2})$
– cube $(^3)$
Working out the square root first will give you a smaller number to work with.

Q11a hint

The power $-\frac{1}{2}$ is telling you two things:
– work out the square root $(\frac{1}{2})$
– write the reciprocal
$25^{-\frac{1}{2}} = \dfrac{1}{25^{\frac{1}{2}}}$

Q1 hint

Write each number as $\square \times \square$.
See if one of the numbers can be a square number.

Q2a hint

$\sqrt{10} \times \sqrt{2}$
$= \sqrt{10 \times 2}$
$= \sqrt{\square}$
$= \square\sqrt{\square}$

Q3 Strategy hint

ABC is a right-angled triangle so you can use Pythagoras' theorem.

Q4 hint

A rational number can be written as an integer, a fraction, a terminating decimal or a recurring decimal.

5 State whether the rational numbers you identified in Q4 are terminating or recurring decimals.

6 Cindy worked out the answer to $\sqrt{9 \times 5}$ but couldn't decide which answer to write down. Which of these answers is the most accurate?
   A 6.71 (to 3 s.f.)
   B 6.708 203 932
   C $3\sqrt{5}$
   D 6.7 (to 1 d.p.)

Q6 hint

Rounded answers are always slightly inaccurate.

Enrichment

1 **Problem-solving** How thick is a single page in this book?
Follow these steps to find out.
   a Find out how many sheets of paper are in the book.
   b Use a ruler to measure the total thickness of the pages in the book (in mm).
   c Use your calculator to find the thickness of one sheet in mm. Write the answer in standard form.
   d Convert your answer in part **c** to nanometers (nm). Give your answer to 1 decimal place.

Q1d hint

$1\,nm = 10^{-6}\,mm$

2 **Real** Write these countries in order of population size, from smallest to largest.

Country	Population (July 2014)
UK	6.411×10^7
New Zealand	4.540×10^6
Iceland	3.263×10^5
Japan	1.271×10^8
St Lucia	1.8×10^5
Brazil	2.028×10^8

3 **Reflect** Nikole says, 'Working with indices, powers and roots is all about adding, subtracting, multiplying and dividing'.
Look back at the questions you answered in these strengthen lessons.
Describe when you had to:
   • add
   • subtract
   • multiply
   • divide.
Do you agree with Nikole's statement? Give some examples to explain why.

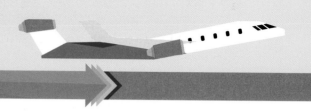

1 Extend

You will:

• Extend your understanding with problem solving.

 1 Write down the reciprocal of each number. Give your answer as a decimal.

    a 8   **b** 18   **c** 55

    d 0.625   **e** 0.025   **f** 0.005

> **Q1 hint**
>
> The reciprocal is the number you need to multiply by to get 1.

2 Write down five fractions that are greater than $\left(\frac{1}{3}\right)^4$ but less than $\left(\frac{1}{4}\right)^3$

3 a Calculate the volume of a cube with sides

    i $\frac{1}{3}$ cm   **ii** $\frac{3}{5}$ cm

  b Calculate the side of a cube with volume

    i $\frac{27}{64}$ cm^3 **ii** $\frac{216}{125}$ cm^3

4 STEM There are 100 trillion microorganisms in the human intestines. This is 10 times the number of cells in a human body. Write the number of cells in a human body, in standard form.

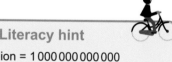

> **Q4 Literacy hint**
>
> 1 trillion = 1 000 000 000 000

5 Problem-solving Write these numbers in order, from smallest to largest.

  1.26×10^{-3} 0.12×10^{-2} 0.00124 1205×10^{-6} $\dfrac{1}{8 \times 10^2}$

> **Q5 Strategy hint**
>
> Write each number in standard form first.

6 Put the answers to these calculations in order, from smallest to largest.

  A $(2.3 \times 10^{-3}) \times (7.4 \times 10^{-2})$

  B $(1.3 \times 10^{-2})^2$

  C $(5.3 \times 10^{-2}) \div (3.2 \times 10^2)$

  D $(1.091 \times 10^{-4}) + (6 \times 10^{-5})$

  E $(1.8 \times 10^{-4}) - (1.8 \times 10^{-5})$

7 Real The table shows how people accessed information about a football tournament.

	Number of people (to 3 s.f.)
Connected with the official site	1.12×10^8
Apps downloaded	2.20×10^7
Facebook users	4.55×10^8
Tweets during the match	3.66×10^7

Use the data to work out the missing number in each sentence.

  a There were roughly _____ times more Facebook users than people connected to the official site.

  b There were roughly _____ times more Facebook users than tweets in the match.

  c There were roughly _____ times more tweets in the match than people who downloaded apps.

8 Real / STEM Scientists often use units written with negative indices. For example: $30\,\text{m/s} = 30\,\text{ms}^{-1}$.
Write these units using negative indices.
  a km/h   **b** m/s^2 **c** kg/m^3 **d** mi/h

9 Work out the reciprocals of these numbers. Give your answers in standard form.
  a 2×10^9 **b** 8×10^7 **c** 4×10^{-5} **d** 1.6×10^{-4}

10 Real The number of app downloads in July 2008 was 1.0×10^7. There were 10 times as many in September 2008 and 10 times as many again in April 2009.
In June 2014 there were 7.5×10^{10} app downloads.
  a How many downloads were there in April 2009?
  b What was the increase from July 2008 to June 2014?

11 STEM / Reasoning The smallest size the human eye can see is $10^{-4}\,\text{m}$.
The diameter of a virus particle is 170 nm.
Could you see a group of 1 million virus particles with the naked eye?
Explain your answer.

12 STEM The formula for working out the frequency of a wave in the electromagnetic spectrum is:

$f = \dfrac{c}{\lambda}$, where c is the speed of light and λ is the wavelength.

$c = 3 \times 10^8\,\text{m/s}$
Work out the frequency of
  a red light with wavelength $6.9 \times 10^{-7}\,\text{m}$
  b blue light with wavelength $4.65 \times 10^{-7}\,\text{m}$.
Give your answers in standard form to 2 significant figures.

> **Q12 Literacy hint**
>
> λ is the Greek letter *lambda*. It is sometimes used instead of a letter from our alphabet.
> The unit for frequency is hertz (Hz).

13 Real The populations of Bangladesh, China, India and Pakistan are shown in the table.
  a Write these countries in order of population size, from smallest to largest.
  b What is the difference between the population of India and China?

Country	Population in 2014
Bangladesh	1.556×10^8
China	1.366×10^9
India	1.247×10^9
Pakistan	1.880×10^8

  c How many times larger is the population of India than that of Pakistan?
  d What is the total population of these 4 countries?
The world population is 7.183×10^9.
  e What proportion of the world's population lives in China or India?

14 Real / STEM / Modelling A science museum wants to make a scale model of the Solar System.
The diagram shows the real distances between the Earth, Moon and Sun.
In the model the Earth and the Moon are 10 cm apart.
How far away from the Earth will the Sun need to be?
Discussion Is this a good scale for the model? Suggest some distances that might work better.

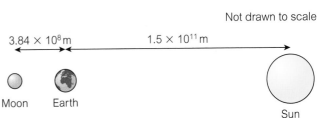

Not drawn to scale

15 Work out

a $\left(\frac{1}{2}\right)^{-3}$ **b** $\left(\frac{2}{3}\right)^{-2}$ **c** $\left(\frac{1}{2}\right)^{-4}$

16 Write as a single power.

a $11^7 \times 11^{-3} \div 11^{-2}$ **b** $3^{-13} \times 3^4 \div 3^{-5} \div 3^2$

c $\dfrac{7^{-7} \times 7^{-2}}{7^{-1} \div 7^8}$ **d** $\dfrac{5^{-3} \div 5^3}{5^{10} \times 5^{-6}}$

17 Work out

a $3^{-3} \times 2^{-2} \times 2^{-1} \times 3^4$ **b** $\left(\frac{1}{2}\right)^{-3} \times \left(\frac{1}{3}\right)^{-1} \times \left(\frac{1}{2}\right)^{2} \times \left(\frac{1}{3}\right)^{-1}$

c $\left(\frac{1}{2}\right)^{-5} \times \left(\frac{1}{3}\right)^{-1} \times \left(\frac{1}{2}\right)^{3} \times \left(\frac{1}{3}\right)^{-2}$ **d** $\left(\frac{1}{2}\right)^{-3} \times \left(\frac{1}{2}\right)^{3}$

18 Reasoning   **a** Which of these numbers have the same value?

 $(0.5)^3$ 8^{-2} $\left(\frac{1}{4}\right)^{2}$ $\left(\frac{1}{2}\right)^{3}$ 2^{-3} $\left(\frac{1}{64}\right)^{\frac{1}{2}}$

b How many different ways can you write $\frac{1}{9}$?

19 Work out

a $\left(2\frac{1}{4}\right)^{\frac{1}{2}}$ **b** $\left(2\frac{7}{9}\right)^{\frac{3}{2}}$ **c** $\left(15\frac{5}{8}\right)^{\frac{1}{3}}$

d $\left(\frac{8}{1000}\right)^{-\frac{5}{3}}$ **e** $\left(1\frac{9}{16}\right)^{-\frac{3}{2}}$ **f** $\left(2\frac{10}{27}\right)^{-\frac{2}{3}}$

Q19a hint

Write the mixed number as an improper fraction.

20 Work out

a $\sqrt{7} \times \sqrt{28}$ **b** $\sqrt{3} \times \sqrt{48}$ **c** $\sqrt{5} \times \sqrt{6} \times \sqrt{30}$

d $\left(\sqrt{36}\right)^3$ **e** $\sqrt[3]{216} \div \sqrt{16}$ **f** $\sqrt[4]{81} \times \sqrt{10} \times \sqrt{40}$

21 Simplify, leaving your answers in surd form.

a $\sqrt{24} \times \sqrt{18}$ **b** $\sqrt{30} \times \sqrt{210}$

c $\sqrt{10} \times \sqrt{18} \times \sqrt{45} \times \sqrt{12}$ **d** $\sqrt{\left(\sqrt[3]{27}\right)} \times \sqrt{15}$

Q21 hint

You can simplify expressions involving surds in the same way as you simplify algebraic expressions. $\sqrt{3}$ and $\sqrt{5}$ are not like terms.

22 Simplify, leaving your answers in surd form.

a $2\sqrt{2} + 3\sqrt{2} = \square\sqrt{2}$ **b** $5\sqrt{3} - 2\sqrt{3}$

c $3\sqrt{5} + 2\sqrt{3} + 2\sqrt{5} = \square\sqrt{3} + \square\sqrt{5}$ **d** $10\sqrt{7} + 4\sqrt{2} + 3\sqrt{2} - 6\sqrt{7}$

23 Problem-solving AC is the diameter of the circle.
Give an **exact answer** for
a the area of the circle
b the area of triangle ABC
c the ratio AB : BC

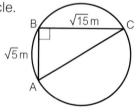

Q23 Literacy hint

An **exact answer** has π and surds instead of rounded decimals.

24 Reasoning AB = $\sqrt{20}$ cm and BC = 6 cm.
Show that the area of the isosceles triangle ABC is $3\sqrt{11}$ cm^2.

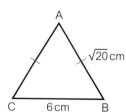

25 Reasoning The side of a regular hexagon is 8 cm.
Show that the perpendicular height (h) is $8\sqrt{3}$ cm.

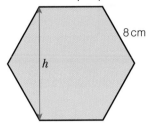

8 cm

h

26 Which of these cube roots are irrational?

a $\sqrt[3]{1}$ b $\sqrt[3]{3}$ c $\sqrt[3]{5}$

d $\sqrt[3]{8}$ e $\sqrt[3]{12}$ f $\sqrt[3]{27}$

> **Q26 hint**
> Which cannot be simplified to give an integer?

27 In a test students were asked to calculate the length of the arc AB.
The radius of the circle is 5 cm.

A

5 cm   B

a Which of the answers that students gave are correct?

A $7.85\,\text{cm}^2$ (to 2 d.p.)

B $19.6\,\text{cm}^2$ (to 3 s.f.)

C $2.5\pi\,\text{cm}^2$

D $6.25\pi\,\text{cm}^2$

E $10\pi\,\text{cm}^2$

b Which answer is the most accurate? Explain your answer.

Investigation   **Problem-solving**

Use the numbers in the boxes to find close approximations to 17.
Choose a number from the first box and raise it to a power from the second box.

2.6	4.1	290
$\frac{1}{18}$	27	$\frac{1}{70}$
5000	16.9	70

to the power of

-1	$\frac{1}{2}$	3
2	$\frac{2}{3}$	1
$-\frac{1}{3}$	$\frac{1}{3}$	5

is roughly _____

For example, $2.6^3 = 17.576$, which is a close approximation to 17.
Are there any numbers you can't use?

---

28 Reflect In this unit you have learned a lot of new vocabulary.
Write a list of all the new vocabulary you have used.
Write, in your own words, a definition for each.
Compare your definitions with your classmates.
Did you all learn the same thing?

Reflect

1 Unit test

Log how you did on your Student Progression Chart.

1 Write as a fraction

  a $\left(\frac{1}{3}\right)^2$ **b** $\left(\frac{3}{5}\right)^3$

2 Write down the reciprocal of

  a 9   **b** $\frac{5}{8}$

  c $3\frac{2}{7}$ **d** $\frac{1}{4}$

3 Write each number in standard form.

  a 820   **b** 0.000 091 5

4 Put these numbers in order, from smallest to largest.

  1.24×10^{-2} 1.21×10^{-4} 1.2×10^{2} 1.23×10^{3} 1.24×10

5 Work out each calculation. Give your answers in standard form.

  a $\dfrac{8.8 \times 10^{8}}{2.2 \times 10^{3}}$ **b** $(2.5 \times 10^{4}) \times (5 \times 10^{-7})$

6 Work out each calculation. Give your answers in standard form.

  a $(1.505 \times 10^{-9}) \times (8.3 \times 10^{4})$ **b** $\dfrac{48.96 \times 10^{5}}{5.1 \times 10^{-5}}$

7 Write as a single power.

  a $6^{3} \times 6^{-4}$ **b** $3^{-4} \div 3^{-2}$

  c $(7^{-3})^{2}$ **d** $\dfrac{4^{-4} \div 4^{-1}}{4^{-1} \times 4^{-1}}$

8 Simplify

  a $\sqrt{72}$ **b** $\sqrt{77}$ **c** $\sqrt{3} \times \sqrt{24}$

9 Simplify, leaving your answers in surd form.

  a $7\sqrt{5} + 2\sqrt{5}$ **b** $5\sqrt{7} + 3\sqrt{2} - 2\sqrt{7}$

10 Work out

  a $27^{\frac{2}{3}}$ **b** $\left(\frac{1}{25}\right)^{\frac{3}{2}}$

11 Work out

  a $144^{-\frac{1}{2}}$ **b** $\left(\frac{8}{27}\right)^{-\frac{2}{3}}$

12 Show that the area of triangle ABC is $\sqrt{30}$ cm².

A $\sqrt{20}$ cm   B

$\sqrt{26}$ cm

C

13 Say whether each number is rational or irrational.

a $\sqrt{3}$ **b** $\frac{1}{6}$

c $\sqrt{4}$ **d** $\frac{2}{\pi}$

14 ABC is a right-angled triangle. What is the most accurate answer for the length BC?

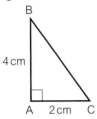

A 4.472 135 955 cm
B 4.5 cm (to 2 s.f.)
C $2\sqrt{5}$ cm
D 4.47 cm (to 2 d.p.)

Challenge

15 Simplify

a $\left(2\frac{2}{3}\right)^{-1}$ **b** $\left(6\frac{1}{4}\right)^{\frac{1}{2}}$

16 Simplify

a $5\sqrt{2} + 10\sqrt{2}$ **b** $6\sqrt{5} + \sqrt{3} + 4\sqrt{5}$

17 An African elephant weighs about 6 tonnes.
The Earth weighs 5.97×10^{24} kg.

a How many kg are in a tonne?
b How many tonnes does the Earth weigh?
c What is the mass of the Earth, measured in elephants? Give your answer in standard form.
d Look back at the data in Exercise 1.3 Q8. How many elephants do you need to make the mass of each planet?

18 Reflect Which of the questions in this unit test took:
  • the shortest time to answer? Why?
  • the longest time to answer? Why?
  • the most thought to answer? Why?

MASTER | Check P36 | Strengthen P38 | Extend P42 | Test P46

2.1 Sequences

You will learn to:
- Generate sequences using quadratic expressions
- Find an expression for the nth term of a quadratic sequence.

CONFIDENCE

Why learn this?
Sequences and patterns occur in nature and scientific experiments. They can be used to make predictions.

Fluency
What is the result of
- multiplying 1 by 3 and adding 7
- multiplying 2 by 3 and adding 7
- multiplying 3 by 3 and adding 7?

Explore
There are 100 rabbits on an island. How many will there be in 6 months' time?

Exercise 2.1

Warm up

1 Work out the first four terms and the 10th term of the sequence with nth term

  a $6n$

  b $n - 7$

  c $3n + 2$

  d $2n - 3$

2 Work out the nth term of each sequence.

  a 5, 10, 15, 20, …

  b 5, 6, 7, 8, …

  c 2, 5, 8, 11, …

  d −3, 1, 5, 9, …

> **Key point**
> An nth term that includes n^2 (and no higher power of n) generates a **quadratic sequence**.

3 Decide whether each sequence is **arithmetic** or **quadratic**.

  a 5, 9, 13, 17, …

  b 1, 4, 9, 16, …

  c −3, −1, 1, 3, …

  d 32, 28, 24, 20, …

  e 2, 8, 18, 32, …

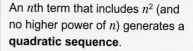

> **Q3 Literacy hint**
> An **arithmetic** sequence goes up or down in equal steps.

Topic links: Expressions

4 Write the next three terms in each sequence.

a 2, 5, 10, 17, …

b 0, 3, 8, 15, …

c 6, 14, 24, 36, …

d −1, 5, 15, 29, …

e 2, 3, 5, 8, …

f −4, −2, 1, 5, …

Key point

$T(n)$ is another way of writing the nth term.

5 Work out the first four terms and the 10th term of the quadratic sequence with

a $T(n) = n^2$

b $T(n) = 3n^2$

c $T(n) = -2n^2$

d $T(n) = 5n^2$

Q5a hint

$T(1) = 1^2 = \square$
$T(2) = 2^2 = \square$

6 Work out the first four terms and the 10th term of the quadratic sequence with

a $T(n) = 2n^2 + 4$

b $T(n) = 3n^2 - 3$

c $T(n) = -3n^2 + 7$

d $T(n) = 4n^2 - 5$

7 **Reasoning** Find the 5th and 10th terms of the sequence $T(n) = 2n^2 + 5$. Explain why the 10th term is not double the 5th term.

8 a Copy and complete this table for the sequence of square numbers.

Term number	1	2	3	4	5	6
Term	1	4	9	16		

Difference   +3   +$\square$

Key point

When the difference isn't constant, you can work out the difference between the differences. This is known as the **second difference**.

b What happens to the differences for this sequence?

c Add another row to your table below the difference row and calculate the **second difference**.

Worked example

Find the nth term of the sequence that begins 3, 6, 11, 18, …

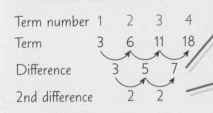

Term number   1   2   3   4

Term   3   6   11   18

Difference   3   5   7

2nd difference   2   2

Work out the differences between each term.

Work out the second difference. Any sequence that has a second difference of 2 is based around n^2.

Term number   1   2   3   4

Term   3   6   11   18

n^2 1   4   9   16

)+2)+2)+2)+2

nth term is $T(n) = n^2 + 2$

Write the sequence of square numbers (n^2). 2 is added to each of the square numbers.

Describe the sequence.

9 Find the nth term of each sequence.

　　a 5, 8, 13, 20, …

　　b –2, 1, 6, 13, …

　　c 5, 11, 21, 35, …

Key point

If the second difference is 4, the sequence is based around $2n^2$. If the second difference is 6, the sequence is based around ☐.

10 a Write down the first five terms of the sequence with

　　　i $T(n) = 2n + 1$

　　　ii $T(n) = n^2$

　　b Write down the first five terms of the sequence with nth term $n^2 + 2n + 1$

　　c A quadratic sequence and a linear sequence have been added together to give:

　　　3, 8, 15, 24, 35, …

　　　i What is the quadratic sequence?

　　　ii What is the linear sequence?

　　　iii What is the nth term of 3, 8, 15, 24, 35, …?

11 Find the nth term of each sequence.

　　a 2, 6, 12, 20, …

　　b 0, 2, 6, 12, …

　　c 3, 7, 13, 21, …

　　d –1, 3, 9, 17, …

　　e 3, 8, 17, 30, …

Investigation   Reasoning / Problem-solving

The diagram shows the first 3 triangle numbers.

$T_1 = 1$ $T_2 = 3$ $T_3 = 6$

1 Work out the sum of adjacent pairs of triangle numbers. What do you notice? Use a diagram to help explain why this happens.

2 Use the techniques used in Q8 and 9 above to find an expression for the nth term in the sequence of triangle numbers.

---

12 Explore There are 100 rabbits on an island. How many will there be in 6 months' time?

Is it easier to explore this question now you have completed the lesson? What further information do you need to be able to answer this?

13 Reflect Deepak says, 'A lot of maths is about looking for hidden patterns.' Which questions in this lesson do you think Deepak was thinking of when he said this?

Explore

Reflect

2.2 Expanding

You will learn to:
- Multiply pairs of brackets
- Square a linear expression
- Use quadratic identities.

Why learn this?
Expanding brackets can help promoters work out what price to put concert tickets at for the greatest profit.

Fluency
- What is $7(3 + 7)$?
- Expand $5(x - 6)$.
- Factorise $8x + 4$.

Explore
What is the area of a rectangle that is $(x + 2)$ by $(x - 2)$?

Exercise 2.2

1 Expand and simplify
   a $5(x + 2) + 2x$
   b $6(a - 5) + 6$
   c $2(z + 3) + 3(z - 5)$
   d $5(3 - t) - 2(t + 4)$

2 Expand and simplify
   a $2x(x^2 + 2) + 3x$
   b $3y(4 - y) + y^2$
   c $2b + b^2(b + 3) + 3$
   d $w^3(3w - 2) - 2w(w + 3)$

Worked example

Expand and simplify $(x + 2)(x + 4)$.

$(x + 2)(x + 4) = x^2 + 4x + 2x + 8$
$\qquad\qquad\quad = x^2 + 6x + 8$

$(x + 2)(x + 4) = x^2 + \underbrace{4x + 2x}_{6x} + 8$
$\qquad\qquad\quad = x^2 + \quad 6x \quad + 8$

Key point

When you **expand** double brackets, you multiply each term in one set of brackets by each term in the other set of brackets.

$(a + b)(c + d) = ac + ad + bc + bd$

3 Expand and simplify the double brackets.
   a $(x + 3)(x + 2)$
   b $(y + 2)(y + 3)$
   c $(d + 5)(d + 2)$
   d $(m + 3)(m + 4)$
   e $(v + 6)(v + 3)$
   f $(h + 6)(h + 7)$

   Discussion What do you notice about your answers to parts **a** and **b**?

4 Expand and simplify the double brackets.
   a $(p + 3)(p - 2)$
   b $(w - 3)(w + 2)$
   c $(x + 4)(x - 2)$
   d $(e - 3)(e + 6)$
   e $(s - 8)(s - 2)$
   f $(j - 5)(j - 4)$

Q4 hint

Be careful with negative numbers.
$-8 \times -2 = +16$

5 **Problem-solving / Reasoning** Adam and Kari both expand and simplify the quadratic expression $(x - 3)(-5 + x)$.
   Adam says the answer is $x^2 + 2x - 15$.
   Kari says the answer is $x^2 - 8x + 15$.
   Only one of them is correct. Who is it? What mistakes were made?

Warm up

6 Expand and simplify

a $(x + 5)^2$ **b** $(x + 6)^2$

c $(x + 7)^2$ **d** $(x - 1)^2$

e $(x - 4)^2$ **f** $(x - 7)^2$

Q6a hint

$(x + 5)^2 = (x + 5)(x + 5)$

7 Expand and simplify

a $(x + 8)(x - 2) + x(4x - 2)$ **b** $(n - 2)(n - 6) - 10(n + 4)$

Q7a hint

Work out $(x + 8)(x - 2)$.
Expand $x(4x - 2)$.
Add them together.

8 Problem-solving / Reasoning Show that

$n(n + 8) - 2(n + 5) = (n + 4)(n - 2) + 2(2n - 1)$

Investigation   **Problem-solving / Reasoning**

1 Expand and simplify the double brackets.

   a $(x + 1)(x - 1)$

   b $(x + 3)(x - 3)$

   c $(x + 4)(x - 4)$

   d $(x + 5)(x - 5)$

   e $(x + 6)(x - 6)$

   f $(x + 7)(x - 7)$

   g $(x + 8)(x - 8)$

2 What do you notice about your answers?

3 Why do you think expressions of the form $(x + n)(x - n)$ are called the **difference of two squares**?

---

9 Problem-solving / Modelling A farmer has a square-shaped field of length a metres.

   a Write an expression for the area of his field.

   b He changes the shape of the field by adding b metres to one pair of opposite sides, and subtracting b metres from the other pair of opposite sides. Write an expression for the area of this field.

   c What has been the impact of changing the shape of his field on the area?

10 Expand the double brackets and simplify where possible.

a $(2x + 7)(x - 5)$ **b** $(2x - 4)(x - 3)$

c $(x + 7)(2x - 2)$ **d** $(3x + 6)(2x - 4)$

e $(2x - 3)(4x + 5)$ **f** $(3x - 7)(3x - 8)$

Q10 hint

Follow the same rules as you did in Q3, 4, 5 and 6.

11 Expand and simplify

a $(3x + 7)^2$ **b** $(2x - 4)^2$

c $(5x + 6)^2$ **d** $(4x + 9)^2$

e $(7x - 3)^2$ **f** $(8x - 9)^2$

12 Expand and simplify

a $(2x + 1)(2x - 1)$ **b** $(3x + 4)(3x - 4)$

c $(2x - 5)(2x + 5)$ **d** $(c + d)(c - d)$

13 Explore What is the area of a rectangle that is $(x + 2)$ by $(x - 2)$?
Is it easier to explore this question now you have completed the lesson?
What further information do you need to be able to answer this?

14 Reflect Q9 is a pictorial example of the difference of two squares. Can you think of other examples where a picture helps to explain abstract ideas?

Explore

Reflect

MASTER

Check
P36

Strengthen
P38

Extend
P42

Test
P46

2.3 Factorising

You will learn to:
- Factorise quadratic expressions into two brackets.

CONFIDENCE

Why learn this?
The path of a cricket ball can be described using a quadratic expression. It is useful to be able to factorise such expressions in order to find out more about the ball, such as the maximum height reached by the ball.

Fluency
Which pair of numbers
- adds up to 7 and multiplies to make 10
- adds up to 13 and multiplies to make 30
- adds up to 5 and multiplies to make −24?

Explore
Does $x^2 + a^2$ factorise?

Exercise 2.3

1 Expand and simplify

  a $(x + 4)^2$ **b** $(x - 3)^2$

  c $(x + y)^2$ **d** $(2x + 4)^2$

  e $(3x - 4)^2$ **f** $(2x + y)^2$

2 Expand and simplify the double brackets.

  a $(x + 5)(x - 5)$ **b** $(a + 7)(a - 7)$

  c $(y + 2)(y - 2)$ **d** $(x + y)(x - y)$

3 Factorise

  a $4x^2 + 12x$ **b** $25x^3 - 15x$

  c $y^2 - 9y^3$ **d** $3x^4 + 15x^2$

Worked example

Factorise $x^2 + 7x + 10$.

$2 + 5 \qquad 2 \times 5$

$x^2 + 7x + 10 = (x + 5)(x + 2)$

The **factor pairs** of 10 are 1×10 and 2×5.
Only the 2 and 5 add together to make 7 so these are the numbers that go in the brackets.

$x^2 + 7x + 10 = (x + 5)(x + 2)$

Check: $(x + 2)(x + 5) = x^2 + 5x + 2x + 5 \times 2$

$= x^2 + 7x + 10$

Check your answer by expanding.

4 Factorise each quadratic expression. Check your answers.

  a $x^2 + 7x + 12$ **b** $x^2 + 9x + 18$

  c $x^2 + 9x + 14$ **d** $x^2 + 12x + 27$

  e $x^2 - 3x + 2$ **f** $x^2 - 7x + 12$

Q4f hint

Remember that $-3 \times -4 = 12$ as well as $3 \times 4 = 12$.

Warm up

5 Factorise each quadratic expression. Check your answers.
  a $x^2 + 3x - 18$
  b $x^2 + 4x - 12$
  c $x^2 + 8x - 33$
  d $x^2 - 7x - 44$
  e $x^2 - 9x - 36$
  f $x^2 - 12x - 28$

6 Match the equivalent expressions.

A $x^2 + 8x + 12$	**i** $(x - 7)(x - 4)$
B $x^2 + 9x + 20$	**ii** $(x + 9)(x - 4)$
C $x^2 - 11x + 28$	**iii** $(x + 2)(x - 5)$
D $x^2 - 7x + 10$	**iv** $(x + 4)(x + 5)$
E $x^2 + 5x + 36$	**v** $(x - 4)(x + 3)$
F $x^2 + 4x - 21$	**vi** $(x + 6)(x + 2)$
G $x^2 - x - 12$	**vii** $(x + 7)(x - 3)$
H $x^2 - 3x - 10$	**viii** $(x - 5)(x - 2)$

> **Key point**
>
> A **perfect square** is of the form
> $(x + a)^2 = (x + a)(x + a) = x^2 + 2ax + a^2$

7 Write these as **perfect squares**.
  a $x^2 + 6x + 9$
  b $x^2 + 14x + 49$
  c $x^2 - 8x + 16$
  d $x^2 - 12x + 36$

> **Q7a hint**
>
> Find the value of a in this equation and then substitute it in.
> $x^2 + 2ax + a^2 = x^2 + 6x + 9$

8 Factorise each quadratic expression. Check your answers.
  a $x^2 - 25$
  b $x^2 - 64$
  c $x^2 - 81$
  d $x^2 - 121$
  e $p^2 - q^2$

> **Q8 hint**
>
> The middle term has cancelled out when collecting terms.

9 **Problem-solving** The area of a rectangle is $x^2 + 11x + 24$.
  What could the side lengths of the rectangle be?

10 **Problem-solving** Abrahim adjusts the sides of a rectangle so that its perimeter remains the same and its new area is $x^2 - 49$.
  a How did he change the two sides?
  b Describe the original shape.

11 **Explore** Does $x^2 + a^2$ factorise?
  Is it easier to explore this question now you have completed the lesson? What further information do you need to be able to answer this?

12 **Reflect** Factorising quadratic expressions often involves 'trial and error'. Is trial and error simply guesswork, or can you devise a system to make it more efficient?

*Active*Learn Delta 3, Section 2.3

2.4 Solving quadratic equations

You will learn to:
- Solve quadratic equations by factorising.

Why learn this?
The police solve quadratic equations to work out how fast cars were travelling before a collision.

Fluency
Work out x when
- $x - 8 = 14$
- $7x = 56$
- $3x + 4 = 19$

Work out
- 2×0
- $8 \times 0 \times 6$
- $15 \times -3 \times 0$
- 5×0

Explore
How far will a car travel once the brakes are applied?

CONFIDENCE

Exercise 2.4

1 Solve each equation.
  a $x^2 = 36$
  b $2x^2 = 32$
  c $3x^2 = 12$
  d $x^2 + 9 = 25$

2 Factorise each expression.
  a $x^2 - 3x + 2$
  b $x^2 - 81$
  c $x^2 - 2x - 35$
  d $x^2 + 10x + 25$

Warm up

Worked example

Solve $x^2 + 6x = 27$.

$x^2 + 6x = 27$ → Rearrange the equation so it equals 0.
$x^2 + 6x - 27 = 0$ → Factorise the quadratic expression.
$(x + 9)(x - 3) = 0$
$x + 9 = 0 \qquad x = -9$ → 0 multiplied by any number is 0.
$x - 3 = 0 \qquad x = 3$ So either $x + 9 = 0$
$x = -9$ or $x = 3$ or $x - 3 = 0$.

Check by substitution:
$x = -9$
$(-9)^2 + (6 \times -9) = 27$
$\qquad 81 - 54 = 27$ ✓
$x = 3$
$3^2 + (6 \times 3) = 27$
$\qquad 9 + 18 = 27$ ✓

Key point
You can solve some quadratic equations by setting them equal to 0 and factorising.

3 Solve each quadratic equation by factorising. Check your answers.
  a $x^2 + x = 2$
  b $x^2 + 15x = -54$
  c $x^2 + x = 20$
  d $x^2 + 4x = 21$
  e $x^2 - 9x = 22$
  f $x^2 - 14x = 51$

Q3 hint
Rearrange the equations so that they equal 0.

4 Solve each quadratic equation by factorising. Check your answers.

    a $x^2 + 4x = -4$ **b** $x^2 + 14x = -49$

    c $x^2 - 6x = -9$ **d** $x^2 - 10x = -25$

5 **Problem-solving** The length of a rectangle is 4 m more than its width. The area is 96 m². What is the

    a length   **b** width of the rectangle?

    Discussion How did you decide which solution to use?

6 **Problem-solving** Bonita is 2 years older than Kimberley. The product of their ages is 399. How old are they both?

7 **Problem-solving** Ben is 4 years younger than Josh. The product of their ages is 437. How old are they both?

8 **Problem-solving** The square of a number is equal to 10 times the number subtract 24.
Write down two possible values for the number.

9 Solve these equations to work out x.

    a $x^2 + 11 = 47$ **b** $x^2 - 6 = 19$ **c** $x^2 - 24 = 25$

10 **Problem-solving** Stephen thinks of a number, squares it and adds 9 to get an answer of 25.

    a Write an equation to show this.

    b Solve the equation.

    c Why can't we be sure about which number Stephen thought of?

Investigation   **Reasoning / Problem-solving**

  1 Without expanding and rearranging, solve $(x + 5)^2 = 16$.

  2 Explain why the solutions are the same as $x^2 + 10x + 9 = 0$.

  3 Write $x^2 + 4x + 4$ as a perfect square.

  4 Use your answer to part **3** to solve $x^2 + 4x + 10$ in two different ways.

---

11 **Explore** How far will a car travel once the brakes are applied? Is it easier to explore this question now you have completed the lesson? What further information do you need to be able to answer this?

12 **Reflect** This lesson has several problem-solving questions. How did your methods for solving them change as you progressed through the lesson? Did finding the solutions get easier by the time you reached the last question?

     *Active*Learn   Delta 3, Section 2.4

2 Check up

Log how you did on your
Student Progression Chart.

Sequences

1 Arsheen says the sequence 1, 4, 7, 10, 13, … is quadratic.
Is she right? Explain how you know.

2 Write the next three terms in each sequence.
  a 0, 3, 8, 15, …
  b −1, 2, 7, 14, …
  c 3, 5, 9, 15, …
  d −3, 0, 7, 18, …

3 Work out the first four terms and the 10th term of the quadratic
sequence with
  a $T(n) = 4n^2$
  b $T(n) = -7n^2$

4 Work out the first four terms and the 10th term of the quadratic
sequence with
  a $T(n) = 4n^2 - 2$
  b $T(n) = -2n^2 + 4$
  c $T(n) = -3n^2 - 5$
  d $T(n) = -n^2 + 2n - 3$

5 Find the nth term of each sequence.
  a 2, 6, 12, 20, …
  b 1, 6, 13, 22, …
  c −2, 0, 4, 10, …
  d −5, −2, 3, 10, …

Expanding

6 Expand and simplify
  a $(x + 2)(x + 7)$
  b $(x + 8)(x - 5)$
  c $(x - 4)(x + 6)$
  d $(x - 7)(x - 9)$

7 Molly has squared the expression $(x - 6)$ and written the answer $x^2 + 36$.
Is Molly correct? Explain how you know.

8 Expand and simplify
  a $(x - 2)(x + 2)$
  b $(x + 7)(x - 7)$
  c $(x + 5)^2$

9 Expand and simplify
  a $(2x + 3)(x - 6)$
  b $(3x + 8)(2x - 5)$
  c $(4x - 3)(3x - 8)$
  d $(2x - 7)(2x + 7)$

10 A rectangle has a length of $2x + 1$ and a width of $3x - 2$.
Write an expression for the area of the rectangle.

Factorising

11 Factorise each quadratic expression.
  a $x^2 + 5x + 6$
  b $x^2 + 7x - 18$
  c $x^2 - 5x + 4$
  d $x^2 - 4x - 45$

12 Factorise each quadratic expression.
  a $x^2 + 6x + 9$
  b $x^2 - 10x + 25$
  c $x^2 - 49$

13 The area of a rectangle is $x^2 - 4x - 21$.
Write down an expression for the width and the length of
the rectangle.

Solving quadratic equations

14 Solve each equation.
  a $x^2 + 8x = -15$
  b $x^2 + 11x = -24$
  c $x^2 - x = 30$
  d $x^2 + 6x = 7$

15 Milo is 5 years older than Vlad.
The product of their ages is 414.
How old are they both?

16 **How sure are you of your answers? Were you mostly**
  😖 **Just guessing**   😐 **Feeling doubtful**   🙂 **Confident**
  What next? Use your results to decide whether to strengthen or
  extend your learning.

Challenge

17 a Factorise each of the expressions on the grid.

$x^2 + 8x + 12$	$x^2 + 7x + 10$	$x^2 - 2x + 1$
$x^2 - 4x + 3$	$x^2 - 9$	$x^2 + 9x + 18$
$x^2 + 5x - 6$	$x^2 + 4x - 5$	$x^2 - x - 6$

  b Make a list of all the factors used.
  c Using only these factors, make as many new expressions as you can.

2 Strengthen

You will:
- Strengthen your understanding with practice.

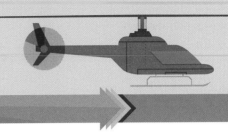

Sequences

1 Which of these are quadratic sequences?

   a   2, 5, 10, 17 …

      +3   +5   +7   1st difference: the difference between terms

        +2   +2   2nd difference: the difference between differences

   b 5, 11, 17, 23, …

   c 48, 40, 32, 24, …

   d 3, 5, 9, 15, …

> **Q1 hint**
>
> In a quadratic sequence the *first difference* changes by a constant amount.

2 Write the next three terms of these quadratic sequences.

   a 1, 5, 13, 25, …

   b 0, 2, 6, 12, …

   c 96, 48, 24, 12, …

   d 3, 6, 11, 18, …

> **Q2a hint**
>
>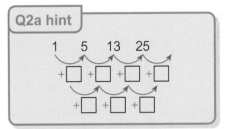

3 A quadratic sequence has a general term $T(n) = n^2$.

   a Work out the first four terms.

   b Work out the 10th term.

> **Q3a hint**
>
> 1st term: $T(1) = 1^2$
> 2nd term: $T(2) = 2^2$

4 Work out the first four terms and the 10th term of the quadratic sequence with

   a $T(n) = n^2 + 4$

   b $T(n) = n^2 - 3$

   c $T(n) = 4n^2$

   d $T(n) = 3n^2 + 7$

   e $T(n) = -2n^2 + 5$

> **Q4 hint**
>
> Follow the same method as in Q3.

5 Find the nth term of each sequence.

   a 4, 7, 12, 19, …

      4   7   12   19

      +3 +5 +7   Look at the pattern in the differences

       +2   +2   Now look at the second difference

   b 2, 5, 10, 17, …

   c 7, 10, 15, 22, …

   d -3, 0, 5, 12, …

> **Q5a hint**
>
> The second difference is 2 so the sequence starts with n^2.
> $1^2 + \square = 4$
> $2^2 + \square = 7$

6 Find the nth term of each sequence.

   a 3, 8, 15, 24, …

   b 3, 7, 13, 21, …

   c 4, 12, 24, 40, …

   d 2, 14, 30, 50, …

   e 0, 5, 14, 27, …

   f 4, 11, 24, 43, …

Expanding

1 Expand and simplify the double brackets.

   a $(a + 5)(a + 4)$

   b $(n + 3)(n + 2)$

   c $(x + 7)(x + 4)$

   d $(p + 3)(p + 2)$

   e $(y + 7)(y + 1)$

2 Expand and simplify the double brackets.

   a $(b - 6)(b + 3)$

   b $(y + 4)(y - 3)$

   c $(x - 8)(x + 2)$

   d $(a + 3)(a - 4)$

   e $(b - 6)(b - 5)$

   f $(x - 3)(x - 5)$

   g $(g - 3)(g - 7)$

   h $(n - 9)(n - 3)$

3 Expand and simplify

   a $(c + 7)^2$

   b $(y - 5)^2$

   c $(n + 8)^2$

   d $(n - 1)^2$

   e $(p - 6)^2$

4 Expand and simplify

   a $(x - 3)(x + 3)$

   b $(x + 2)(x - 2)$

   c $(x - 9)(x + 9)$

   d $(x + y)(x - y)$

5 Expand and simplify

   a $(2x + 4)(x - 3)$

   b $(2x - 5)(x - 2)$

   c $(x + 4)(2x - 3)$

   d $(2x + 7)(2x - 4)$

   e $(x + 2)(3x - 5)$

   f $(2x + 9)(3x - 2)$

Q1a hint

To expand $(a + 5)(a + 4)$, use a grid method like this:

×	a	+5
a	$+a^2$	$+5a$
+4	$+4a$	+20

Answer: $a^2 + 5a + 4a + 20$

Simplify: □ + □ + □

Q2a hint

To expand $(b - 6)(b + 3)$, use a grid method like this:

×	b	−6
b	b^2	$-6b$
+3	$+3b$	−18

Q3a hint

$(c + 7)^2 = (c + 7)(c + 7)$

Q4 hint

Look at what happens to the middle two terms.

Q5 hint

$2x \times x = 2x^2$

$2x \times 2x = 2 \times x \times 2 \times x$

$= 4 \times x^2$

$= 4x^2$

Factorising

1 a Which two numbers

    i add together to make 8 and multiply together to make 15

    ii add together to make 11 and multiply together to make 28?

  b Factorise each quadratic expression.
Check your answers by expanding the brackets.

    i $x^2 + 5x + 6 = (x + \square)(x + \square)$

    ii $x^2 + 12x + 35 = (x + \square)(x + \square)$

    iii $x^2 + 9x + 8 = (x + \square)(x + \square)$

    iv $x^2 + 10x + 24$

    v $x^2 + 11x + 24$

    vi $x^2 + 11x + 18$

> **Q1b i hint**
>
> Which two numbers add together to make 5 and multiply together to make 6?

2 a Which two numbers

    i add to make –5 and multiply to make 6

    ii add to make –10 and multiply to make 21?

  b Factorise each quadratic expression.

    i $x^2 - 7x + 12 = (x - \square)(x - \square)$

    ii $x^2 - 6x + 8 = (x - \square)(x - \square)$

    iii $x^2 - 9x + 20 = (x - \square)(x - \square)$

    iv $x^2 - 8x + 7$

    v $x^2 - 15x + 44$

    vi $x^2 - 13x + 42$

> **Q2b hint**
>
> negative × negative = **positive**
> negative + negative = **negative**

3 Factorise

  a $x^2 - 2x - 8 = (x + \square)(x - \square)$

  b $x^2 - 3x - 10 = (x + \square)(x - \square)$

  c $x^2 - 3x - 18 = (x + \square)(x - \square)$

  d $x^2 - 8x - 48$

  e $x^2 - 6x - 27$

  f $x^2 - x - 12$

> **Q3 hint**
>
> negative × positive = **negative**
> negative + positive = **positive**
>   or **negative**

4 Factorise

  a $x^2 + 7x - 18 = (x - \square)(x + \square)$

  b $x^2 + 2x - 24 = (x - \square)(x + \square)$

  c $x^2 + x - 56 = (x - \square)(x + \square)$

  d $x^2 + 3x - 54$

  e $x^2 + 4x - 21$

  f $x^2 + 5x - 24$

5 Factorise

  a $x^2 + 4x + 4$

  b $x^2 - 6x + 9$

  c $x^2 + 12x + 36$

  d $x^2 - 4x + 4$

6 Factorise
  a $x^2 - 4$
  b $x^2 - 16$
  c $x^2 - 144$

Solving quadratic equations

1 Solve each quadratic equation by factorising.
  a $x^2 + 6x = 0$
  b $x^2 - 4x = 0$
  c $x^2 - 8x = 0$
  d $x^2 - 7x = 0$
  e $x^2 + 5x = 0$

2 Solve each quadratic equation by factorising.
  a $x^2 + 3x = -2$
  b $x^2 + 5x = -4$
  c $x^2 + 3x = 10$
  d $x^2 - x = 12$
  e $x^2 + 9x = -20$
  f $x^2 - 7x = 18$
  g $x^2 + 12x = -36$
  h $x^2 - 6x = 16$

3 Problem-solving The length of a rectangle is 3 m more than its width. The area is 130 m². Find the length and the width of the rectangle.

4 Problem-solving Hamid is 5 years older than his sister Shanaz. Their ages multiplied together is 176.
  a How old is Hamid?
  b How old is Shanaz?

Enrichment

1 Choose pairs of these linear expressions to expand. You can square expressions too.
  a How many different quadratic expressions can you make?
  b What are the similarities and differences between them?

  $x + 3$ $x - 2$ $x - 3$ $x + 2$

2 Reflect How would you explain the difference between linear and quadratic sequences to a friend who has missed out on this unit?

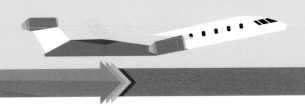

2 Extend

You will:
• Extend your understanding with problem-solving.

1 Find the next three terms of each sequence.

  a 7, 14, 23, 34, …

  b 0, 9, 22, 39, …

  c –6, 6, 30, 66, …

  d 3, –7, –25, –51, …

2 Work out the first four terms, the 20th term and the 100th term of each sequence.

  a $T(n) = n^2 + 6n - 2$

  b $T(n) = 2n^2 + 3n - 1$

  c $T(n) = 4n^2 - 2n + 5$

  d $T(n) = -2n^2 - 2n + 4$

  e $T(n) = -4n^2 + 2n - 3$

  f $T(n) = 8n^2 + 2n - 16$

> **Q2 hint**
>
> Substitute into the expression with the term number.

3 Find an expression for the nth term of these sequences.

  a 4, 14, 28, 46, …

  b 4, 19, 40, 67, …

  c 7, 17, 35, 61, …

  d 3, 0, –7, –18, …

  e –9, –20, –37, –60, …

  f 4, 16, 38, 70, …

> **Q3 hint**
>
> A second difference of 2 means n^2, a second difference of 2 × 2 means $2n^2$, …

4 **Problem-solving / Modelling** A virus is infecting a city.

After 1 day there is just 1 case.

After 2 days there are 18 cases.

After 3 days there are 43 cases.

After 4 days there are 76 cases.

  a Find an expression for the number of cases after n days.

  b Assuming the infection continues to grow in this sequence, how many people will be infected after 10 days?

  c How long will it be before more than 50 000 people are infected?

  d Explain why the number of people infected would be unlikely to continue to grow in this sequence.

5 **Problem-solving / Modelling** A popular video on a website has received these numbers of hits.

Day 1   135 hits

Day 2   455 hits

Day 3   975 hits

Day 4 1695 hits

Predict how many hits the video will have after 25 days.

> **Q5 hint**
>
> Find an expression for n days based on the sequence.

Investigation

Problem-solving

The diagram shows the first 3 hexagons in a pattern.

H_1 H_2 H_3

How many dots will there be in H_{15}?

> **Hint**
>
> Find an expression for the nth term and use it to find the 15th term.

6 Problem-solving / Reasoning In a basketball league, each team plays every other team twice.

   a How many games are there when there are
     i 2 teams   **ii** 3 teams   **iii** 4 teams?
   b Write an expression for the number of games when there are n teams.
   c How many teams do you need to have a league season with 132 matches?

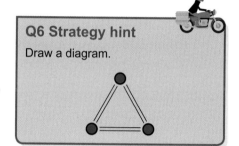

Q6 Strategy hint

Draw a diagram.

7 You can expand and simplify two sets of double brackets like this:

$$(x + 7)(x + 2) - (x + 3)(x + 8) = [x^2 + 2x + 7x + 14] - [x^2 + 8x + 3x + 24]$$
$$= [x^2 + 9x + 14] - [x^2 + 11x + 24]$$
$$= x^2 + 9x + 14 - x^2 - 11x - 24$$
$$= -2x - 10$$
$$= -2(x + 5)$$

Expand and simplify
   a $(x + 13)(x + 3) - (x + 10)(x + 4)$
   b $(x - 4)(x + 7) - (x + 5)(x - 3)$

8 You can expand three sets of brackets, $(x + 4)(x + 1)(x + 5)$, like this:
First expand and simplify the first two sets of brackets.

$$(x + 4)(x + 1) = x^2 + x + 4x + 4 = x^2 + 5x + 4$$

Then multiply the expression you get by the third set of brackets.

$$(x + 5)(x^2 + 5x + 4) = x^3 + 5x^2 + 4x + 5x^2 + 25x + 20$$

Expand and simplify
   a $(x + 2)(x + 3)(x + 4)$
   b $(x + 5)(x + 10)(x - 2)$
   c $(x - 6)(x + 2)(x - 9)$

9 Expand and simplify
   a $(2x + 4)(-3x - 6)$ **b** $(3x + 4)(-6x - 5)$
   c $(-5x - 4)(3x + 7)$ **d** $(-3x + 6)(-3x - 9)$
   e $(-2x - 4)(-4x - 2)$ **f** $(-4x - 4)(-3x - 6)$

Q9 hint

Take care when squaring or multiplying with negative numbers.

43   **Topic links:** Scale factors   **Subject links:** Science (Q4, Q21, Q22)

10 Expand and simplify

a $(2x + 4)^2$

b $(3x - 2)^2$

c $(-4x - 3)^2$

d $(-5x + 6)^2$

e $(4x + 1)(4x - 1)$

f $(-2x + 3)(-2x - 3)$

g $(-4x - 7)(-4x + 7)$

h $(ax + b)(ax - b)$

11 Problem-solving A square is changed into a rectangle by doubling two parallel sides and adding 2 cm, and trebling the other parallel sides and subtracting 3 cm.

a Write an expression for the area of the rectangle.

b The original side was 12 cm. What is the difference between the area of the rectangle and the area of the original square?

Q11 hint

Form an expression for each side in terms of x.

12 Problem-solving A photograph with dimensions x cm by y cm is enlarged so that both sides are 4 times longer but with 1 cm removed from each side to form a border.

a Write an expression for the area of the new photograph.

b What is the scale factor of enlargement?

Q12 hint

The scale factor is the number that multiplies the original dimension to make the new one.

Investigation

Reasoning

1 a Expand $(x + 8)^2$.

b Now expand $(x + 7)(x + 9)$.

c What do you notice?

2 a Now expand $(x + 6)^2$ and $(x + 5)(x + 7)$.

b What do you notice?

3 Try with other examples.

4 Write down a **generalisation**.

Check that your rule works for negative values.

Literacy hint

A **generalisation** usually uses only letters, for example, $(x + n)^2$.

---

13 Factorise each quadratic expression.

a $2x^2 - 7x - 4 = (2x - \square)(x - \square)$

b $3x^2 - 4x - 4 = (3x - \square)(x - \square)$

c $5x^2 - 4x - 36$

d $-5x^2 - 14x - 8$

e $-3x^2 - 18x + 48$

f $2x^2 - 11x + 12$

14 Factorise each quadratic expression.

a $4x^2 + 4x - 3$

b $6x^2 - 8x - 8$

c $4x^2 - 1$

d $12x^2 - 9x - 3$

e $12x^2 - x - 6$

f $9x^2 + 26x - 3$

Q14 hint

The factor pairs of $4x^2$ are x and $4x$, $2x$ and $2x$, $-x$ and $-4x$, and $-2x$ and $-2x$.

15 Problem-solving The area of a rectangular field is $6x^2 + x - 15$. Write down an expression for the length and width of the field.

16 Problem-solving The area of a triangle is $2x^2 + 9x + 7$. Write an expression for the base and the height of the triangle.

Q16 hint

Remember the area of a triangle is $\frac{1}{2}$ × base × height.

17 Solve
 a $6x^2 + 13x = -6$
 b $9x^2 - 3x = 2$
 c $8x^2 + 14x = 15$
 d $-5x^2 - 57x = 22$
 e $9x^2 = 64$
 f $16x^2 + 22x = 20$

18 **Problem-solving** Mohamed thinks of a number. He squares it, then subtracts 15. His answer is twice his original number. What is his number?

Q18 hint

Start by forming an equation for the number.

19 **Problem-solving** There is a 5-year age difference between two brothers.
The product of their ages is 546 years.
How old are they both?

20 Two **consecutive** integers multiplied together make 306.
What are the integers?

Q20 Literacy hint

Consecutive means one after the other.

21 **STEM** The formula
 $$s(t) = -\tfrac{1}{2}gt^2 + vt + h$$
 is used in the study of moving objects.
 $s(t)$ is an object's height after t seconds, v is the velocity in m/s and h is the initial height in metres. g is the acceleration due to gravity ($9.8 \, \text{m/s}^2$).
 An object is launched with a velocity of 29.4 m/s from a height of 78.4 m.
 Use the formula to work out how long will it be (in seconds) before it hits the ground.

Q21 hint

Substitute the values you have into the equation.
The ground is at zero height.
Look for a common factor in each term. It could be a decimal.

22 **STEM** An object is launched from the ground at 41.65 m/s.
Use the formula in Q21 to work out how long will it be, in seconds, before the object returns to the ground.

23 Solve each equation by completing the square.
 a $x^2 + 10x = -16$
 b $x^2 + 20x = -36$
 c $x^2 + 6x + 5 = 0$
 d $x^2 + 16x = -28$
 e $x^2 + 14x = -40$

24 **Reflect** Jenny says, 'You always need to sense check your answers when finding unknowns in real-life questions.' What do you think Jenny means by 'sense check'? Can you think of any questions where you needed to do this?

Reflect

2 Unit test

Log how you did on your Student Progression Chart.

1 Write the next three terms in each sequence.
  a −1, 2, 7, 14, …
  b 0, 6, 16, 30, …
  c 1, 10, 25, 46, …
  d 0, −5, −12, −21, …

2 Expand and simplify
  a $(x + 5)(x - 5)$
  b $(x + 10)(x - 10)$
  c $(a + b)(a - b)$

3 Expand and simplify
  a $(x + 3)(x + 1)$
  b $(x + 7)(x + 11)$
  c $(x + 13)(x + 3)$
  d $(x + a)(x + b)$

4 Find the nth term of each sequence.
  a 5, 20, 45, 80, …
  b 9, 36, 81, 144, …
  c −2, −8, −16, −26, …

5 Expand and simplify
  a $(x + 8)(x - 2)$
  b $(x - 6)(x - 10)$
  c $(x - 9)(x + 3)$
  d $(x + a)(x - b)$

6 Expand and simplify
  a $(x + 5)^2$
  b $(x - 4)^2$
  c $(x + a)^2$
  d $(x - a)^2$

7 Find the nth term of each sequence.
  a 9, 18, 33, 54, …
  b 1, 25, 65, 121, …
  c 1, −8, −23, −44, …
  d 5, 17, 33, 53, …
  e 3, 12, 29, 54, …
  f −3, 2, 13, 30, …

8 Expand and simplify
  a $(2x + 7)(x - 2)$
  b $(4x - 5)(x - 3)$
  c $(2x - 5)(2x + 3)$
  d $(3x + 4)(2x - 3)$

9 A rectangle has side lengths $2x + 7$ and $4x - 1$.
  Write an expression, without brackets, for the area of the rectangle.

10 The diagram shows the start of a pattern of rectangles.

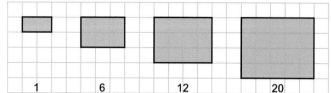

1	6	12	20

Write an expression for the number of squares in the nth pattern.

11 Factorise
   a $x^2 + 6x$
   b $x^2 + 12x + 27$
   c $x^2 + 9x + 20$

12 Factorise
   a $x^2 + x - 30$
   b $x^2 - x - 12$
   c $x^2 - 11x + 24$
   d $x^2 + 3x - 54$

13 Factorise
   a $x^2 - 144$
   b $p^2 - q^2$
   c $4x^2 - 36$
   d $x^2 + 8x + 16$

14 Solve
   a $x^2 + x = 12$
   b $x^2 - 7x = -10$
   c $x^2 + 4x = 5$

15 Factorise
   a $2x^2 + 11x + 5$
   b $4x^2 + 15x + 9$

16 Is 360 a term in the sequence with $T(n) = 2n^2 + 4$? Explain.

Challenge

17 Copy and complete the multiplication square below.

×		$(x - 3)$
	$x^2 + 10x + 21$	$x^2 - 9$
		$x^2 - 7x + 12$

18 Reflect Make a list of any topics in this unit that
   • you need more help with or
   • you could help another student to understand.

MASTER   Check P61   Strengthen P63   Extend P67   Test P71

3.1 Inequalities

You will learn to:
- Solve linear inequalities and represent the solution on a number line
- Multiply both sides of an inequality by a negative number.

Why learn this?
Businesses use inequalities to work out maximum and minimum profits based on different sales.

Fluency
Write < or > between each pair of numbers.
- 5 ☐ 1
- 4 ☐ 2
- −3 ☐ −5
- −10 ☐ −20
- 3 ☐ −9

Explore
How are inequalities used in optimization problems?

Exercise 3.1

1 Work out
  a −4 + 9
  b 10 − 17
  c −8 − −3
  d 5 × −2
  e $-\frac{6}{3}$
  f −4 × −8

2 Solve each of these equations.
  a $x + 12 = 19$
  b $5x = 45$
  c $2x - 5 = 9$
  d $\frac{x}{3} + 7 = 16$

Worked example

Use a number line to show the values that satisfy these **inequalities**.
a $x < 4$
b $5 > y \geqslant -2$

a $x < 4$

This includes all the numbers less than 4 (*excluding* 4).

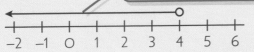

b $5 > y \geqslant -2$

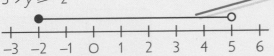

This includes all the numbers less than 5 (*excluding* 5) and greater than or equal to −2 (*including* −2).

Key point
You can show **inequalities** on a number line.
An empty circle ○ shows that the value is not included.
A filled circle ● shows that the value is included.
An arrow ○→ shows that the solution continues to plus or minus infinity.

3 Show these inequalities on a number line.
  a $x > 5$
  b $x \leqslant 2$
  c $-3 \leqslant y < 3$
  d $7 > y \geqslant 1$
  e $-4 \leqslant z \leqslant -1$
  f $6 \geqslant z \geqslant -2$

Warm up

4 Write inequalities for each of these and show them on a number line.
  a a number less than or equal to 5
  b a number greater than −4
  c a number less than 6 and greater than or equal to −2
  d a number greater than or equal to −8 and less than or equal to −1

Q4 hint

Choose a letter to represent the number.

5 Write the inequalities shown by each of these number lines.

  a

  b

  c
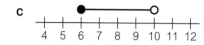

6 Solve these inequalities. Show each solution on a number line. The first one has been started for you.
  a $x + 12 \geqslant 15$

  $x \geqslant 15 - 12$

  $x \geqslant \square$

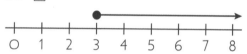

Key point

You can solve inequalities in a similar way to solving equations.

  b $x + 9 < 11$ **c** $y - 4 \geqslant -9$
  d $2y \leqslant 14$ **e** $3z > -15$
  f $\dfrac{x}{5} \geqslant -1$ **g** $\dfrac{x}{2} < 3$

7 **STEM** In a science experiment, Greg mixes vinegar and calcium carbonate to make a 'volcano'.
  He uses 150 m*l* of vinegar. In order to get the volcano to erupt Greg must use x grams of calcium carbonate, where $3x \leqslant 150$.
  a Solve the inequality.
  b Greg has 35 g of calcium carbonate. Does this satisfy the inequality?

8 Solve these inequalities. Show each solution on a number line.
  a $-2 < x + 4 < 5$ **b** $0 \leqslant y - 5 \leqslant 3$

  c $8 \geqslant 2y > 2$ **d** $2 > \dfrac{x}{4} \geqslant -1$

  Discussion Is $3 \geqslant z > -1$ the same as $-1 < z \leqslant 3$?

Q8 hint

Do the same operation to all three parts of the inequality so that the variable is on its own in the middle.

9 **Problem-solving** Kyle says, 'I think of an integer and double it. The answer is greater than 2 but smaller than 14'.
  a Write an inequality to represent this information.
  b Solve the inequality and show the solution on a number line.
  c Write down all the numbers Kyle could have chosen.

Q9 hint

$\square < 2x < \square$

10 Solve these inequalities. Show each solution on a number line.
  a $2n + 1 \leqslant 5$ **b** $3n - 8 > 1$

  c $\dfrac{x}{2} + 7 < 11$ **d** $\dfrac{x}{3} - 2 \geqslant -4$

Subject links: Science (Q7)

11 Solve these inequalities. Show each solution on a number line.
The first one has been started for you.
a $-1 \leqslant 2y + 3 < 9$
$-1 - 3 \leqslant 2y < 9 - 3$
$-4 \leqslant 2y < 6$
$-\dfrac{4}{2} \leqslant y < \dfrac{6}{2}$
$\square \leqslant y < \square$

b $1 \leqslant 3x - 2 < 10$
c $19 > 5n - 1 > 4$
d $29 \geqslant 4p + 1 \geqslant -7$

12 **Problem-solving** Lucy says, 'I think of an integer, multiply it by 3 and then subtract 5. The answer is greater than 7 but smaller than 12'.
a Write an inequality to represent this information.
b Solve the inequality and show the solution on a number line.
c Write down all of the numbers Lucy could have chosen.

Investigation   Reasoning

On a number line you can see that $-6 < -4$.
1 Multiply both sides of the inequality $-6 < -4$ by -1.
Is the statement you wrote as your answer to part **1** still true?
2 Divide both sides of the inequality $-6 < -4$ by -1.
Is the statement you wrote as your answer to part **1** still true?
3 a For what values of x is $x < 5$?
b For what values of x is $-x < -5$?
4 a For what values of x is $2x < 10$?
b For what values of x is $-2x < -10$?

Discussion What happens to the inequality sign when you multiply or divide both sides by a negative number?

---

13 Solve these inequalities.
a $-x < 8$
b $-3x > 15$
c $-2x \leqslant -18$
d $8 - x < 3$
e $3 < -x < 5$
f $-12 \leqslant -4x \leqslant 20$

Q13a hint

$-x$ is less than 8, so x is greater than $\square$.

14 **Explore** How are inequalities used in optimization problems?
Is it easier to explore this question now you have completed the lesson?
What further information do you need to be able to answer this?

15 **Reflect** In what ways are inequalities similar to equations?
In what ways are they different?

MASTER

Check
P61

Strengthen
P63

Extend
P67

Test
P71

3.2 Using index laws

You will learn to:
- Use index laws with zero and negative powers.

CONFIDENCE

Why learn this?
Negative indices are used in lots of mathematical functions and terms.

Fluency
Work out
- 4^2
- 4^{-2}
- 4^0

Explore
What expressions will simplify to x^{-4}?

Exercise 3.2

Warm up

1 Work out the value of these expressions when $x = 1$.

a $12x - 15$ **b** $11 - 8x$ **c** $\dfrac{15x + 21}{9x}$

2 Write each fraction in its simplest form.

a $\dfrac{3}{24}$ **b** $\dfrac{18}{22}$ **c** $\dfrac{14}{6}$

3 Copy and complete the sequence.
Write your answers as whole numbers and fractions.

$$5^5 = 3125$$
$$5^4 = 625$$
$\Big\}\div 5$
$\Big\}\div 5$
$$5^3 =$$
$$5^2 =$$
$$5^1 =$$
$$5^0 =$$
$$5^{-1} =$$
$$5^{-2} =$$
$$5^{-3} =$$
$$5^{-4} =$$
$$5^{-5} =$$

4 Reasoning Write down the value of
a 1^0 **b** 2^0 **c** 3^0 **d** 4^0 **e** a^0 **f** x^0 **g** $2p^0$ **h** $5t^0$

> **Key point**
> Any number to the power of zero is 1.

5 Work out the value of each of these expressions.

a $7x^0 - 4y^0$ **b** $4m^0 \times 8n^0$ **c** $\dfrac{45}{5y^0}$

d $\dfrac{36 - 4a^0}{8b^0}$ **e** $18c^0 - \dfrac{10^2}{5d^0}$ **f** $8z^0\left(12^0 - \dfrac{12y^0}{2^2}\right)$

> **Q5 hint**
> $x^0 = 1$ and $y^0 = 1$

Topic links: Simplifying fractions

1 Copy and complete.

a $\dfrac{7^3}{7^6} = 7^{3-6} = 7^{\square}$

$\dfrac{7^3}{7^6} = \dfrac{7 \times 7 \times 7}{7 \times 7 \times 7 \times 7 \times 7 \times 7} = \dfrac{1}{7^{\square}}$

b $\dfrac{x^2}{x^3} = x^{2-3} = x^{\square}$

$\dfrac{x^2}{x^3} = \dfrac{x \times x}{x \times x \times x} = \dfrac{1}{x^{\square}}$

c $\dfrac{y^6}{y^{10}} = x^{6-10} = y^{\square}$

$\dfrac{y^6}{y^{10}} = \dfrac{1}{y^{\square}}$

2 Write down what it means when a number has a negative power.

Discussion For what values of x is $x^{-1} < 1$?

6 Simplify these expressions. Write each one as a negative power and
   as a fraction. The first one has been started for you.

a $\dfrac{x^4}{x^7} = x^{4-7} = x^{\square} = \dfrac{1}{x^{\square}}$

b $\dfrac{y^2}{y^8}$ c $\dfrac{p^4}{p^5}$ d $\dfrac{z}{z^9}$

Q6d hint

$z = z^1$

Worked example

Simplify $\dfrac{20x^5}{4x^8}$.

Write your answer as a negative power and as a fraction.

$\dfrac{20x^5}{4x^8} = \dfrac{20}{4} \times \dfrac{x^5}{x^8}$ ⟵ Write the fraction as the product of two simpler fractions.

$\dfrac{20}{4} \times \dfrac{x^5}{x^8} = 5 \times x^{-3} = 5x^{-3}$ ⟵ Simplify the two fractions.

$20 \div 4 = 5$

$\dfrac{x^5}{x^8} = x^{5-8} = x^{-3}$

$5x^{-3} = 5 \times \dfrac{1}{x^3} = \dfrac{5}{x^3}$ ⟵ A negative power as a fraction is 1 over the positive power. $x^{-3} = \dfrac{1}{x^3}$.

7 Simplify these expressions. Write each one as
   i   a negative power   ii   a fraction.

a $\dfrac{6x^7}{2x^9}$ b $\dfrac{24y^3}{4y^7}$ c $\dfrac{56y}{7y^8}$ d $\dfrac{7p^8}{21p^{12}}$ e $\dfrac{8r^3}{72r^{10}}$ f $\dfrac{9q}{45q^{11}}$

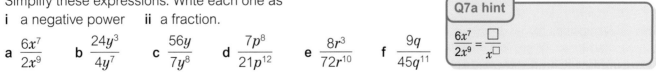

Q7a hint

$\dfrac{6x^7}{2x^9} = \dfrac{\square}{x^{\square}}$

8 **Explore** What expressions will simplify to x^{-4}?
   Is it easier to explore this question now you have completed the
   lesson?
   What further information do you need to be able to answer this?

9 **Reflect** What was familiar to you in this lesson and what
   surprised you?

Explore

Reflect

3.3 Solving equations

You will learn to:
- Explain the difference between equations, formulae and functions
- Construct and solve complex equations.

CONFIDENCE

Why learn this?
Engineers designing roller coaster rides have to solve equations to make sure the ride is safe.

Fluency
Work out the value of these expressions when $x = 4$.
- $5x - 3$
- $7(2x + 1)$
- $\dfrac{x + 5}{3}$
- $\dfrac{5x - 6}{7}$

Explore
Do all equations have a solution?

Exercise 3.3

1 Work out the lowest common multiple (LCM) of
   a 5 and 15   **b** 4 and 3   **c** 2 and 5

2 Write down whether each of these is an expression or a formula.
   a $3x + 4y$ **b** $P = 4t + 5$
   c $s = 5d - 2x$ **d** $v + 10t$
   e $8x^2 - 7x + 24$ **f** $t = 4m^2 - 3n + mn$

> **Q2 hint**
> An expression doesn't have an equals sign.

3 Solve these equations.
   a $3(y + 5) = 9$ **b** $7(p - 3) = 2(2p + 6)$ **c** $\dfrac{y + 9}{4} = 5$

4 Solve these equations.
   a $3x - 11 = \dfrac{4x + 2}{3}$ **b** $2x + 5 = \dfrac{5x + 1}{2}$
   c $\dfrac{11x + 6}{5} = 3x - 2$ **d** $\dfrac{8x - 2}{6} = 2x - 5$

> **Q4a hint**
> Start by multiplying both sides by 3.
> $3(3x - 11) = 4x + 2$

> **Key point**
> An **equation** has two expressions (one could be constant) either side of an equals sign. When there is just one variable, you can solve it.
> A **formula** is a rule showing a relationship between two or more variables.
> A **function** gives instructions for changing one number into another.
> $x \rightarrow 2x + 5$ is a function.

5 Decide whether each of these is an **equation**, a **function** or a **formula**.
   a $2x + 1 = 11$ **b** $s \rightarrow 10t - 2$
   c $a = \dfrac{(a + b)h}{2}$ **d** $y \rightarrow 3x + 5$
   e $3x + 5 = 32$ **f** $F = ma$

Topic links: Perimeter and area, Angles in a triangle

Warm up

6 Problem-solving Aaron and Fiona are thinking of the same number.
Aaron multiplies it by 3, then adds 5.
Fiona multiplies it by 12, subtracts 3, then divides the result by 3.
They both get the same answer.
What number did they start with?

Q6 Strategy hint
Use a letter to represent the number.
Write expressions for Aaron's and
Fiona's calculations.

7 Problem-solving The diagram shows an equilateral triangle.
Work out the perimeter of the triangle.
Discussion Does it matter which two sides of the triangle you used?
How can you check your answer is correct?

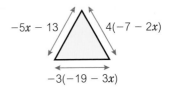

$-5x - 13$ $4(-7 - 2x)$
$-3(-19 - 3x)$

Worked example

Solve the equation $\dfrac{3x + 6}{3} = \dfrac{x - 4}{2}$

$\dfrac{6(3x + 6)}{3} = \dfrac{6(x - 4)}{2}$ — To remove the fractions, multiply both sides of the equation by the LCM of 2 and 3, which is 6.

$\dfrac{^2\cancel{6}(3x + 6)}{\cancel{3}} = \dfrac{^3\cancel{6}(x - 4)}{\cancel{2}}$ — Cancel the denominators. $6 \div 3 = 2$ and $6 \div 2 = 3$.

$2(3x + 6) = 3(x - 4)$ — Expand the brackets.

$6x + 12 = 3x - 12$

$6x - 3x = -12 - 12$ — Collect like terms.

$3x = -24$

$x = -8$ — $-24 \div 3 = -8$

Check: LHS: $\dfrac{3x + 6}{3} = \dfrac{3 \times (-8) + 6}{3} = \dfrac{-18}{3} = -6$

RHS: $\dfrac{x - 4}{2} = \dfrac{-8 - 4}{2} = \dfrac{-12}{2} = -6$ — Check the solution is correct by substituting $x = -8$ into both sides of the equation.

8 Solve

a $\dfrac{x - 2}{3} = \dfrac{x + 3}{6}$

b $\dfrac{11x + 6}{5} = \dfrac{3x + 8}{2}$

c $\dfrac{4x - 9}{3} = \dfrac{3x + 2}{4}$

d $\dfrac{4x + 23}{9} = \dfrac{2x + 14}{6}$

Q8 Strategy hint
Check your solutions are correct by
substituting.

9 The diagram shows an isosceles triangle ABC.

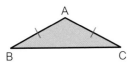

In triangle ABC, $\angle ABC = \dfrac{11x - 10}{10}$ and $\angle ACB = \dfrac{7x + 46}{8}$.

a Write an equation using the fact that $\angle ABC = \angle ACB$.
b Solve your equation to find the value of x.
c Work out the size of $\angle ABC$ and $\angle ACB$.
d Work out the size of $\angle BAC$.

10 Problem-solving The diagram shows a square.

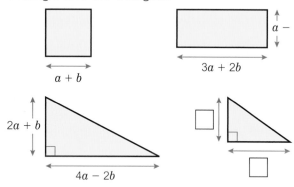

$\frac{7x-1}{5}$ $\frac{5x+1}{4}$

Work out the perimeter of the square.

Q10 Strategy hint

Write an equation using the fact that the sides of a square are the same length. Solve it to find the value of x. Then work out the side length of the square.

11 Problem-solving / Reasoning The diagram shows a square, a rectangle and two triangles.

$a + b$

$a - b$

$3a + 2b$

$2a + b$

$4a - 2b$

The total area of the square and the rectangle is the same as the total area of the two triangles.

a Write an expression for the length and the height of the small triangle in terms of a and b.

b Is your answer to part **a** the only answer? Explain why.

12 Problem-solving

a For which values of x are these statements true?

  i $\frac{2x}{3} = \frac{4x}{6}$

  ii $\frac{3x+1}{2} = \frac{2x+1}{3}$

  iii $\frac{3x^2+3}{9} = \frac{x^2+1}{3}$

  iv $\frac{3x}{8} = \frac{8x}{3}$

b Write whether each one is an equation or an **identity**.

Discussion Why do you think equations like the one in part **iv** are sometime called 'trivial cases'?

Q12 Literacy hint

An **identity** is true for all value of x.

13 Explore Do all equations have a solution?
Is it easier to explore this question now you have completed the lesson?
What further information do you need to be able to answer this?

14 Reflect Q11 is tagged as a Problem-solving and Reasoning question. What is the difference between Problem-solving and Reasoning? Which part of the question is which, or do both parts need both skills?

3.4 Changing the subject

You will learn to:
- Change the subject of a formula.

Why learn this?
If you know the formula to convert °C to °F, you can also convert °F to °C by changing the subject.

Fluency
Match each blue expression to its equivalent red expression.

$6x + 3$ $x(x + 2)$
$4y - 6$ $3(2x + 1)$
$x^2 + 2x$ $2y(4x - 5)$
$8xy - 10y$ $2(2y - 3)$

Explore
How can you work out the radius of a sphere from the volume?

Exercise 3.4

1 Solve these equations.

a $5x = 20$

b $\dfrac{x}{3} = 8$

c $2x + 1 = 9$

d $5x - 6 = 4$

2 Factorise these expressions.

a $7x + 14$

b $9y - 6$

c $4ab + 8ac$

d $3x^2 - 9xy$

> **Key point**
> The **subject** of a formula is the variable on its own on one side of the equals sign.
> A is the subject of $A = l \times b$.

3 Make x the **subject** of each formula.

a $y = x + 5$ b $z = x - 12$ c $h = 5x$ d $k = \dfrac{x}{4}$

> **Q3a hint**
> Rearrange the formula so it starts '$x =$'.

4 **STEM** The formula to work out the force (F) acting on an object is $F = ma$, where m is the mass and a is the acceleration of the object.

a i Make a the subject of the formula.
   ii Work out the value of a when $F = 24$ and $m = 3$
b i Make m the subject of the formula.
   ii Work out the value of m when $F = 35$ and $a = 10$.

> **Q4a i hint**
> $F = m \times a$
> $m \times a = F$
> $a = \dfrac{\square}{\square}$

5 Make x the subject of each formula.

a $y = 2x + 3$ b $t = 5x - 9$ c $v = 3x + 8m$

> **Q5a hint**
> $y - 3 = 2x$
> $x = \dfrac{y - 3}{\square}$

6 The equation of a straight line can be written in the form $y = mx + c$.
Make y the subject of each of these by writing them in the form $y = mx + c$.

a $y - 5x = 12$ b $y + 4x - 11 = 0$ c $2y - 6x = 18$

Discussion In what order did you rearrange the terms in part **c**?

7 Make r the subject of each formula.

   a $C = 2\pi r$

   b $A = \pi r^2$

   c $A = 4\pi r^2$

   d $V = \pi r^2 h$

   Discussion What are each of these formulae for?

Q7b hint

$r^2 = \dfrac{A}{\pi}$

$r = \square$

8 Problem-solving The diagram shows a trapezium with area 72 cm².

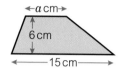

   a Write down the formula for the area of a trapezium.

   b Rearrange the formula to make a the subject.

   c Work out the value of a.

9 Problem-solving A company wants to make a cylindrical tin with radius 8 cm and capacity 1 litre.
Work out the smallest integer height of the tin.

Q9 hint

1 litre = 1000cm³

10 Reasoning Jacinda rearranges the formula for the surface area of a cylinder to make h the subject.
This is what she writes.

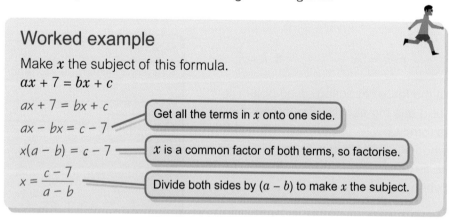

   a Explain the mistake that Jacinda has made.

   b Work out the value of h when $A = 205$ cm² and $r = 3.4$ cm.
Give your answer correct to 3 significant figures.

Worked example

Make x the subject of this formula.

$ax + 7 = bx + c$

$ax + 7 = bx + c$ Get all the terms in x onto one side.

$ax - bx = c - 7$

$x(a - b) = c - 7$ x is a common factor of both terms, so factorise.

$x = \dfrac{c - 7}{a - b}$ Divide both sides by $(a - b)$ to make x the subject.

Key point

The subject of a formula should only appear once in the formula.

11 Make x the subject of each formula.

   a $5x = kx + p$

   b $mx + t = x + 10$

   c $xy - 5 = 12 + 4x$

   d $r^2 x = m^2 x + mr$

Topic links: Equation of a straight line, Area and volume formulae

Subject links: Science (Q4, Q12, Q14)

12 STEM In an experiment Gareth works out the speed of two balls after they collide.
This is one of the formulae that he writes.
$6eu - ev = 2v + u$
a Make u the subject of this formula.
b Work out the value of u when $v = 4$ and $e = 0.5$.

13 Make y the subject in each of these formulae.
a $a = 2b + \sqrt{y}$
b $T = 2x + \sqrt{y}$
c $L = 2x + \dfrac{\sqrt{5y}}{k}$

Q13 Strategy hint
Rearrange each formula to make $\sqrt{y}$ or $\sqrt{5y}$ the subject first. Then square both sides of the equation.

14 STEM Two formulae used in physics are $w = \sqrt{\dfrac{k}{m}}$ and $b = a\sqrt{1 - e^2}$
a Make k the subject of the first formula.
b Make e the subject of the second formula.

Q14a hint
Square both sides of the equation first.

15 This formula is used to work out the distance, d, travelled by an object that starts from rest.
$$d = \dfrac{at^2}{2}$$
a = acceleration and t = time taken.
a Rearrange the formula to make a the subject.
b Work out the acceleration when $d = 100$ and $t = 8$
c Work out the time taken when $a = 25$ and $d = 50$

16 Explore How can you work out the radius of a sphere from the volume?
Is it easier to explore this question now you have completed the lesson?
What further information do you need to be able to answer this?

17 Reflect Choose one of the formulae in Q13 to write out as a Worked Example for another student. Do you think this is a useful way to strengthen your learning?

Explore

Reflect

3.5 Algebraic fractions

You will learn to:
- Change algebraic fractions to equivalent fractions
- Solve problems with fractions in formulae.

Why learn this?
Designers of containers rearrange formulae to work out dimensions of different containers with the same volume.

Fluency
What are the missing numbers in each of these equivalent fractions?

- $\dfrac{2}{3} = \dfrac{\square}{21}$
- $\dfrac{\square}{48} = \dfrac{3}{4}$
- $\dfrac{4}{5} = \dfrac{32}{\square}$
- $\dfrac{100}{\square} = \dfrac{5}{7}$

Explore
Make u the subject of $\dfrac{1}{u} + \dfrac{1}{v} = \dfrac{1}{f}$.

Exercise 3.5

1 Work out

a $\dfrac{2}{5} + \dfrac{1}{10}$ b $\dfrac{1}{4} + \dfrac{1}{3}$ c $\dfrac{2}{3} - \dfrac{1}{5}$ d $\dfrac{7}{8} - \dfrac{5}{6}$

2 Make x the subject of each formula.

a $T = x + m$ b $y = mx + c$ c $px + 2v = mx + 7u$

3 Expand and simplify

a $(x + 2)(x + 5)$ b $(y + 7)(y - 3)$ c $(z - 8)(z - 2)$

4 Solve

a $\dfrac{x}{10} = 30$ b $6 = \dfrac{y}{12}$ c $\dfrac{2x}{5} = 6$

5 Copy and complete these equivalent fractions.

a $\dfrac{3x}{5} = \dfrac{6x}{\square}$ (×2, ×2)

b $\dfrac{1}{m} = \dfrac{n}{\square}$ (×n, ×n)

c $\dfrac{1}{b} = \dfrac{\square}{2bc}$

d $\dfrac{nx}{2m} = \dfrac{3nx^2}{\square}$

Worked example

Write the expression $\dfrac{1}{a} + \dfrac{1}{b}$ as a single fraction.

$\dfrac{1}{a} + \dfrac{1}{b} = \dfrac{b}{ab} + \dfrac{a}{ab}$ — Multiply one fraction by a and the other by b to get a common denominator.

$\dfrac{b}{ab} + \dfrac{a}{ab} = \dfrac{b + a}{ab}$ — The denominators are equal so the numerators can be added.

$\dfrac{b + a}{ab} = \dfrac{a + b}{ab}$ — $b + a$ is the same as $a + b$. Write the terms in alphabetical order.

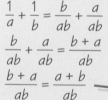

6 Write each expression as a single fraction.

a $\dfrac{1}{m} + \dfrac{1}{n}$ b $\dfrac{3}{a} + \dfrac{5}{b}$ c $\dfrac{a}{c} + \dfrac{b}{d}$ d $\dfrac{1}{x} - \dfrac{1}{y}$ e $\dfrac{a}{p} - \dfrac{3b}{q}$

Subject links: Science (Q9, Q10, Q12)

Worked example

$$\frac{1}{x} = y + 5$$

Make x the subject.

$1 = x(y + 5)$ — Multiply both sides by x so it is not the denominator of a fraction but don't expand the bracket.

$\dfrac{1}{y + 5} = x$ — Divide both sides by $y + 5$ to make x the subject.

$x = \dfrac{1}{y + 5}$ — You could rewrite so the x is on the left-hand side.

7 Make x the subject of each formula.

a $\dfrac{1}{x} = 9 - y$ **b** $\dfrac{1}{x} + 3 = z$ **c** $\dfrac{1}{x} - 5 = w + 2$

d $\dfrac{2}{x} = a + b$ **e** $\dfrac{5}{x} + 9 = d$ **f** $t + \dfrac{4}{x} = 2s$

8 Make x the subject of each formula.

a $\dfrac{1}{x} = \dfrac{1}{m} + \dfrac{1}{n}$ **b** $\dfrac{3}{x} - \dfrac{2}{p} = \dfrac{1}{q}$ **c** $\dfrac{4}{x} + \dfrac{a}{b} = 5$ **d** $\dfrac{m}{n} + \dfrac{a}{x} = \dfrac{y}{3}$

> **Q8 hint**
> Rearrange so the x term is alone on one side of the equals sign first.

9 **STEM** The formula to work out the energy E stored in a spring is $E = \dfrac{kx^2}{2l}$

    a Make k the subject of the formula.
    b Make l the subject of the formula.

10 **STEM** The formula to work out the optical power of a lens is $P = \dfrac{1}{f}$

    a Make f the subject of the formula.
    b Work out the value of f when $P = 10$.

11 Match each yellow card with its equivalent blue card.

$\dfrac{1}{x} + \dfrac{1}{y}$ $\dfrac{2}{x} + \dfrac{1}{y}$ $\dfrac{1}{x} + \dfrac{1}{2y}$ $\dfrac{1}{2x} + \dfrac{1}{y}$

$\dfrac{x + 2y}{xy}$ $\dfrac{2x + y}{2xy}$ $\dfrac{x + y}{xy}$ $\dfrac{x + 2y}{2xy}$

12 **STEM / Problem-solving** A formula used by electrical engineers is $\dfrac{V_p}{V_s} = \dfrac{I_p}{I_s}$

    Work out the value of I_s when $V_p = 120\,000$, $V_s = 240$ and $I_p = 50\,000$.

13 Multiply out the brackets in these expressions and simplify.

    a $\dfrac{(w + z)^2 - (w - z)^2}{6}$ **b** $\dfrac{(a + b)^2 - (a - b)(a + b)}{3}$

> **Q13 hint**
> $(w + z)^2 = (w + z)(w + z)$

14 **Explore** Make u the subject of $\dfrac{1}{u} + \dfrac{1}{v} = \dfrac{1}{f}$

    Is it easier to explore this question now you have completed the lesson?
    What further information do you need to be able to answer this?

15 **Reflect** Wai Lin says, 'In Q6, I checked my answers were right by substituting numbers for the unknowns.'
    Is this a good way to check your answers?
    Explain.

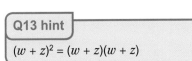

Active Learn   Delta 3, Section 3.5

Explore

Reflect

Master
P48

CHECK

Strengthen
P63

Extend
P67

Test
P71

3 Check up

Log how you did on your
Student Progression Chart.

Inequalities

1 Write the inequalities shown by each of these number lines.

a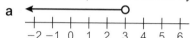

b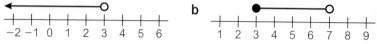

2 Represent these inequalities on a number line.

    a $x > 4$
        b $-4 \leqslant y < 2$

3 Solve these inequalities.

    a $x + 2 < 5$
        b $2y \leqslant -6$

    c $-5 \leqslant y - 3 \leqslant 1$
        d $2 \geqslant \dfrac{x}{3} > -1$

4 Solve these inequalities.

    a $4n + 1 \leqslant 9$
        b $\dfrac{x}{2} - 3 \geqslant -1$

    c $2 \leqslant 3y + 5 < 17$
        d $6 > 2n - 2 > -6$

5 Solve these inequalities.

    a $-x > 2$
        b $-5x \leqslant -30$

    c $5 > -x \geqslant 8$
        d $-4 < -x < 7$

Indices and fractions

6 Work out the value of $4y^0$.

7 Write $\dfrac{x^2}{x^4}$ as a single power of x.

8 Copy and complete these equivalent fractions.

    a $\dfrac{1}{x} = \dfrac{\Box}{5xy}$
        b $\dfrac{ab}{2c} = \dfrac{5ab^2}{\Box}$

9 Write each calculation as a single fraction.

    a $\dfrac{1}{c} + \dfrac{1}{d}$
        b $\dfrac{a}{b} - \dfrac{1}{c}$
        c $\dfrac{x}{y} + \dfrac{m}{2n}$

10 Multiply out the brackets in this expression and simplify.

$$\dfrac{(2x + 3y)^2 - (2x - 3y)(2x + 3y)}{6}$$

Equations and formulae

11 Solve these equations.

    a $3x + 7 = \dfrac{9x - 1}{2}$
        b $\dfrac{15x + 1}{4} = 2x - 5$

12 The diagram shows an isosceles triangle.

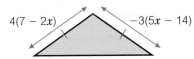

$4(7 - 2x)$ $-3(5x - 14)$

a Work out the value of x.

b What is the length of the equal sides in this isosceles triangle?

13 Make x the subject of each formula.

a $u = x + v$ **b** $y = 4x - 9$ **c** $A = 7x^2$

14 Make x the subject of each formula.

a $xy - a = x + b$ **b** $p^2x = q^2x + pq$ **c** $T = \sqrt{\dfrac{x}{2}}$

15 Solve $\dfrac{x - 4}{3} = \dfrac{x + 2}{4}$.

16 Make x the subject of each formula.

a $\dfrac{1}{x} = y + 2$ **b** $\dfrac{1}{x} = \dfrac{1}{a} + \dfrac{1}{b}$ **c** $\dfrac{2}{x} + \dfrac{3}{p} = \dfrac{5}{q}$

17 The formula to work out the volume (V) of an object is $V = \dfrac{M}{D}$

where M is the mass of the object and D is the density of the object.

a Rearrange the formula to make D the subject.

b A triangular prism has a mass of $750\,g$ and a volume of $25\,cm^3$.
Work out the value of D.

18 How sure are you of your answers? Were you mostly

☹ **Just guessing**   😐 **Feeling doubtful**   🙂 **Confident**

What next? Use your results to decide whether to strengthen or extend your learning.

Challenge

19 Here are two inequalities.

A ☐ $< 5x - 7 \leqslant$ ☐   **B** ☐ $< \dfrac{x}{3} + 5 \leqslant$ ☐

The solution to both of the inequalities is $-3 < x \leqslant 6$.
What are the missing numbers in each of the inequalities?

20 Use the terms from the cloud to complete these equivalent fractions.

9   x^2
$2xy^2$ $3y^2$
$2xy$

a $\dfrac{4x}{\square} = \dfrac{8xy}{6y^3}$ **b** $\dfrac{x}{2y} = \dfrac{\square}{\square}$ **c** $\dfrac{xy}{\square} = \dfrac{\square}{18y}$

3 Strengthen

You will:
- Strengthen your understanding with practice.

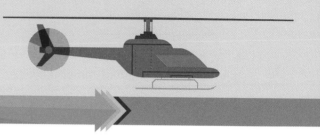

Inequalities

1 Match each of these inequalities with the correct number line diagram.

a $x < 2$

b $x \geqslant 2$

c $-2 < x \leqslant 2$

d $2 > x \geqslant -2$

i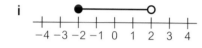

ii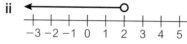

iii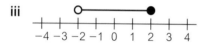

iv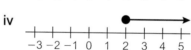

Q1 hint

○ shows the value is not included.
● shows the value is included.

Q1d hint

$2 > x \geqslant -2$ is the same as $-2 \leqslant x < 2$

2 Write whether A, B or C is the correct inequality shown by each of these number lines.

a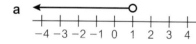

b

A $x \leqslant 1$ **B** $1 < x$ **C** $x < 1$

A $6 \leqslant x \leqslant 10$ **B** $6 \leqslant x < 10$ **C** $6 < x < 10$

3 Write inequalities for each of these sentences and show them on a number line.
Some of them have been started for you.

a A number is less than or equal to −1.

 $x \ \square \ -1$

b A number is greater than or equal to 3.

c A number is less than 4 and greater than or equal to −3.

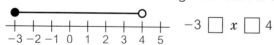 $-3 \ \square \ x \ \square \ 4$

d A number is greater than or equal to −7 and less than or equal to 0.

4 Solve these inequalities.
Represent the solution on a number line.

a $x + 7 < 12$
$x < 12 - 7$
$x < \square$

b $n - 4 > 9$

c $3y \leqslant 15$

d $\dfrac{z}{5} \geqslant -1$

e $8n + 3 < 19$

f $2z - 8 > 4$

Q4a hint

Choose any number that fits your inequality. Add 7. Is it less than 12?

Subject link: Science (Equations and formulae Q8)

5 Mia uses this method to solve a double inequality.

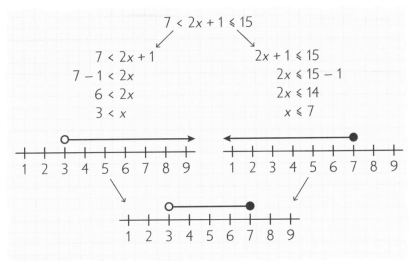

$$7 < 2x + 1 \leqslant 15$$

$$7 < 2x + 1 \qquad\qquad 2x + 1 \leqslant 15$$
$$7 - 1 < 2x \qquad\qquad 2x \leqslant 15 - 1$$
$$6 < 2x \qquad\qquad 2x \leqslant 14$$
$$3 < x \qquad\qquad x \leqslant 7$$

Solve these double inequalities.
Represent the solution on a number line.

a $-1 \leqslant y + 2 \leqslant 8$

b $4 < 2x < 16$

c $3 \geqslant \dfrac{x}{3} > -1$

d $-7 \leqslant 2y + 3 < 15$

e $14 > 3n - 1 > 5$

Q5c hint

Rewrite as $-1 < \dfrac{x}{3} \leqslant 3$.

6 Solve these inequalities.

a $8 - x < 3$

b $12 - y > 18$

c $-7x \geqslant -21$

d $-3y \leqslant 24$

e $2 < -x < 9$

f $-18 \leqslant -6x \leqslant 30$

Q6a hint

Add x to both sides so it is no longer negative.

Indices and fractions

1 Copy and complete the workings to work out $7x^0$.

$$7x^0 = 7 \times 1 = \square$$

2 Simplify these expressions.
Write each one as

   i a fraction   **ii** a negative number

a $\dfrac{x^2}{x^5}$

b $\dfrac{y^5}{y^7}$

c $\dfrac{z}{z^6}$

Q2a hint

$\dfrac{x^2}{x^5} = \dfrac{x \times x}{x \times x \times x \times x \times x} = \dfrac{1}{x^{\square}} = x^{-\square}$

3 Copy and complete these equivalent fractions.

a $\dfrac{5y}{9} = \dfrac{\square}{18}$

b $\dfrac{8}{x} = \dfrac{\square}{5x}$

c $\dfrac{2y}{x} = \dfrac{\square}{xz}$

d $\dfrac{1}{m} = \dfrac{3mp}{\square}$

e $\dfrac{2}{b} = \dfrac{4ab}{\square}$

Q3d hint

What has the numerator been multiplied by to get $3mp$? Multiply the denominator by the same expression.

4 Copy and complete.

a $\dfrac{1}{g} + \dfrac{1}{k} = \dfrac{1 \times k}{g \times k} + \dfrac{1 \times g}{k \times g} = \dfrac{\square + \square}{gk}$

b $\dfrac{3}{a} + \dfrac{4}{b} = \dfrac{3 \times b}{a \times b} + \dfrac{4 \times \square}{b \times a} = \dfrac{\square + \square}{ab}$

c $\dfrac{p}{q} + \dfrac{b}{3c} = \dfrac{p \times 3c}{q \times \square} + \dfrac{b \times \square}{3c \times \square} = \dfrac{\square + \square}{\square}$

Q4c Strategy hint

Multiply the numerator and the denominator of one fraction by the denominator of the other.

$\dfrac{\blacksquare}{\bigstar} + \dfrac{\bullet}{\blacktriangle} = \dfrac{(\blacksquare \times \blacktriangle) + (\bullet \times \bigstar)}{\bigstar \times \blacktriangle}$

5 a Expand and simplify.
  i $(3x + 4y)^2$
  ii $(3x - 4y)^2$
  b Use your answers to part **a** to simplify
   i $(3x + 4y)^2 + (3x - 4y)^2$
   ii $(3x + 4y)^2 - (3x - 4y)^2$
   iii $\dfrac{(3x + 4y)^2 - (3x - 4y)^2}{12}$

6 Simplify $\dfrac{(x + 2y)^2 + (x - 2y)^2}{2}$

Q5a hint

$(3x + 4y)^2 = (3x + 4y)(3x + 4y)$

$= 9x^2 + 12xy + \square + \square$

Equations and formulae

1 Solve these equations.
  a $5x + 3 = \dfrac{11x + 2}{2}$
  b $\dfrac{10x + 9}{3} = 6x - 5$

Q1a hint

First multiply both sides by 2.

$2(5x + 3) = \dfrac{2(11x + 2)}{2}$

2 The diagram shows a square.

$$-3x + 2$$

$$4(-8 - 5x)$$

  a Write an equation involving x.
  b Solve your equation to work out the value of x.
  c Work out the side length of the square.

Q2c hint

Substitute your value for x into one of the expressions.

3 Make x the subject of each formula.
  The first one has been done for you.
  a $b = x + m$

  $b = x + m$ $x \longrightarrow \boxed{+m} \longrightarrow b$

  $x = b - m$ $x \longleftarrow (-m) \longleftarrow b$

  b $y = 3x$
  c $y = mx + c$
  d $h = gx - 2$
  e $T = 2x^2$
  f $h = px^2$

Q3e hint

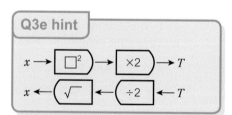

4 Make x the subject of these formulae.
  Some of them have been started for you.
  a $5x = bx + c$
  $5x - bx = c$
  $x(5 - b) = c$
  $x = \dfrac{c}{\square - \square}$

  b $xp + m = x + n$

  c $7x + 12 = 20 - xy$

  d $a^2x = b^2x + cd$

  e $R = \sqrt{\dfrac{x}{4}}$
  $R^2 = \dfrac{x}{4}$
  $x = \square R^2$

  f $M = \dfrac{\sqrt{2x}}{p}$

Q4b hint

Rearrange to get only the terms in x on the left hand side of the equation.

5 a What is the lowest common multiple (LCM) of 3 and 6?

b Multiply $\dfrac{2x + 3}{3}$ by the LCM of 3 and 6.

c Multiply $\dfrac{5x + 2}{6}$ by the LCM of 3 and 6.

d Solve $\dfrac{2x + 3}{3} = \dfrac{5x + 2}{6}$

6 Solve these equations. Check your solutions are correct.

a $\dfrac{x + 3}{3} = \dfrac{3x - 7}{5}$ **b** $\dfrac{5x - 1}{8} = \dfrac{2x + 1}{4}$ **c** $\dfrac{3x - 2}{6} = \dfrac{4x - 1}{9}$

7 Make x the subject of each formula.
Some of them have been started for you.

a $\dfrac{1}{x} = y - 8$ **b** $\dfrac{1}{x} = \dfrac{1}{y} + \dfrac{1}{z}$ **c** $\dfrac{1}{x} - \dfrac{2}{p} = \dfrac{3}{q}$ **d** $\dfrac{5}{x} + \dfrac{3}{m} = \dfrac{1}{k}$

$1 = x(y - 8)$ $\dfrac{1}{x} = \dfrac{\square + \square}{yz}$

$x = \dfrac{1}{\square - \square}$ $yz = x(\square + \square)$

$x = \square$

> **Q7c hint**
>
> Rearrange to get only the $\dfrac{1}{x}$ term on the left hand side of the equation.

8 STEM The formula to work out the pressure (P) on a surface is $P = \dfrac{F}{A}$ where F is the force and A is the area.

a Rearrange the formula to make A the subject.

b Use your formula to work out A when $F = 240$ and $P = 30$.

> **Q8 hint**
>
>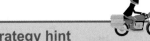

Enrichment

1 Here are two inequalities involving x.

$2x + 1 < 7$

$4x - 9 > -5$

x is a whole number.

What is the value of x?

> **Q1 Strategy hint**
>
> Solve each inequality and represent both solutions on the same number line.

2 Becky says, 'I think of a number, add 2 then divide the result by 5. This gives me the same answer as when I start with the same number, subtract 4 and divide the result by 3'.

a Write an equation using x to represent the number Becky thinks of.

b Solve the equation to work out the value of x.

3 Which of these fractions is not equivalent to the others?

$\dfrac{2a}{3}$ $\dfrac{10a^2}{15a}$ $\dfrac{26ab^2}{39b^2}$ $\dfrac{36a^2b^2}{52ab^2}$ $\dfrac{54acd}{81cd}$

4 Reflect How would you explain index notation to someone who has never used it?

Master
P48

Check
P61

Strengthen
P63

EXTEND

Test
P71

3 Extend

You will:
- Extend your understanding with problem-solving.

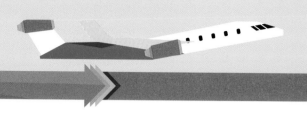

1 Problem-solving The area of the blue rectangle is twice the area of the red rectangle.
   a Work out the value of x.
   b Work out the areas of the two rectangles.

4 cm

$(3x - 7)$ cm

Area = $(36 - 4x)$ cm²

2 Simplify

   a $\dfrac{18x^7}{4x^{10}}$

   b $\dfrac{22x^4}{6x^7}$

   c $\dfrac{12m}{15m^5}$

   d $\dfrac{y^2 \times y^5}{y^9}$

   e $\dfrac{x^4}{x^3 \times x^6}$

   f $\dfrac{8p^3}{6p \times p^4}$

> **Q2e hint**
>
> Simplify the denominator first.

3 The three boxes below contain terms involving the letter x.

   $4x^5$ $10x^3$ $8x^2$ $6x^4$

   $3x^3$ $5x$ $9x^4$ $7x^6$

   $2x^{15}$ $4x^{12}$ $6x^{13}$ $10x^{18}$

   a Choose one term from each box and simplify $\dfrac{\text{Yellow} \times \text{Blue}}{\text{Red}}$.
   b Repeat part a two more times using different terms each time.
   c Which terms from each box will give the answer with the smallest possible power of x? What is this answer?
   d Which terms from each box will give the answer with the greatest possible power of x? What is this answer?

4 Solve these inequalities. Write your answer as a mixed number. Represent the solution on a number line.
   a $x + 1\frac{1}{3} \geqslant 5\frac{2}{3}$ **b** $x - 3\frac{3}{4} < 2\frac{1}{8}$ **c** $3x > 13$ **d** $\dfrac{x}{2} \leqslant 1\frac{2}{5}$

> **Q4a hint**
>
> $x \geqslant 5\frac{2}{3} - 1\frac{1}{3}$

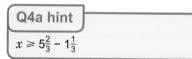

5 Real Arjay makes a fertiliser from nettle juice. He mixes $\frac{1}{4}$ litre of nettle juice with some water.
   So that the fertiliser is not too strong, he must mix the nettle juice with w litres of water, where $4w \geqslant 10$.
   a Solve the inequality.
   b i What is the smallest whole number of litres of water that he can use?
      ii How much fertiliser will this make?
   c i What is the smallest whole number of litres of fertiliser that he can make?
      ii How much water will he use for this amount of fertiliser?

6 Solve these inequalities. Write your answers as decimals. Represent the solution on a number line.
   a $2 \leqslant 10x < 8$ **b** $-6 < 4x \leqslant 10$

Topic links: Ratio, Working with fractions and mixed numbers, Perimeter, Area and perimeter of circles

Subject links: Science (Q13, Q15)

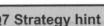

7 **Problem-solving** Ella solves the inequality $\square < 8x \leqslant \square$.
The number line shows her solution.

What is the inequality that Ella solved?

Q7 Strategy hint

Start by using the number line to write the solution as an inequality.

8 Solve these inequalities. Write your answers as mixed numbers or decimals. Represent the solution on a number line.
   a $4n + 3 \leqslant 16$
   b $\frac{x}{3} - \frac{1}{2} < \frac{1}{8}$
   c $2 \leqslant 3x - 5 < 6$
   d $9 > 5n + 3 > -1$

9 **Problem-solving** Here are two inequalities.
   $5 \leqslant 4y - 7 < 17$
   $-1 < 2y + 13 < 21$
   y is an integer.
   What is the value of y?

Q9 Strategy hint

Solve each inequality and represent both solutions on the same number line.

10 For each of these statements:
   i write an equation using x as the unknown number
   ii solve the equation to find the value of x.
   a I think of a number, add 3 and divide the result by 3. The answer is the same when I think of the same number subtract 3 and divide the result by 2.
   b I think of a number, multiply it by 5, add 3 and divide the result by 4. The answer is the same when I think of the same number multiply it by 7, subtract 3 and divide the result by 5.

Q10a hint

$\frac{x + 3}{3} = \frac{x - 3}{2}$

11 The diagram shows a regular pentagon and octagon.
   The perimeter of the pentagon is given as $3x - 4$
   and the perimeter of the octagon as $4x + 8$.

$P = 3x - 4$ $P = 4x + 8$

   a Write an expression for the side length of the
      i pentagon
      ii octagon.
   b The side length of the pentagon is the same as the side length of the octagon. Write an equation to show this.
   c Solve your equation to find the value of x.
   d Work out
      i the side length of each shape
      ii the perimeters of each shape.

12 **Problem-solving** This rectangle is made of two squares joined together.

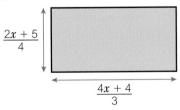

$\frac{2x + 5}{4}$

$\frac{4x + 4}{3}$

Q12 Strategy hint

Set up an equation using length = 2 × height.

Work out the value of x. Write your answer as a mixed number in its simplest form.

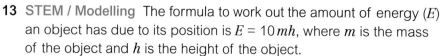

13 STEM / Modelling The formula to work out the amount of energy (E) an object has due to its position is $E = 10mh$, where m is the mass of the object and h is the height of the object.
  a i Make h the subject of the formula.
   ii Work out the value of h when $E = 75$ and $m = 3$.
  b i Make m the subject of the formula.
   ii Work out the value of m when $E = 340$ and $h = 8$.

14 Write each of these equations in the form $y = mx + c$.
  a $3y + 9x = 5$
  b $8x - 4y - 9 = 0$
  c $5y - 8x - 12 = 0$

Q14 hint

Leave any numbers that don't divide exactly as top heavy fractions or mixed numbers.

15 STEM / Modelling A formula used to work out the speed (v) of an object is $v = u + at$ where u is the starting speed, a is the acceleration and t is the time.
  a i Make u the subject of the formula.
   ii Work out the value of u when $v = 25$, $a = 3$ and $t = 5$.
  b i Make a the subject of the formula.
   ii Work out the value of a when $v = 32$, $u = 12$ and $t = 4$.

16 Make r the subject of each formula.
  a $V = \dfrac{\pi r^2 h}{3}$
  b $V = \dfrac{4\pi r^3}{3}$

Q16a hint

$3V = \pi r^2 h$

$\dfrac{3V}{\pi h} = r^2$

$r = \square$

17 Problem-solving The diagram shows a quarter-circle.
  a Write a formula for the area (A) of the quarter-circle.
  b Work out the radius of the quarter-circle when $A = 23\,\text{cm}^2$. Give your answer correct to 1 decimal place.

18 Make x the subject of each formula.
  a $2x + p = 5(x - 4)$
  b $y(2x + 9) = 7 - 5x$
  c $3(4 + 2x) = 5m(3x - 5)$

Q18a hint

Start by expanding the brackets.

19 Problem-solving The diagram shows a semicircle.
  a Write a formula for the perimeter (P) of the semicircle.
  b Work out the radius of the semicircle when $P = 33\,\text{cm}$. Give your answer correct to 1 decimal place.

20 Problem-solving / Reasoning The diagram shows the ages of two people in terms of x and y.
Gina is three times the age of Kyle.

Kyle   Gina
$3y + 4$ $ay + 60$

  a Write an equation using the information given and make y the subject of the formula.
  b When $a = 1$, work out the value of y and the ages of Kyle and Gina.
  c When $a = 2$, work out the value of y and the ages of Kyle and Gina.
  d Explain why a cannot be equal to 6.

Q20a Strategy hint

Start by writing an equation which includes brackets.

21 Copy and complete these expressions.
  a $\dfrac{1}{2x} + \dfrac{2}{5y} = \dfrac{\square + \square}{10xy}$
  b $\dfrac{m}{3a} + \dfrac{n}{4b} = \dfrac{\square + \square}{12ab}$
  c $\dfrac{a}{2p} - \dfrac{5b}{6q} = \dfrac{\square - \square}{6pq}$
  d $\dfrac{3p}{8g} - \dfrac{p}{6h} = \dfrac{\square - \square}{24gh}$

22 Make x the subject of each formula.

   a $\dfrac{1}{x} + 6 = y^2$ **b** $\dfrac{1}{x} = \dfrac{1}{p^2} + \dfrac{1}{q^2}$

   c $\dfrac{1}{x^2} = \dfrac{1}{m} + \dfrac{1}{n}$ **d** $\dfrac{5}{x^2} - \dfrac{2}{a} = \dfrac{3}{b}$

   e $\dfrac{2}{x} - \dfrac{a}{x} = \dfrac{1}{c} + \dfrac{1}{d}$

23 **Problem-solving / Reasoning** The diagram shows a small circle cut out from a larger circle.
Show that the formula for the shaded area (A) can be written as $A = \pi x(2R - x)$.

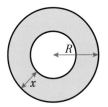

> **Q23 hint**
>
> Shaded area = area of large circle
>   − area of small circle
> Radius of small circle = ☐ − ☐

Investigation   **Reasoning**

Here is part of a number grid.

1 A cross of five numbers is shaded green.
You can work out the answer to:
left × bottom − top × right
like this:
$9 \times 18 - 2 \times 11 = 162 - 22 = 140$

1	2	3	4	5	6	7	8
9	10	11	12	13	14	15	16
17	18	19	20	21	22	23	24
25	26	27	28	29	30	31	32
33	34	35	36	37	38	39	40

2 Do the same for the
   a red cross
   b blue cross.

3 What do you notice about your answers and the number in the centre of the cross?

4 On the same number grid is a cross shaded yellow.
The number in the middle is n.
Copy the cross shape of five numbers and write an expression for each number in terms of n.

> **Hint**
>
> The bottom number is 8 more than middle number, or $n + 8$.

5 For the yellow cross, work out:
left × bottom − top × right.
Expand and simplify your answer.

6 What do you notice about your answer?

7 Investigate cross shapes of five squares on different number grids. For example rows of 6, 9, 12 etc.

8 What do you notice about your answers?

---

24 **Reflect** Look back at the questions in this unit.
Were there any questions that you could not answer straight away?
How did you deal with this? Write down some strategies that will help you with difficult questions in the future.

3 Unit test

Log how you did on your Student Progression Chart.

1 Work out the value of $7x^0 \times 5y^0$.

2 Solve the equation $2x + 1 = \dfrac{7x - 19}{2}$

3 A cube has a mass of $3(-5x - 7)\,\text{kg}$.
A cuboid has a mass of $-2(7x + 9)\,\text{kg}$.
The mass of the cube and the cuboid is the same.
a Work out the value of x.
b What is the mass of the cube and the cuboid?

4 Write $\dfrac{q^8}{q^{15}}$ as a single power of q.

5 Represent these inequalities on a number line.
a $x \leqslant -2$
b $-1 < y < 5$

6 Write the inequality that each number line represents.

a 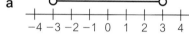 **b**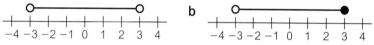

c  **d**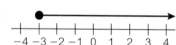

7 Solve
a $x + 3 < 7$ **b** $3y \leqslant -3$
c $5 > \dfrac{x}{2} > 3$ **d** $-5 \leqslant 2x + 3 < 7$
e $-x > -6$ **f** $2 - x < -3$

8 Solve $\dfrac{7x + 1}{6} = \dfrac{9x + 3}{8}$

9 Make x the subject of each formula.
a $m = x + t$
b $F = ax$
c $g = 3x - 5$
d $T = rx^2$

10 Make x the subject of each formula.
a $12x = xy + p$ **b** $mx - 4 = nx + 9$
c $a^2x = bx + 5d$ **d** $P = \dfrac{\sqrt{3x}}{r}$

11 Simplify $\dfrac{12xy}{18xz}$

12 Simplify
a $\dfrac{2}{k} + \dfrac{3}{g}$ **b** $\dfrac{x}{y} - \dfrac{5}{z}$ **c** $\dfrac{a}{2b} - \dfrac{5}{c}$ **d** $\dfrac{x}{y} + \dfrac{3y}{5n}$

13 Make x the subject of each formula.

a $\dfrac{1}{x} = u - v$

b $\dfrac{1}{x} - \dfrac{1}{y} = \dfrac{3}{z}$

c $\dfrac{3}{x^2} + \dfrac{2}{a} = \dfrac{5}{b}$

14 The formula to work out the acceleration (a) of an object is

$a = \dfrac{v - u}{t}$ where u is the starting speed and v is the finishing speed

of the object and t is the time taken.

a i Make v the subject.

 ii Work out the value of v when $u = 10$, $a = 5$ and $t = 3$.

b i Make t the subject.

 ii Work out the value of t when $u = 25$, $a = 8$ and $v = 65$.

15 Multiply out the brackets in this expression and simplify.

$$\dfrac{(3x + 4y)^2 - (2x + 6y)^2}{5}$$

Challenge

16 The diagram shows a rectangle and a triangle.

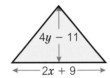

Carrie makes this pattern using the triangle and the rectangle.

a Write two equations using the information given and solve them to work out the value of x and y.

b Work out the area of the rectangle and the triangle.

c What can you say about the areas of the rectangle and the triangle?

17 Reflect This unit covered equations, formulae, inequalities and indices. Which topics did you like most and which did you like least? Can you explain why?

Reflect

4.1 STEM: Data collection

You will learn to:

- Identify sources of primary and secondary data
- Choose a suitable sample size
- Understand how to reduce bias in sampling and questionnaires
- Identify a random sample.

CONFIDENCE

Why learn this?
Governments carry out surveys called censuses to find out information about the population of the country.

Fluency
Round 5.56 cm to the nearest
- mm
- cm
- m

Work out 10% of
- 50
- 400
- 2000

Explore
When the UK government carries out a census, what sample of the population does it ask? What proportion respond?

Exercise 4.1

Warm up

1 What unit would you use to measure
   a the distance between two cities
   b the length of a caterpillar
   c the width of a garden?

2 Michelle wants to test whether this spinner is **biased**. Should she spin it 5, 30 or 100 times?

> **Q2 Literacy hint**
>
> **Biased** means it is more likely to land on one colour than another.

3 Real / STEM Choose the most appropriate measurement from the cloud for these investigations.
   a How deep in the ocean can fish survive?
   b Do genetically engineered fish grow longer than wild fish?
   c How far can a remote-controlled helicopter fly?

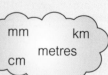

mm   km   metres   cm

4 Real / STEM Select an appropriate level of accuracy for these investigations.
   a The times taken to run 800 m at your school sports day to the nearest
      A millisecond   B second   C minute.
   b The masses of frogs to the nearest
      A gram   B 0.1 kg   C kg.
   c The speeds of vehicles on the motorway to the nearest
      A 0.1 mph   B 1 mph   C 10 mph.

Subject links: Science (Q3–5, Q7, Q8, Q10), Geography (Q7)

5 Real / STEM Decide on an appropriate level of accuracy for these investigations.

    a The times taken to run 800 m at an Olympic Games

    b The capacity of petrol tanks

    c The masses of sunflower seeds

6 For the following data:

    i decide whether it is **primary** or **secondary data**

    ii if it is primary data, give a suitable method for collecting it.

    a The total time spent in A&E in every hospital in the UK from April 2010 to June 2011

    b Numbers given by people who were asked to choose their favourite number

    c Percentage of the UK population that used the internet in 2013

    d GCSE results of all pupils in England in 2014

    e The percentage of people who write with their right hand

    f The number of people in cars on a main road

> **Key point**
>
> **Primary data** is data I collect myself. **Secondary data** is collected by someone else.
> Different ways of collecting primary data include questionnaires, surveys and data logging.

> **Key point**
>
> The total number of items your survey relates to is called the **population**.
> The group of items you test is called a **sample**.
> Sampling can be time consuming and expensive but the greater the sample, the more reliable it can be.
> For a sample to be reliable and unbiased, it should
> - be at least 10% of the population
> - represent the population.

7 Reasoning / STEM Select the most appropriate **sample size** for each survey. Explain your choice.

    a There are 50 000 trees in a forest. Researchers want to find out what proportion of trees are taller than 20 m.

        i 5000   **ii** 1000

        iii 500   **iv** 10

    b The UK **population** is approximately 64 000 000. An organisation wants to find out how many people have had a flu vaccination.

        i 100   **ii** 10 000

        iii 1 000 000   **iv** 20 000 000

    c The population of Manchester is 510 000. The council wants to find out how many people visit the doctor at least once a year.

        i 100 000   **ii** 6000

        iii 100   **iv** 5

8 Real / STEM A hospital wants to know the age of people in the local area. They put questionnaires in the local pet shop. Why will this give a biased sample?

9 Real A town council wants to know how the public library is being used. They give questionnaires to everyone in the library every Thursday afternoon for a month. Why is this sample biased?

10 **STEM** A school wants to investigate the type of food students eat at lunchtime.
There are 1500 students at the school.
 a Suggest a sensible number of students to be sampled.
 b Which of these surveying methods will give a biased result?
   Explain your answers.
   i Sending a questionnaire to all Year 10 email accounts.
   ii Sending a questionnaire to all students.
   iii Asking students in the lunch queue at the beginning of lunchtime.
   iv Asking students with a packed lunch.
 c Will the data be primary or secondary?

> **Key point**
>
> A question in a survey can be biased if it encourages people to give a particular answer.
> A good survey question should not be
> • vague
> • **leading**
> • restrictive.

11 Explain why each of these **leading questions** is unsuitable to use in a survey.
For each question write a more suitable question to replace it.
 a What methods of travel have you used in the last 12 months?
   car   bus   train   taxi   none
   ☐   ☐   ☐   ☐   ☐
 b Petrol prices keep rising, so do you intend to use your car less during the next year?
 c What do you do at weekends?
 d Should the inadequate bus service in our town be improved?
 e The main cause of bad behaviour in lessons is because the
   lesson is boring   teacher is not strict enough   lesson is too long
          ☐   ☐   ☐
 f Because killing animals is cruel, should more people become vegetarians?
 g What kind of food do you eat most of?

> **Q11 Literacy hint**
>
> A **leading question** encourages people to give a particular answer.

12 **Reasoning / Real** The table shows some survey questions and the sampling method used for each one. For each survey
 a write down the population
 b decide if the sample is **random**. Explain your answer.

> **Key point**
>
> In a **random** sample, the whole population has an equal chance of being chosen, so it reduces the chances of bias.

	Survey	Sample
1	How long do patients spend in A&E at a hospital?	Every person leaving A&E on a Saturday night
2	What is the most common second language of people living in Denmark?	Students at a university in Denmark
3	What proportion of UK secondary school teachers are male?	Teachers at the local secondary school
4	What proportion of UK secondary school teachers are male?	Teachers in secondary schools in Leicester, Birmingham, Swansea and Aberdeen

13 **Explore** When the UK government carries out a census, what sample of the population does it ask? What proportion respond?
Is it easier to explore this question now you have completed the lesson? What further information do you need?

14 **Reflect** Look back at the questions you have answered in this lesson.
What mathematical skills do you need when planning a survey?

Active Learn Delta 3, Section 4.1

Reflect Explore

4.2 Presenting and comparing data

You will learn to:
- Draw and interpret stem and leaf diagrams
- Construct and interpret frequency polygons
- Use frequency polygons to compare data.

Why learn this?
Pharmaceutical companies can use frequency polygons to compare the effects of new medicines.

Fluency
What is the midpoint of each group?
- $0 < t \leqslant 10$
- $5 < m \leqslant 25$
- $60 < h \leqslant 63$

Explore
What types of career use frequency polygons most?

Exercise 4.2

1 What is the difference between discrete and continuous data
  a in a frequency table
  b in a frequency diagram?

2 This table shows the age of customers who visit a leisure centre one day.

Age (years)	0–9	10–19	20–29	30–39	40–49	50–59	60–69	70+
Frequency	16	31	8	27	15	8	15	10

  a Draw a **frequency diagram** to display this data.
  b What is the modal class?

> **Q2 Literacy hint**
> A **frequency diagram** is sometimes called a bar chart.

Worked example

Here are the lengths of some earthworms (in cm).
4.5   1.3   0.9   3.6   3.2   2.2   4.8   4.0   3.2   2.9
Construct a **stem and leaf diagram** for this data.

```
0 | 9
1 | 3
2 | 2 9
3 | 6 2 2
4 | 5 8 0
```

> Decide on a stem. For decimals use the whole-number part. Write in the leaves as you work along the data list.

```
0 | 9
1 | 3
2 | 2 9
3 | 2 2 6
4 | 0 5 8
```

> Write out your diagram again, putting the leaves in order.

Key: 1 | 3 means 1.3 cm

> Give your diagram a key.

> **Key point**
> A **stem and leaf diagram** shows numerical data split into a 'stem' and 'leaves'.
> The key shows you how to read the values.

3 Here are some heights of sunflower seedlings (in mm).

35	28	22	41	33	19	55	48	29	31
49	30	18	25	50	39	21	47	38	39

  a Draw a stem and leaf diagram for this data.

  b Use your diagram to answer these questions.

    i How many of the seedlings were more than 35 mm tall?

    ii What percentage of the seedlings were less than 25 mm tall?

Q3a hint

Use the tens digit as the stem.
Remember the key.

4 The stem and leaf diagram shows students'
results for a Year 9 maths test.
Find

  a the mode

  b the range

  c the median.

```
0 | 9
1 | 1 3 8
2 | 2 3 5 8 8
3 | 0 1 4 4 6 7 7 7 9
4 | 1 2 2 5 8 9
5 | 0
```

Key
2 | 5 means 25

  Discussion Which average can you find
most easily from a stem and leaf diagram?

5 A group of Year 9 students were tested on their knowledge
of countries of the world before and after watching a video.
This back-to-back stem and leaf diagram shows the results.

  a Work out the median and range before and after the
students watched the video.

  b Write two sentences comparing the median and range
for before and after.

Before video		After video
8 5 3 2	1	2
9 6 6 4 1 0	2	1 7 9
2 0	3	0 6 7 7 8
8 4 3	4	2 2 5 9
	5	0 0

Key
2 | 3 means 32

Key
3 | 6 means 36

Worked example

This table shows the sea temperature in
Woolacombe in Devon.
Draw a **frequency polygon** for this data.

Work out the midpoint of each group.

Temperature, T (°C)	Frequency	Midpoint
$6 < T \leqslant 8$	8	7
$8 < T \leqslant 10$	14	9
$10 < T \leqslant 12$	18	11
$12 < T \leqslant 14$	25	13
$14 < T \leqslant 16$	23	15
$16 < T \leqslant 18$	15	17
$18 < T \leqslant 20$	3	19

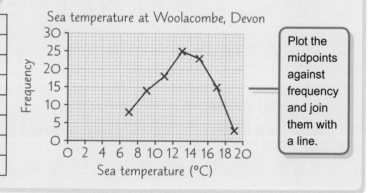

Sea temperature at Woolacombe, Devon

Plot the midpoints against frequency and join them with a line.

6 This table shows the ages of
people visiting a doctors'
surgery in one week.

  a Draw a frequency polygon
for this data.

  b Which age group made the
fewest visits to the
doctors' surgery?

Age, a (years)	Frequency
$0 < a \leqslant 10$	63
$10 < a \leqslant 20$	69
$20 < a \leqslant 30$	75
$30 < a \leqslant 40$	68
$40 < a \leqslant 50$	51
$50 < a \leqslant 60$	46
$60 < a \leqslant 70$	52
$70 < a \leqslant 80$	75
$80 < a \leqslant 90$	58
$90 < a \leqslant 100$	55

Key point

You can draw a **frequency
polygon** by plotting the midpoint of
each group against its frequency.
A frequency polygon helps show
trends in grouped data.

7 **Reasoning** These two frequency polygons show the ages of British adults who used the internet for social networking and for banking in one year.

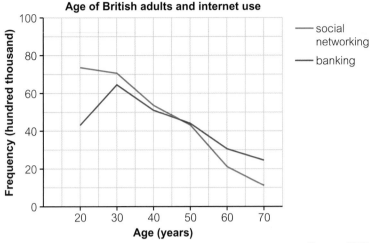

Age of British adults and internet use

—— social networking
—— banking

Source: ONS

a What is the same about the ages of adults who used the internet for social networking and banking?

b What is different?

Q7 hint

Find the modal class for each set of data. What is the trend in each set of data?

8 **Real** The frequency tables show how much employees earn in two companies.

Company A

Earnings per year, e (£ thousands)	Number of employees
0 < e ≤ 10	2
10 < e ≤ 20	26
20 < e ≤ 30	49
30 < e ≤ 40	16
40 < e ≤ 50	11
50 < e ≤ 60	3

Company B

Earnings per year, e (£ thousands)	Number of employees
0 < e ≤ 10	5
10 < e ≤ 20	9
20 < e ≤ 30	26
30 < e ≤ 40	62
40 < e ≤ 50	5
50 < e ≤ 60	2

a Draw a frequency polygon for each set of data, using the same axes.
Use a different colour for each line.

b Compare the two frequency polygons.

Discussion Which company would you choose to work for and why?

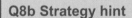

Q8b Strategy hint

What is the modal group for earnings in the two companies?

9 **Explore** What types of career use frequency polygons most? Is it easier to explore this question now you have completed the lesson? What further information do you need?

10 **Reflect** Look at your answers to Q8. The hint suggested finding the modal group. Are there other features you could find to help your comparison?

Explore

Reflect

4.3 Estimating statistics

You will learn to:
- Estimate the mean and range from a grouped frequency table
- Draw conclusions from tables and charts.

Why learn this?
Scientists use grouped data to analyse geographical features.

Fluency
What is the range of this set of data?
5 cm, 3 cm, 0 cm, 2 cm, 10 cm, 5 cm, 6 cm

Explore
Is it better to have a high average with a large range or a low average with a small range?

Exercise 4.3

1 The frequency table shows how many siblings each pupil in a class has.

Number of siblings	0	1	2	3	4
Frequency	5	13	7	4	1

a Work out the mean.

b How many pupils have 2 siblings?

> **Key point**
> When data has been grouped, you cannot work out the exact mean but you can work out an **estimate**.

Worked example

The table shows the results of a survey into the lengths of long rivers in the United Kingdom.

Work out an **estimate** for **a** the mean **b** the range.

a

Length of river, L (km)	Frequency	Midpoint of class (km)	Midpoint × frequency
110 ≤ L < 140	17	125	2125
140 ≤ L < 170	5	155	775
170 ≤ L < 200	3	185	555
200 ≤ L < 230	2	215	430
230 ≤ L < 260	1	245	245
260 ≤ L < 290	0	275	0
290 ≤ L < 320	1	305	305
320 ≤ L < 350	1	335	335
250 ≤ L < 380	1	365	365
Total	31	Total	5135

> You don't know the exact value of each length, so estimate it as the midpoint of each class.
> Draw a column for the midpoints.
> Calculate an estimate of the total length for each class (midpoint × frequency).

> Calculate the total number of rivers and an estimate for the sum of their lengths.

Estimated mean = Estimated sum of lengths ÷ total number of rivers
= 5135 ÷ 31
= 165.65 km (to 2 d.p.)

b An estimate of the range is 380 − 110 = 270 km

> From the frequency table, the smallest possible value is 110 km and the largest possible value is 380 km.

Topic links: Imperial measures

Subject links: Geography (Q2, Q4)

2 The table shows the results of a survey into the lengths of river systems in Europe.
Work out an estimate for
a the range
b the mean.

Length of river, L (miles)	Frequency
$0 \leqslant L < 300$	5
$300 \leqslant L < 600$	13
$600 \leqslant L < 900$	8
$900 \leqslant L < 1200$	1
$1200 \leqslant L < 1500$	2
$1500 \leqslant L < 1800$	1
$1800 \leqslant L < 2100$	0
$2100 \leqslant L < 2400$	1

3 Problem-solving Class 9Y carried out a survey to find out how many miles people drive each year. The frequency polygon shows their results.
Work out an estimate for
a the range
b the mean.

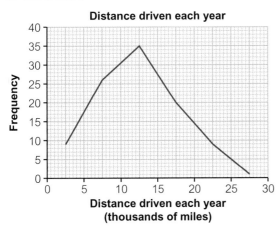

Distance driven each year

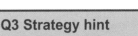

Q3 Strategy hint
Make a table with these four columns:
- class
- frequency
- midpoint of class
- midpoint × frequency.

4 The table shows the results of a survey into the lengths of rivers in North America.

Length of river, L (miles)	Frequency
$0 < L \leqslant 400$	21
$400 < L \leqslant 800$	18
$800 < L \leqslant 1200$	4
$1200 < L \leqslant 1600$	3
$1600 < L \leqslant 2000$	3
$2000 < L \leqslant 2400$	2
$2400 < L \leqslant 2800$	1
$2800 < L \leqslant 3200$	2

a How many items are there in the sample?
b Which number item is the median?
c In which group will the median value be?
d What is the modal class?
e Work out an estimate for
   i the mean   **ii** the range.

Key point
You can't work out the median from grouped data but you can find out which group the median value is in.

5 Explore Is it better to have a high average with a large range or a low average with a small range?
Look back at the maths you have learned in this lesson.
How can you use it to answer this question?

6 Reflect Ed says, 'On average, a human has slightly less than two legs.' What point do you think Ed is trying to make with this statement?

Explore

Reflect

4.4 Box plots

You will learn to:
- Interpret statistics
- Draw and interpret box plots
- Compare data using box plots.

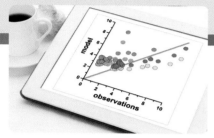

Why learn this?
Scientists and engineers need to identify outliers in sets of data to stop them skewing the results.

Fluency
Work out
- $(19 + 1) \div 2$
- $(19 + 1) \div 4$
- $55 \div 11$
- $105 - 47$

Explore
Compare the mean, median, mode, range and interquartile range of 3, 3, 3, 3, 33 with and without the outlier.

CONFIDENCE

Warm up

Exercise 4.4

1 For these sets of data, work out
    i the mean   **ii** the mode   **iii** the median   **iv** the range.

  a 3 5 11 11 12 15 20

  b 1 cm 5 cm 7 cm 10 cm 10 cm 15 cm 16 cm 18 cm 18 cm 18 cm 25 cm

2 The data in the table shows the number of pets each child in a class has.
Work out the median.

Number of pets	0	1	2	3
Frequency	12	8	5	1

3 Shoshana researches the amount of grams of sugar 5 of her friends eat in one day.

    1 ☐ ☐ ☐ 7

The mode is 1. The mean is 2.4. The range is 6. All the amounts are given as whole numbers. Work out the missing data items.

Q3 hint

What should all the numbers add up to?

Worked example

Marcus measures the height of 11 plants, to the nearest centimetre.
  8 cm   9 cm   10 cm   11 cm   12 cm   13 cm
  14 cm   17 cm   18 cm   22 cm   22 cm
Work out
a the **median**   **b** the **lower quartile**   **c** the **upper quartile**.

a Median = 13 cm — There are 11 items, so the middle item is the $(11 + 1) \div 2 = $ 6th item in the ordered list.

b Lower quartile = 10 cm — The lower quartile is $\frac{1}{4}$ of the way up the ordered list. The median is the 6th item, so the lower quartile is the $6 \div 2 = $ 3rd item.

c Upper quartile = 18 cm — The upper quartile is $\frac{3}{4}$ of the way up the list. It is the $6 + (6 \div 2) = $ 9th item.

Key point

The **median** divides the data into two halves.
The **lower quartile** shows where the bottom 25% of the data is.
The **upper quartile** shows where the top 25% of the data is.

Subject links: Food technology (Q6, Q8)

4 For each set of data, work out
   i the median
   ii the lower quartile
   iii the upper quartile.
   a 63 64 67 67 73 76 78 80 81 84 86
   b 2 4 6 7 8 8 9 9 10 10 12 13 15 16 16
   c 17 18 20 20 19 17 19 17 17 16 17

Q4c hint

Put the data items in order first.

5 Here are the temperatures for 15 days in November in Sheffield.
    10°C 8°C 9°C 10°C 5°C 8°C 3°C
    6°C 4°C 8°C   8°C 9°C 5°C 6°C 7°C
  Work out
  a the median
  b the upper quartile
  c the lower quartile
  d the **interquartile range**.

Key point

The **interquartile range** is the difference between the upper quartile and lower quartile. It tells you how spread out the middle 50% of the data is.

6 This **box plot** shows the number of grams of potatoes the Frost family eat per day in one week.

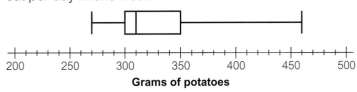

Grams of potatoes

  a Work out
    i the median
    ii the lower quartile
    iii the upper quartile
    iv the range
    v the interquartile range.
  b Copy and complete this sentence.
    On half the days, they ate between 300 g and ☐ g.

Key point

A **box plot** (or box and whisker diagram) displays information about the range, the median and the quartiles. It is drawn above or below a number line.

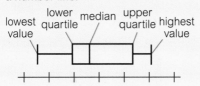

7 Draw a box plot to represent the data in Q5.
  Discussion Do you think the temperatures in Sheffield were consistent? How does your box plot show this?

Q7 hint

The number line should go from the lowest value to the highest value.

8 **Reasoning** Here is the amount of potatoes the Carr family eat in one week.
    200 g 360 g 380 g 350 g 300 g 280 g 310 g
  Draw a box plot to show this data.
  Discussion Compare the box plots for Q6 and Q8. Which data is more spread out?

9 **Explore** Compare the mean, median, mode, range and interquartile range of 3, 3, 3, 3, 33 with and without the outlier.
  Look back at the maths you have learned in this lesson.
  How can you use it to answer this question?

10 **Reflect** In this lesson, real data about weather and diet is analysed using box plots. What other areas of research might use box plots?

Explore

Reflect

4.5 Cumulative frequency graphs

You will learn to:
- Draw cumulative frequency graphs for grouped data
- Interpret cumulative frequency graphs.

CONFIDENCE

Why learn this?
Supermarkets use cumulative frequency graphs to work out the proportion of customers who get through the checkout in under 5 minutes.

Fluency
Which item is the median in
- 51 items
- 65 items
- 80 items?

Explore
What shape are most cumulative frequency graphs?

Exercise 4.5

Warm up

1 Draw the box plot for this set of data.

    0   4   4   5   7   8   9   12   13   17   20

2 This table shows the amount of time people waited at a dentist's one morning.

Time, t (minutes)	Frequency
$1 < t \leqslant 5$	8
$6 < t \leqslant 10$	12
$11 < t \leqslant 15$	13
$16 < t \leqslant 20$	9
$21 < t \leqslant 25$	3
$25 < t \leqslant 30$	5

   a How many people waited 10 minutes or less?
   b How many people waited longer than 16 minutes?
   c How many people waited between 11 and 25 minutes?
   d In which group does the median time lie?

Key point
The **cumulative frequency** is the sum of consecutive frequencies. You can use it to plot a **cumulative frequency graph**.

Worked example

The table shows the times taken by female athletes to run a marathon. Draw a **cumulative frequency graph** to represent this data.

Time, T (h : min)	Frequency	Cumulative frequency
$2:20 < T \leqslant 2:30$	1	1
$2:30 < T \leqslant 2:40$	10	11
$2:40 < T \leqslant 2:50$	18	29
$2:50 < T \leqslant 3:00$	36	65
$3:00 < T \leqslant 3:10$	43	108
$3:10 < T \leqslant 3:20$	15	123
$3:20 < T \leqslant 3:30$	9	132

Add a **cumulative frequency** column to the table.

This is the frequency of the first group.

Add the frequency of the second group to the cumulative frequency in the first row. This shows everyone who completed the marathon in 2 : 40 or less.

Add the frequency in the third group to the cumulative frequency in the second group, and so on.

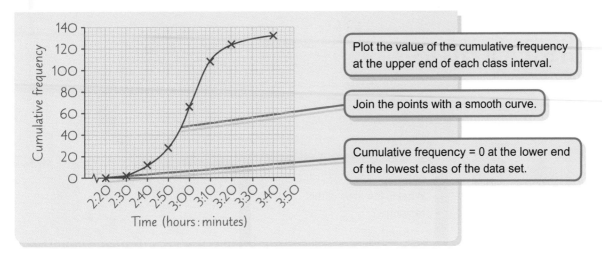

Plot the value of the cumulative frequency at the upper end of each class interval.

Join the points with a smooth curve.

Cumulative frequency = 0 at the lower end of the lowest class of the data set.

3 This table shows the time taken by male athletes to complete a marathon. Draw a cumulative frequency graph for this data.

Time, T (hours : minutes)	Frequency
$2 : 00 < T \leqslant 2 : 10$	4
$2 : 10 < T \leqslant 2 : 20$	7
$2 : 20 < T \leqslant 2 : 30$	13
$2 : 30 < T \leqslant 2 : 40$	18
$2 : 40 < T \leqslant 2 : 50$	36
$2 : 50 < T \leqslant 3 : 00$	43
$3 : 00 < T \leqslant 3 : 10$	15
$3 : 10 < T \leqslant 3 : 20$	10
$3 : 20 < T \leqslant 3 : 30$	4

4 **Reasoning** This cumulative frequency graph shows the ages of the members of a tennis club.
  a How many members does the tennis club have?
  b Use the graph to estimate
    i the median
    ii the lower quartile
    iii the upper quartile.
  c Work out
    i the range   ii the interquartile range.

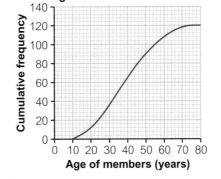

Ages of tennis club members

Key point

You can use the cumulative frequency graph to estimate the median, lower quartile and upper quartile.
Read off the middle, $\frac{1}{4}$ and $\frac{3}{4}$ values.

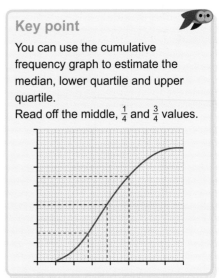

5 Use the cumulative frequency graph you drew in Q3 to estimate
  a the median   b the lower quartile
  c the upper quartile   d the range
  e the interquartile range.

6 **Explore** What shape are most cumulative frequency graphs?
  Look back at the maths you have learned in this lesson.
  How can you use it to answer this question?

7 **Reflect** 'Box plots tell us the same things as cumulative frequency graphs.' Do you agree with this statement? Explain your answer.

4.6 Histograms

You will learn to:
• Construct and interpret histograms.

Why learn this?
Television producers use histograms to show the ages of people who watch different programmes.

Fluency
What is the area of this rectangle?

5 cm
4.2 cm

Explore
What kinds of data can you draw a histogram for? What kinds of data can you draw a frequency diagram for?

Exercise 4.6

1 A bird survey was done on a Scottish island in the first 2 months of 2014. The frequency diagram shows the number of avocets observed per week.

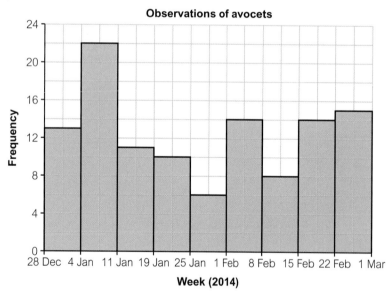

Observations of avocets

a How many avocets altogether were observed between 28 December and 1 March?
b Which time period had the most observations?
c In which weeks were fewer than 10 avocets observed?
d What is the mean number of avocets observed per week?

2 This frequency table shows the number of different species of birds that were observed over a week.
a Draw a bar chart for the data.
b During the same week there were 1919 observations of chaffinches. How would including these affect your bar chart?

Species	Frequency
Bittern	13
Ruddy duck	9
White-tailed eagle	4
Goshawk	5
Golden eagle	8
Common sandpiper	15
Bean goose	3
Herring gull	6
Corn bunting	15

Subject link: Science (Q5)

3 These were the weekly earnings, in pounds, during January 2001 of 25 people working in the UK.

266	257	137	103	119
507	99	278	93	141
488	130	126	165	680
179	220	172	110	191
250	190	140	202	100

Copy this frequency table, and fill in the frequency column.

Weekly earnings, E (£)	Frequency
$0 < E \leqslant 100$	
$100 < E \leqslant 150$	
$150 < E \leqslant 200$	
$200 < E \leqslant 300$	
$300 < E \leqslant 700$	

Key point

Sometimes it is useful to have different class widths when grouping data, for example when a lot of values are close together and other values are more spread out.

Worked example

This table shows the population of cities in the UK (excluding Birmingham and London).
Draw a histogram to show the data.

Key point

A **histogram** looks similar to a bar chart but the area of the bar, rather than its height, gives the frequency. The vertical axis is labelled **frequency density**.

Population, P (thousands)	Frequency	Class width	Frequency density
$0 < P \leqslant 20$	8	20	0.4
$20 < P \leqslant 50$	12	30	0.4
$50 < P \leqslant 100$	10	50	0.2
$100 < P \leqslant 150$	8	50	0.16
$150 < P \leqslant 200$	6	50	0.12
$200 < P \leqslant 300$	12	100	0.12
$300 < P \leqslant 500$	6	200	0.03
$500 < P \leqslant 1000$	5	500	0.01

Draw a 'Class width' and 'Frequency density' column.

$$\text{Frequency density} = \frac{\text{frequency}}{\text{class width}}$$

for each class.
Work it out for each class.

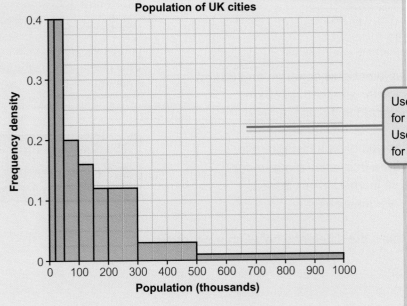

Population of UK cities

Use the Population column for the width of each bar. Use the Frequency density for the height of each bar.

4 Reasoning The grouped frequency table gives the distances that employees at a factory travel to work.

Distance, d (km)	Frequency
$0 < d \leqslant 2$	32
$2 < d \leqslant 5$	45
$5 < d \leqslant 10$	38
$10 < d \leqslant 20$	29
$20 < d \leqslant 40$	18
$40 < d \leqslant 60$	6
$60 < d \leqslant 100$	5

Draw a histogram for the data.

Discussion Why are some bars tall and thin, and some are short and wide?

5 STEM This histogram shows the diameters of the largest confirmed meteor impact craters found on Earth.

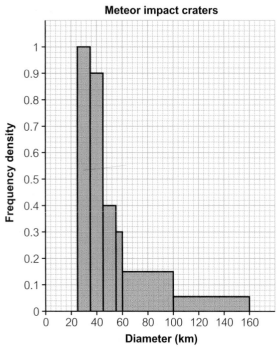

Meteor impact craters

Source: Earth Impact Database

a How many craters had a diameter between 55 km and 65 km?
b How many craters had a diameter greater than 65 km?
c How many craters are represented in the histogram?

6 Explore What kinds of data can you draw a histogram for?
What kinds of data can you draw a frequency diagram for?
Look back at the maths you have learned in this lesson.
How can you use it to answer this question?

7 Reflect In your own words, explain the difference between a bar chart and a histogram.

Q5a hint

Frequency density = $\dfrac{\text{frequency}}{\text{class width}}$

Rearrange the formula to work out the frequency from the frequency density.

Q5c Strategy hint

Create a table showing class width, frequency density and frequency.

ActiveLearn   Delta 3, Section 4.6

4 Check up

Collecting data

1 A school has 1800 students. It wants to investigate how its students travel to school. Select the most appropriate sample size for the survey.
   A 1000　　　　**B** 500　　　　**C** 200　　　　**D** 20

2 A library has 3860 members. How big should a sample of the library members be?

3 Fiona is researching the amount of time teenagers spend on the computer
   a Say whether each of these is primary or secondary data.
      A Sending a survey to the students of a local school
      B Using information from the internet
   She gives questionnaires to all the Year 10 students at her school.
   b Why will the sample be biased?
   c How could Fiona reduce bias in her sample?

Representing and interpreting data

4 These are the marks awarded in a music competition.
   | 67 | 35 | 46 | 39 | 49 | 41 | 67 | 43 | 37 | 46 |
   | 37 | 78 | 31 | 48 | 63 | 55 | 67 | 54 | 70 | 65 |
   a Draw a stem and leaf diagram for this data.
   b What were the marks for 1st, 2nd and 3rd places?
   c How many competitors scored more than 50 marks?

5 For this set of data
   5 cm, 3 cm, 8 cm, 4 cm, □, □, □
   the mean is 5 cm, the mode is 8 cm, and the median is 5 cm.
   Write the full set of data.

6 This table shows the weight of 50 children on their second birthday.
   a Estimate the mean weight.
   b Which class contains the median weight?
   c Estimate the range.

Weight, w (kg)	Frequency
$10 < w \leqslant 11$	8
$11 < w \leqslant 12$	14
$12 < w \leqslant 13$	15
$13 < w \leqslant 14$	7
$14 < w \leqslant 15$	5
$15 < w \leqslant 16$	1

7 These frequency polygons show the heights of 50 boys and 50 girls on their second birthday.
   a Calculate the mean height for each frequency polygon.
   b Compare the heights of the boys and girls using the two frequency polygons.

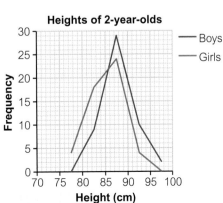

Heights of 2-year-olds
— Boys
— Girls

8 The box plot shows the daily number of sales in a shoe shop over 3 months.

Write

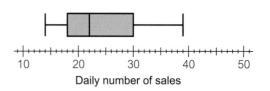

Daily number of sales

a the median   **b** the lower quartile

c the upper quartile   **d** the range

e the interquartile range.

9 This table shows the number of followers of the 50 most popular users of a social networking site in August 2014.

a Draw a cumulative frequency graph to represent this data.

b Use your cumulative frequency graph to work out an estimate for

   i the median

   ii the lower and upper quartile

   iii the interquartile range.

c Which class contains the median?

Followers of the top 50 members in August 2014	
Number of followers, N (millions)	Frequency
$6 < N \leqslant 8$	18
$8 < N \leqslant 10$	13
$10 < N \leqslant 12$	9
$12 < N \leqslant 14$	7
$14 < N \leqslant 16$	2
$16 < N \leqslant 18$	1

10 This histogram shows the amount families from a small town spent on trips abroad in 2014.

a How many families spent less than £1000?

b How many families spent between £1000 and £5000?

c How many families are there in the town?

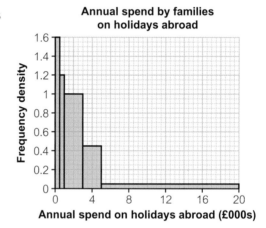

Annual spend by families on holidays abroad

11 How sure are you of your answers? Were you mostly

☹ Just guessing   😐 Feeling doubtful   😊 Confident

What next? Use your results to decide whether to strengthen or extend your learning.

Challenge

12 This table shows information about UK house prices.

Quarter-year	Average price (£)			
	Flat	Terraced house	Semi-detached house	Detached house
Jan–Mar 2012	96769	98754	124269	173607
April–June 2012	96875	96775	129324	173754
July–Sep 2012	100154	99286	129143	176108
Oct–Dec 2012	97344	94761	128157	173991
Jan–Mar 2013	91942	96964	123998	176580
April–June 2013	102165	99666	128507	173490

Source: Land Registry

a Write two questions that the data could help you answer.

b What further data could you collect for your investigation?

Reflect

4 Extend

You will:
- Extend your understanding with problem-solving.

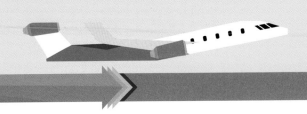

1 **Reasoning / Real** Every year a competition is held in Bognor Regis for human-powered flying machines.
Table A shows the distances travelled in 2004 and 2006.
Table B shows the time spent in the air.

Table A

Distance, D (metres)	Frequency	
	2004	2006
$0 \leqslant D < 2$	1	0
$2 \leqslant D < 4$	4	1
$4 \leqslant D < 6$	10	5
$6 \leqslant D < 8$	5	12
$8 \leqslant D < 10$	5	5
$10 \leqslant D < 12$	1	1

Table B

Airtime, T (seconds)	Frequency	
	2004	2006
$1 \leqslant T < 1.25$	2	4
$1.25 \leqslant T < 1.5$	15	7
$1.5 \leqslant T < 1.75$	6	9
$1.75 \leqslant T < 2$	0	2
$2 \leqslant T < 2.25$	1	2
$2.25 \leqslant T < 2.5$	2	0

Source: Birdman

a Using the same axes, draw frequency polygons for distance travelled in 2004 and in 2006.

b On a new set of axes, draw frequency polygons for airtime in 2004 and 2006.

c Compare the distances and the airtime for the 2 years.

d What can you say about distance and airtime?

> **Q1a hint**
>
> Use a different colour for each polygon and give a colour key.

2 **Reasoning** Students in a Year 9 class took a French test and a Spanish test.
The results for the French test were:

| 35 | 48 | 19 | 25 | 47 | 36 | 33 | 29 | 40 | 35 |
| 49 | 38 | 24 | 28 | 38 | 38 | 12 | 37 | 30 | 41 |

The results for the Spanish test were:

| 50 | 48 | 23 | 28 | 39 | 32 | 34 | 40 | 20 | 28 |
| 38 | 45 | 37 | 29 | 26 | 36 | 38 | 32 | 30 | 21 |

a Draw a back-to-back stem and leaf diagram for this data.

b The pass mark for both tests was 32.
What percentage of students passed

 i the French test

 ii the Spanish test?

Discussion Can you say how many students passed both tests? Explain.

> **Q2a hint**
>
> In a back-to-back stem and leaf diagram, the lowest numbers are closest to the stem.

3 Reasoning Sam wrote a questionnaire about bullying.

Questionnaire about bullying	
Question A	How often have you been bullied?
Question B	What do you do when you see someone being bullied?
Question C	Do you agree that bullies should be sent to prison?

a Say why each of Sam's questions needs to be improved.

b Choose three questions from this list to replace questions A, B and C.

Question P	Why is bullying wrong?
Question Q	If you saw someone being bullied would you ☐ do nothing ☐ try to stop it ☐ tell someone in authority, such as a teacher?
Question R	When were you last bullied?
Question S	When do you think bullying usually happens? ☐ in lessons ☐ after school ☐ on the way home ☐ during luch break ☐ on the school bus ☐ every day
Question T	Do you agree that bullies should be ignored?
Question U	Tick the option that best describes your experience. During the past year I have been bullied ☐ never ☐ once ☐ between 2 and 12 times ☐ at least once per month ☐ at least once a week ☐ daily
Question V	Do you defend people who are being bullied?
Question W	Tick the option that is closest to your view. School bullies should be ☐ sent to prison ☐ dealt with by a teacher who knows them well ☐ made to apologise to the person they bullied ☐ expelled from the school ☐ kept in after school for an hour for a whole term ☐ ignored ☐ banned from all sports

4 Problem-solving

a A data set has 7 items. All the values are whole numbers.
The largest item is 12. The range is 9 and the interquartile range is 4.
The median is 6 and there is no mode.
List the numbers in the data set, smallest first.

b A data set is 9 g, 12 g, 5 g, ☐, ☐, ☐, ☐.
All the values are whole numbers.
The mean is 8 g, the mode is 5 g and the median is 7 g.
Find as many possible data sets as you can.

5 In a survey into eating habits, students recorded the number of
portions of fruit and vegetables they ate for a week. The results are
shown in the table.

Number of portions per week	Frequency
0–9	6
10–19	17
20–29	15
30–39	48
40–49	21
50–59	3

a Work out an estimate for the mean number of portions eaten
each week.

b Which class contains the median number of portions?

6 These graphs show facts about percentages of populations who turned out to vote in UK General Elections.

Graph A shows the percentage of the whole UK population that voted in elections between 1945 and 2010. **Graph B** shows the percentages of the population for a random sample of UK **constituencies**.

Q6 Literacy hint

A **constituency** is an area that votes for a single Member of Parliament.

Graph A

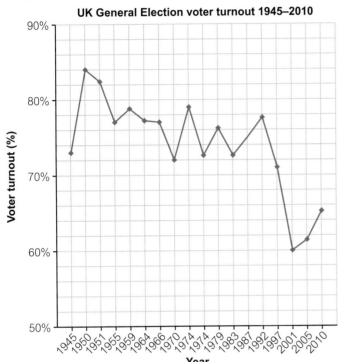

Graph B

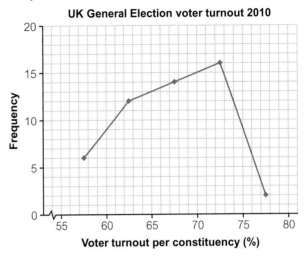

Source: House of Commons

a Explain why graph A is not a frequency polygon.

b Work out an estimate of the mean percentage of eligible people in each constituency who voted in the 2010 General Election.

7 **Reasoning** Each box plot shows the monthly maximum temperature over a particular year. The box plots are all for the same location.

a For each year work out
  i the median
  ii the interquartile range
  iii the range.

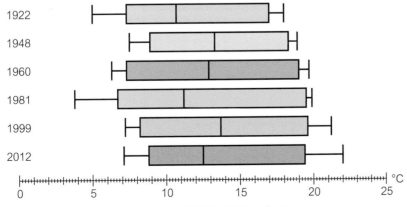

b Comment on the variation in monthly maximum temperature between the different years.

8 Real / Reasoning The table shows the age men lived to after the age of 75 in 1974 and 2013.

Age, A (years)	Frequency	
	1974	2013
$75 \leqslant A < 80$	47529	39630
$80 \leqslant A < 85$	36962	48255
$85 \leqslant A < 90$	21367	44778
$90 \leqslant A < 95$	8145	27641
$95 \leqslant A < 100$	1590	7185
$100 \leqslant A < 105$	134	991

a For the data in each year
  i draw a cumulative frequency graph
  ii work out an estimate for the median, lower quartile and upper quartile
  iii estimate the range and interquartile range
  iv work out which group contains the median.
b What seems to be happening to the expected life-span of the male UK population? How do the cumulative frequency graphs and the statistics that you calculated support your conclusion?

> **Q8a i Strategy hint**
> Round every frequency to the nearest hundred, and mark the cumulative frequency axis in thousands. For example, write 37576 as 37.6 thousands and 1590 as 1.6 thousands.

9 Reasoning The table shows the times of the three-legged race at a village fair in 1967 and in 2005.

a Draw a histogram for the 1967 data.
b Draw a histogram for the 2005 data.
c Write a sentence comparing the times of the races in 1967 and in 2005.

Time, T (minutes)	Frequency	
	1967	2005
$7 \leqslant T < 11$	1	6
$11 \leqslant T < 14$	9	9
$14 \leqslant T < 17$	9	6
$17 \leqslant T < 19$	4	0
$19 \leqslant T < 27$	5	0

Investigation   Reasoning / Problem-solving

These box plots were created from data about four different tomato varieties.
The lightest and heaviest weights were the same for all varieties.
1 Which variety was lightest, on average?
2 Which variety had the most consistent weight?
3 For each box plot, sketch the shape of the cumulative frequency curve to go with it.

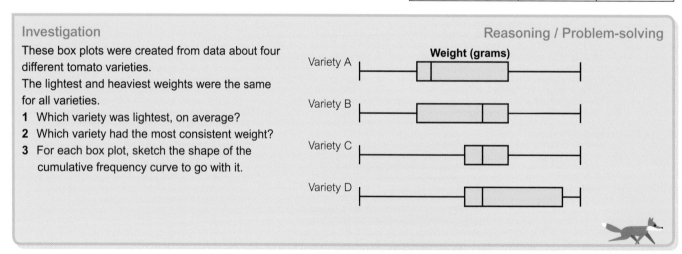

10 Reflect This extend section included a lot of questions using real data. Do you find it easier or harder to understand statistics when real data is used? Explain your answer.

4 Unit test

Log how you did on your Student Progression Chart.

1 A doctor wants to find out her patients' views on waiting times at the surgery, which has 1900 registered patients. Select the most appropriate sample size for the survey.

  A 1900

  B 1000

  C 200

  D 100

2 The table shows the results of a survey into how old people were when they first flew on a plane.

  Construct a frequency polygon for this data.

Age, a (years)	Frequency
$0 < a \leqslant 10$	16
$10 < a \leqslant 20$	32
$20 < a \leqslant 30$	27
$30 < a \leqslant 40$	8
$40 < a \leqslant 50$	5
$50 < a \leqslant 60$	2

3 These are the number of days books in a library were borrowed for:

  5   15   13   8   31   24   21   35   19   11

  18   17   4   22   15   17   21   14   3   15

  a Draw a stem and leaf diagram for this data.

  b What is the mode?

  c Books are initially lent for 3 weeks. How many books needed to be renewed?

4 These frequency polygons show the number of people employed at companies in two towns.

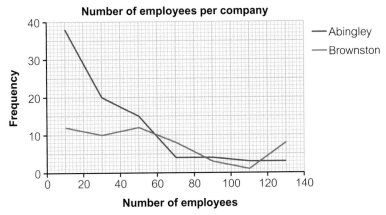

Number of employees per company

— Abingley

— Brownston

  a Calculate the mean number of employees per company for each town.

  b Write a sentence to compare the size of the companies in the two towns.

5 The table shows the diameters of some asteroids.

  a Estimate

    i the range

    ii the mean.

  b In which group is the median?

Diameter, D (metres)	Frequency
$0 < D \leqslant 30$	1600
$30 < D \leqslant 100$	2700
$100 < D \leqslant 300$	2800
$300 < D \leqslant 1000$	3150
$1000 < D \leqslant 2000$	880

6 The box plots show the weights of two different groups of black bears.

Group of bears X

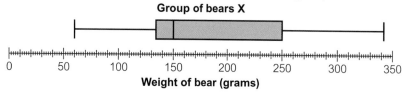

Weight of bear (grams)

Group of bears Y

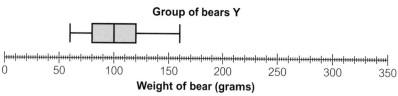

Weight of bear (grams)

a For each group of bears, work out
  i the median   **ii** the lower quartile
  iii the upper quartile   **iv** the range
  v the interquartile range.
b In one of the groups all the bears were the same age.
  i Which group was that? Give reasons for your answer.
  ii Was this group of bears young or old? Explain.

7 The table shows the wingspans of some birds.
  a Draw a cumulative frequency graph for this data.
  b Estimate the median.
  c Work out an estimate for the interquartile range.
  d How many of the birds have a wingspan greater than 50 inches?

Wingspan, W (inches)	Frequency
$10 < W \leqslant 30$	9
$30 < W \leqslant 50$	27
$50 < W \leqslant 70$	11
$70 < W \leqslant 90$	9
$90 < W \leqslant 110$	2

8 The histogram shows the areas of the national parks in the UK.
  a How many parks have an area less than 1000 km²?
  b How many national parks are there in the UK?

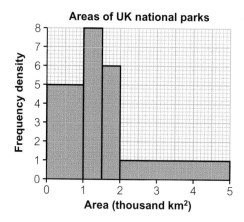

Areas of UK national parks

Challenge

9 Plan how you might investigate the hypothesis 'Men earn more than women'. Make sure you include
  • where you find your data
  • how you collect your data
  • how you will avoid bias
  • what sample size you should consider
  • how you display the data.

10 Reflect Dhia says, 'I enjoy statistics because it is about people as well as maths.' Now you have completed this unit, do you agree with Dhia? Explain your answer.

Reflect

5 Multiplicative reasoning

MASTER

Check
P109

Strengthen
P111

Extend
P115

Test
P119

5.1 Direct proportion

You will learn to:
- Recognise data sets that are in proportion
- Set up equations that show direct proportion.

Why learn this?
Knowing the relationship between quantities can help us to make predictions.

Fluency
Which of these graphs show direct proportion?

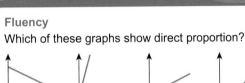
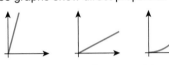

Explore
Are a clothes store's profits in direct proportion to its sales?

Exercise 5.1

1 Which of these are in direct proportion?
  a Exchange rate of pounds (£) and Czech koruna (Kĉ)
  b A plumber who charges a flat fee and then an hourly rate
  c Exchange rate at a bank that charges a £5 flat fee for changing money
  d Distance in miles and distance in kilometres

2 The price of eggs varies in direct proportion to the number sold. The price of 6 eggs is £1.98. How much will
  a 12 eggs cost
  b 15 eggs cost?

> **Q2b hint**
> Work out the cost of 1 egg.

3 **Real** Two friends compare their mobile phone bills.
Andrew's bill is £2.80 for 80 text messages.
Berwyn's bill is £5.10 for 150 text messages.
Who has the better deal?

> **Q3 hint**
> The cost of text messages is in direct proportion to the number sent.

4 **STEM** A laboratory takes these readings for variables x and y in one experiment.

x	0.6	1.7	2.4
y	5.4	15.3	21.6

  a Plot the points for x and y.
  b Does the graph show that the variables are in direct proportion?
  c Work out $\frac{y}{x}$ for each pair. What do you notice?
  d Copy and complete this arrow diagram.
  e Copy and complete this formula linking x and y: $\quad y = \square x$
  Discussion How does the formula relate to the graph?

> **Key point**
> When two quantities x and y are in direct proportion, $\frac{y}{x}$ is **constant**.

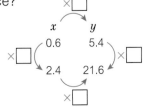

Warm up

5 The table shows the cost of hiring a car.

Number of days	2	5	9
Cost (£)	27	67.50	121.50

  a Work out Cost ÷ Number of days for each pair of values.
  b Is the cost of hiring a car in direct proportion to the number of days?
  c Check your answer to part **b** by drawing a graph, with Number of days on the horizontal axis.
  d Copy and complete: Cost = ☐ × Number of days
  e What is the cost of hiring a car for 15 days?

6 **Real** Russell records the temperature of five cities in Celsius (°C) and Fahrenheit (°F).

City	Cape Town	Chicago	Manchester	Rio de Janeiro	Port Stanley
Temperature C(°C)	16	22	21	26	9
Temperature F(°F)	61	72	70	79	48

  a Is the temperature in Fahrenheit proportional to the temperature in Celsius? Explain.
  b Check your answer to part **a** by drawing a graph, with °C on the horizontal axis.

> **Q6a hint**
> Work out $F ÷ C$ for each city.

7 The values of p and x are in direct proportion. Work out the missing numbers a, b, c and d.

p	x
8	25
12	a
b	50
c	62.5
20	d

> **Q7 hint**
> You could use ratios to find the missing numbers.
>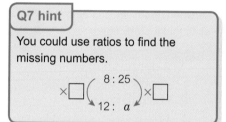

8 **Real** The table below shows the distances (in metres and yards) that a golfer hits a ball with different clubs. Calculate the missing distances x, y and z. Give your answers to the nearest integer.

Club	Distance (yards)	Distance (metres)
9-iron	140	128
7-iron	162	x
4-iron	y	194
Driver	z	306

> **Q8 hint**
> Are metres and yards in direct proportion?

  Discussion How did you find the missing distances?

9 **Modelling** The circumference of Sian's head is 48 cm. Her height is 162 cm.
  a Write Sian's head circumference to height as a ratio.
  Sian assumes that head circumference and height are in direct proportion. Use this model to predict
  b the height of a person with head circumference 35 cm
  c the head circumference of a person 185 cm tall.
  Discussion Is this a reasonable model?

10 **Explore** Are a clothes store's profits in direct proportion to its sales? Is it easier to explore this question now you have completed the lesson? What further information do you need to be able to answer this?

11 **Reflect** The relationship between two variables can be shown on a graph or using a table of values. Do you prefer one method over the other? Why?

Topic links: Graphs, Measures   **Subject links:** Geography (Q6)   *Active*Learn   Delta 3, Section 5.1

5.2 Solving problems using direct proportion

You will learn to:
- Set up equations to show direct proportion
- Use algebra to solve problems involving proportion.

CONFIDENCE

Why learn this?
Scientists use direct proportion to study the relationship between temperature, volume and pressure of gases.

Fluency
$y = 4x$
Work out y when
- $x = 2$
- $x = 3.5$
- $x = 44$

Explore
How much does a 10 kg mass weigh on Mars?

Exercise 5.2

1 Write down the equation of each line on the right.

2 Solve
  a $15 = 30k$
  b $12 = 8k$

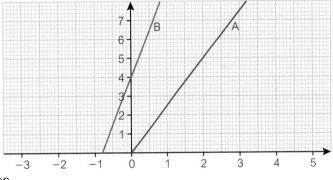

3 **STEM** In a school science experiment, students apply a force to a model car and then measure the acceleration. The table shows some results.

Force, F (newtons)	10	12	25
Acceleration, a (m/s²)	0.5	0.6	1.25

  a Plot a graph of this data.
  b Are force and acceleration in direct proportion? Explain.
  c Write a formula connecting force and acceleration.

4 **Real / Finance** Write a formula linking each pair of quantities.
  a The cost, C, in pence of sending a text message, t, at 5p per text.

  $$C = \square t$$

  b The cost, C, in pounds of x plants at £4 per plant.
  c Yearly earnings, E, in pounds of a footballer who earns £x per week.
  d The number of miles, m, travelled in 2.5 hours at a speed of x miles per hour.
  e The cost, C, in pounds of n biscuits at 35p each.
  Discussion What is the same about all these formulae?

> **Key point**
> When
> - y varies as x
> - y varies directly as x
> - y is in direct proportion to x
> you can write $y \propto x$
> - $y \propto x$ means 'y is proportional to x'.
> When $y \propto x$, then $y = kx$, where k is the **constant of proportionality**.

> **Q4 Literacy hint**
> In the formula $C = 5t$, 5 is the **constant of proportionality**. Its value is constant (stays the same) when t and C vary.

Warm up

5 Which of these equations show direct proportion?

  a $P = 5s$ **b** $C = 5h + 40$

  c $y = \frac{1}{2}x$ **d** $A = d^2$

Worked example

The number of centimetres, C, varies in direct proportion to the number of inches, I.

a 12 inches is equal to 30 centimetres. Write a formula linking C and I.

b How many centimetres are equal to 70 inches?

a $C \propto I$

   $C = kI$ ———— Write the relationship in the form $y \propto x$ and the equation $y = kx$.

   When $I = 12$, $C = 30$

   $30 = k \times 12$ ———— Substitute the values given for I and C into $C = kI$.

   $k = \dfrac{30}{12} = 2.5$

              ———— Solve the equation to find k. Rewrite the equation using the value of k.

   $C = 2.5I$

b When $I = 70$

   $C = 2.5 \times 70$

   $C = 175$ ———— Use your formula to answer the question.

   70 inches = 175 cm

6 The price of potatoes, P, varies in direct proportion to the mass, m, sold.
The price of 2.5 kg of potatoes is £6.05.

  a Write a formula linking P and m.

  b Use your formula to work out the price of 4.2 kg of potatoes.

7 Finance The South African rand, R, varies in direct proportion with the UK pound, P.
One day 801 South African rand = £45.

  a Write a formula for converting pounds to rand.

  b How many South African rand can you buy with £250?

  c How many UK pounds can you buy with 650 South African rand?

  Discussion What level of accuracy should you use for your answer to part **c**?

> **Q7 hint**
> Write a formula $R =$

8 Finance Suzie's commission is in direct proportion to the value of goods sold.
Commission, C, is £51 when £1700 worth of goods, G, is sold.

  a Work out the commission on £2500 of goods sold.

  b Suzie receives £180 commission. What value of goods has she sold?

> **Q8 hint**
> Write a formula $C =$

9 Problem-solving x and y are in direct proportion.

x	0.7	t	3.5
y	4.2	14.4	21

  a Write a formula for y.

  b Work out the missing value t.

> **Q9 hint**
> $y = kx$
> Use a pair of values from the table to find k.

Topic links: Perimeter, Area   **Subject links:** Science (Q3, Q10)

10 **STEM** The weight, W, of an object is in direct proportion to the mass, m, of the object.

On Earth, a 14 kg object weighs 137.2 N.

  a Work out the weight of an 18 kg object on Earth.

  b The formula connecting mass and weight is
$W = m \times$ acceleration due to gravity.
What is the value of the acceleration due to gravity on the Earth?

  c On the Moon, the acceleration due to gravity is 1.6 m/s^2.

    i What is the formula connecting the weight and mass of objects on the Moon?

    ii Work out the weight of the 14 kg object on the Moon.

Q10 Literacy hint

Mass is measured in kg.
Weight is a force and is measured in N (newtons).

Q10b hint

The units for the acceleration due to gravity are m/s^2.

11 **Modelling** An aeroplane travels 720 miles in 90 minutes.
The distance travelled, d, is in direct proportion to the time, t.

  a Work out how far the aeroplane travels at this speed

  i in 140 minutes

  ii in 1 hour 15 minutes.

  The formula connecting distance and time is $d = s \times t$.

  b What is the speed of the plane in miles per hour?

  c The distance from London to New York is 3450 miles.
Use your formula to work out the journey time flying from London to New York.

  Discussion Why does this model not give an exact answer?

Q11b hint

90 minutes = ☐.☐ hours.

12 **Explore** How much does a 10 kg mass weigh on Mars?
Is it easier to explore this question now you have completed the lesson?
What further information do you need to be able to answer this?

13 **Reflect** In this lesson, you met the symbol $\propto$ meaning 'proportional to'. Write down three advantages of using symbols in mathematics. Are there any disadvantages?

Explore

Reflect

5.3 Non-linear proportion

You will learn to:
- Use algebra to solve problems involving different types of proportion.

CONFIDENCE

Why learn this?
The braking distance of a car is proportional to the square of the speed of the car.

Fluency
Find three pairs of numbers that multiply together to make 20.

Explore
How do companies decide on the best prices for their products?

Exercise 5.3

Warm up

1 y is directly proportional to x. When $x = 24$, $y = 42$.
  a Write a formula connecting y and x.
  b Work out the value of y when x is 32.

2 Solve
  a $28 = 4k$
  b $27 = 3^2k$
  c $20 = 5^2k$

Worked example

The distance s travelled by a falling object is proportional to the time t squared.
After 3 seconds, the object has fallen 44.1 m.
How far has the object fallen after 5 seconds?

$s \propto t^2$

$s = kt^2$

> Write the relationship $s \propto t^2$ and the equation $s = kt^2$.

When $t = 3$, $s = 44.1$

$44.1 = k \times 3^2$

> Substitute the values given for t and s into $s = kt^2$.

$k = \dfrac{44.1}{3^2} = 4.9$

$s = 4.9t^2$

> Solve the equation to find k. Rewrite the equation using the value of k.

Substitute $t = 5$.

$s = 4.9 \times 5^2 = 122.5$ m

> Use your equation to answer the question.

Key point

When y is proportional to x^2 you can write $y \propto x^2$
$$y = kx^2$$

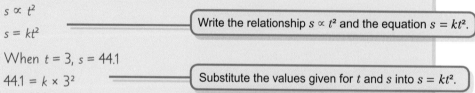

3 STEM The energy stored in a spring, E, is proportional to the square of the extension, x.
When the spring is extended by 5 mm, the stored energy is 500 joules.
  a Write a formula linking E and x.
  b What is the stored energy when the spring is extended by 7 mm?

Topic links: Area

Subject links: Science (Q3, Q6)

4 The table shows data from a science experiment.

x	0.9	2.5	7.5	20
y	40	14.4	4.8	1.8

    a Work out the value of xy for each pair of values.

    b Is y **inversely proportional** to x? Explain.

    c Check whether these sets of data are inversely proportional.

i
P	1	3	9	20
Q	540	440	230	73

ii
r	2.5	8	20	40
s	20	6.25	2.5	1.25

Key point

Two variables are in **inverse proportion** when one is proportional to the reciprocal of the other.

$$y \propto \frac{1}{x}$$

So $y = \frac{k}{x}$ or $xy = k$

    Discussion Jayne says that two variables are inversely proportional if one increases as the other increases. Is Jayne correct?

5 y is inversely proportional to x.

    When $x = 6$, $y = 30$.

    a Copy and complete:

$$y \propto \frac{1}{x}$$
$$y = \frac{k}{x}$$
$$xy = \square$$

    b Work out the value of y when $x = 4.5$.

    c Work out the value of x when $y = 120$.

6 **STEM** The pressure, P, exerted by an object is inversely proportional to the area, A.

    When an object is placed on an area of $8\,cm^2$, the pressure is $180\,N/cm^2$.

    a Work out the pressure when the same object is placed on an area of $30\,cm^2$.

    b Work out the area when the pressure exerted by the object is $576\,N/cm^2$.

Q6 hint

Write a formula linking P and A.

7 **Finance / Modelling** A company calculates that the monthly demand, d, for a games console is inversely proportional to the price, p, of the console.

    When the price of the product is £175, the demand is for 280 units.

    a Predict the monthly demand when the price is £200.

    The company has 600 units to sell next month.

    b What price should they sell them at?

8 **Modelling / Reasoning** When typing a document, the number of mistakes made is inversely proportional to the time taken.

    Rachel types a document in 24 minutes and makes 12 mistakes.

    a Predict how many mistakes she would make typing the document in 32 minutes.

    b Predict how long she should spend typing to make only 2 mistakes.

    Discussion Using this model, is it possible for Rachel to make no mistakes? Explain your answer.

9 **Explore** How do companies decide on the best prices for their products? Is it easier to explore this question now you have completed the lesson? What further information do you need to be able to answer this?

10 **Reflect** David says that plotting a graph of x against y will show whether x and y are inversely proportional. Is David right? If not, is there a graph that could be used?

Explore

Reflect

5.4 Arcs and sectors of circles

You will learn to:
- Work out the length of an arc
- Work out the area of a sector
- Solve problems involving arcs and sectors.

CONFIDENCE

Why learn this?
An arch is a very strong shape so it is often used in building bridges.

Fluency
Write each angle as a fraction of 360° in its simplest form.
- 270°
- 160°
- 210°
- 125°

Explore
How large is the area of grass needed for the javelin event in the Olympics?

Exercise 5.4

Warm up

1 a Draw a circle.
 b Label the centre O.
 c Shade an arc AB.
 d Draw a sector OAB.
 e How many degrees are there at the centre of a circle?

 2 Calculate the area and circumference of this circle.
 Give your answers to 1 d.p.

4 cm

 3 For these shapes, work out
 i the area
 ii the perimeter.

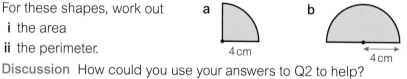
a **b**
4 cm   4 cm

 Discussion How could you use your answers to Q2 to help?

> **Q4 Literacy hint**
> The **arc** of a circle is part of its circumference.

 4 Reasoning / Problem-solving
 a What fraction of the circle is shaded?
 b What fraction of the circumference is **arc** AB?
 c Calculate
  i the circumference of the circle
  ii the length of arc AB.
 d What is the area of
  i the whole circle
  ii the shaded sector?

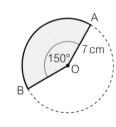
A
150°
O
7 cm
B

> **Q4 hint**
>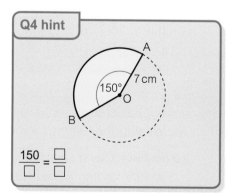
> A
> 150°
> O
> 7 cm
> B
> $\frac{150}{\square} = \frac{\square}{\square}$

Topic links: Rearranging equations

5 For each shape work out
  i the area of the sector
  ii the length of the arc.

a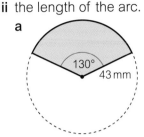

b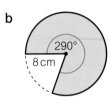

Discussion Are the area of a sector and the area of the whole circle always in direct proportion?

6 The diagram shows a children's sandpit. Work out the area of the sandpit.

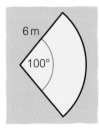

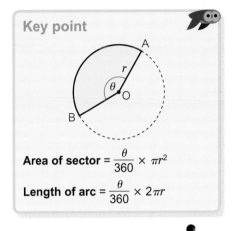

Q5 Literacy hint

θ is the Greek letter 'theta'.

7 **Problem-solving** The diagram shows a company logo.
  On their advertisement the diameter of the logo is 15 m.
  The white and pink sectors are all equal in size.
  Work out the area of pink used.

8 **STEM / Real** The diagram shows a chain on a bike. The radius of the smaller cog is 7 cm and the radius of the larger cog is 13 cm. The angle where the chain is against each cog is shown.
  Work out the length of the chain.

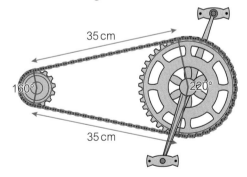

9 **Explore** How large is the area of grass needed for the javelin event in the Olympics?
  Is it easier to explore this question now you have completed the lesson?
  What further information do you need to be able to answer this?

10 **Reflect** The answer to Q7 needs a series of steps.
  Write down what you did in each step. Is there an alternative way of tackling this question?

5 Check up

Log how you did on your Student Progression Chart.

Direct proportion

1 The cost of petrol varies in direct proportion to the number of litres sold.
The cost of 5 litres of petrol is £6.75. What is the cost of
a 15 litres
b 12 litres?

2 The table shows the price and volume of three different bottles of the same shampoo.

Volume (ml)	25	90	150
Cost	£0.90	£3.24	£5.40

a Draw a graph of the data.
b Are volume and cost in direct proportion?
c Write a formula connecting volume and cost.

3 Six toilet rolls cost £1.99. Nine toilet rolls cost £2.69.
Is cost directly proportional to number of toilet rolls?

4 The values of A and B are in direct proportion. Work out the missing numbers w, x and z.

A	B
6	20
9	w
x	60
z	2.5

Proportion equations

5 The value of y is directly proportional to the value of x.
When $y = 6$, $x = 32$.
a Write a formula connecting x and y.
b What is the value of y when x is 46?

6 The value of s is proportional to the value of r^2. When $s = 804$, $r = 8$.
a Write a formula connecting s and r.
b What is the value of s when r is 15?

7 For each set of data, is y inversely proportional to x?
a

x	0.8	2.5	3.2	5
y	30	9.6	7.5	4.8

b

x	2	3	5	14
y	390	250	142	40

8 y is inversely proportional to x. When $y = 16$, $x = 3$.

   a Copy and complete:

$$xy = \square$$

   b What is the value of y when x is 8?

Arcs and sectors

9 What fraction of each circle is shaded?

  a 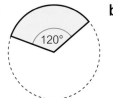   **b**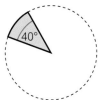

10 Work out

   a the length of arc AB

   b the area of the shaded sector.

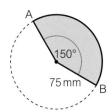

11 **How sure are you of your answers? Were you mostly**

   😞 **Just guessing**   😐 **Feeling doubtful**   🙂 **Confident**

   What next? Use your results to decide whether to strengthen or extend your learning.

Reflect

Challenge

12 Which would you rather have:

   $\frac{1}{6}$ of a 25 cm diameter cake or $\frac{1}{5}$ of a 20 cm diameter cake?

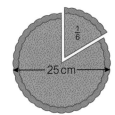 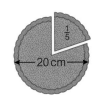

   Explain.

13 Six people take 5 days to dig a ditch.

   Copy and complete this table to show how long it takes different numbers of people to dig the ditch.

People	6	3	1	2	12
Days					

   What type of proportion is this?

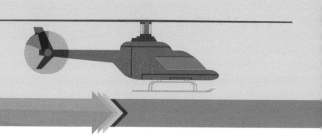

5 Strengthen

You will:
* Strengthen your understanding with practice.

Direct proportion

1 Which graph shows data in direct proportion?

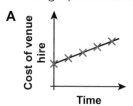

A

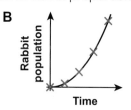

B

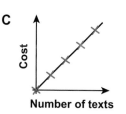

C

Q1 hint

Graphs showing direct proportion are straight lines through the origin.

2 The table shows data from a school science experiment.

p	2	3	5
q	7	10.5	17.5

   a Draw a graph of the data with p on the horizontal axis and q on the vertical axis.

   b Does the graph show that p and q are in direct proportion?

   c Write a formula connecting p and q.

Q2c hint

The formula is the equation of the line.

3 Real / Finance Write each statement as an equation showing direct proportion.

   a The cost, C, of making a phone call for x minutes at 3p per minute

   b The mass, M, of x boxes at 2.3 kg per box

   c The distance travelled, d, by a swimmer with a speed of 1.4 m/s in n seconds

Q3a hint

1 minute: $C = 1 \times 3$ pence
2 minutes: $C = 2 \times 3$ pence
x minutes: $C = x \times 3$ pence
$\quad\quad C = \square x$ pence

4 The cost of potatoes varies in direct proportion to the mass of potatoes bought.

3.5 kg of potatoes cost £8.75. What is the cost of

   a 1 kg

   b 5 kg

   c 6.5 kg?

Q4a hint

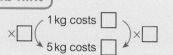

$\div 3.5$ (3.5 kg costs £8.75 / 1 kg costs $\square$) $\div 3.5$

Q4b hint

$\times \square$ (1 kg costs $\square$ / 5 kg costs $\square$) $\times \square$

5 The depth of water in a paddling pool is in direct proportion to the length of time the water runs into it.

After 3 minutes, the water is 48 cm deep.

   a How deep is the water after 4 minutes?

   b How long does it take to fill the pool to a depth of 80 cm?

Q5b hint

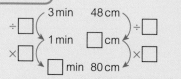

$\div \square$ (3 min   48 cm / 1 min $\square$ cm) $\div \square$
$\times \square$ ($\square$ min   80 cm) $\times \square$

6 X and Y are in direct proportion. Find the missing values a and b in this table.

X	Y
7	12
21	a
b	60

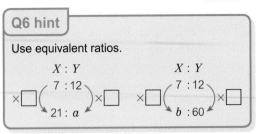

Q6 hint

Use equivalent ratios.

7 S and T are in direct proportion.

S	T
6	15
c	35

Find the missing value c.

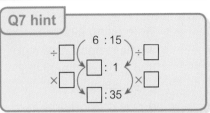

Q7 hint

8 The values of A and B are in direct proportion. Find the missing numbers w, x, y and z.

A	B
4	9
8	w
x	45
y	22.5
22	z

9 An electrician charges £54 for 3 hours' work and £126 for 7 hours' work. Are his charges in direct proportion to the length of time worked?

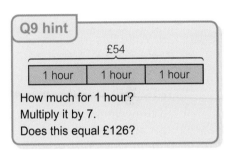

Q9 hint

£54

| 1 hour | 1 hour | 1 hour |

How much for 1 hour?
Multiply it by 7.
Does this equal £126?

10 The distances between pairs of cities are shown in miles, M, and kilometres, K.
The distance in kilometres is directly proportional to the distance in miles.

Distance, M (miles)	Distance, K (km)
12.5	20
19	30.4
24	38.4

a Copy and complete.

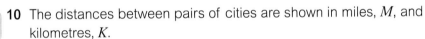

miles : km

b Write a formula that shows the relationship between miles, M, and kilometres, K.
c Check that your formula works for the last pair of distances.

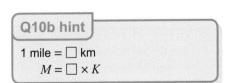

Q10b hint

1 mile = ☐ km
$M = ☐ \times K$

11 **Finance** The Mongolian tughrik, T, varies in direct proportion with the UK pound, P.
One day, £60 is worth 192 000 tughrik.
a How many Mongolian tughrik can you buy with £1?
b Copy and complete this formula relating the Mongolian tughrik, T, to the UK pound, P.

$T = ☐P$

c How many Mongolian tughrik can you buy with £80?

Q11c hint

Substitute $P = 80$ into your formula.

 12 Finance The Mexican peso, M, varies in direct proportion with the UK pound, P.

One day, 880 Mexican pesos = £40.

a How many Mexican pesos can you buy with £90?

b How many UK pounds can you buy with 1430 Mexican pesos?

Proportion equations

1 Write using algebra.

a y is proportional to x

b c is proportional to r

c m varies as t

d p is proportional to q^2

e n varies as the square of x

Q1 hint

$\propto$ means 'is proportional to'.
so $y \propto x$ is another way of writing $y = kx$

2 Match the equivalent statements.

y varies as x

$y = kx$

$y \propto x$

$y = kx^2$

y is directly proportional to x

$y \propto x^2$

y is proportional to x^2

y varies as x^2

 3 y is directly proportional to x.

a Write this as a formula using algebra.

When $x = 4.5$, $y = 11.25$.

b Substitute the values into your '$y = k\square$' formula from part **a**.

c Solve to find k.

d Rewrite the formula as $y = \square k$.

e Use your formula from part **d** to find the value of y when $x = 10$.

Q3a hint

$y \propto \square$
$y = k\square$

 4 r varies directly as t. When $t = 3$, $r = 3.6$.

a Write a formula connecting t and r.

b Find the value of r when $t = 7$.

 5 p is proportional to the square of q.

a Copy and complete.

$p \propto \square$
$p = \square\,\square$

When $q = 4$, $p = 30$.

b Substitute these values into your formula.

c Solve to find k.

d Write the formula $p = \square q^2$

e Use your formula to find the value of p when $q = 6$.

 6 y is proportional to the square of x. When $y = 16$, $x = 5$.

a Write a formula connecting x and y.

b Work out the value of y when $x = 8$.

Q7a hint

In algebra
$y \propto \dfrac{1}{x}$
$y = \dfrac{k}{x}$
Use $x = 4$ and $y = 20$ to work out k.

 7 y is inversely proportional to x. When $x = 4$, $y = 20$.

a Write a formula connecting x and y.

b What will be the value of y when $x = 10$?

c What will be the value of x when $y = 0.2$?

8 This diagram shows the rules for inverse proportion.
Find xy for each pair of values in the table. Is $y \propto \frac{1}{x}$?

a

x	0.5	1	2	3
y	36	18	9	6

b

x	5	10	15	18
y	54	27	18	15

c

x	3	21	16	9
y	19	8	35	24

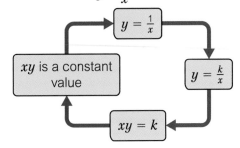

Q8 hint

Does $xy = k$?

Arcs and sectors

1 What fraction of each circle is shaded?
Write your answer as a fraction in its simplest form.

a   **b**   **c**

 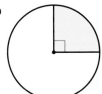 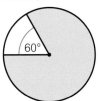

2 The diagram shows a circle with a radius of 7 cm.
  a Work out the circumference of the whole circle.
  b Work out the length of the arc AB.

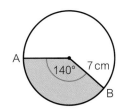

Q2b hint

Arc length
$$= \frac{\text{angle of sector}}{360} \times \text{circumference}$$

3 Work out the length of the arc AB in each sector.

  a   **b**   **c**

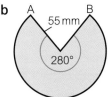

Q3c hint

First work out the angle of the shaded sector.

4 Work out the area of
  a the whole circle
  b the shaded sector.

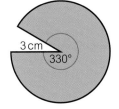

Q4b hint

Area of sector
$$= \frac{\text{angle of sector}}{360} \times \text{area of circle}$$

Enrichment

1 A dog is tethered to a corner of a building by a 5 m rope.
  a Sketch the region the dog can reach.
  b What is the area of the region?

2 **Reflect** Problems about proportion can be solved using ratio, the
unitary method, or algebra. Which is your favourite method, and why?

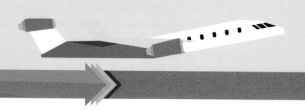

5 Extend

You will:
- Extend your understanding with problem solving.

 1 Real The distance on a map is directly proportional to the corresponding distance on the ground.
On a map, the distance between two places is 5.3 cm. The scale of the map is 1 : 25 000.

  a What is the actual distance between the places in

    i centimetres   **ii** kilometres?

  b Two places are 9.8 km apart. How far apart will they be on the map?

 2 a GPS data showed that a footballer ran 26.4 km in the first 3 matches of the season. There are 38 matches in the full season. Predict how many kilometres he will run in the full season.

  b Another player ran 3.57 km in the 42 minutes she appeared as a substitute. How many kilometres would she run in a full 90-minute game?

3 Real / Modelling Write a formula for

  a the perimeter, P, of a square with side length s

  b the circumference, C, of a circle with radius r

  c the area, A, of a square with side length s

  d the perimeter, P, of a rectangle with length l and width w.

  Discussion Which of these formulae show direct proportion?

4 The diagram shows **similar** triangles.
Work out the missing lengths.

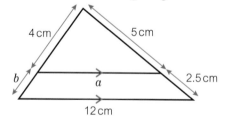

4 cm   5 cm

b a 2.5 cm

12 cm

> **Q4 Literacy hint**
> Two shapes are **similar** if corresponding sides are in proportion.

> **Q4 hint**
> Draw the two triangles separately and label all the sides.

5 Real / STEM The table shows measurements of force and extension of a spring made during a science experiment.

Force, F (newtons)	0.2	0.3	0.5	0.6	1	1.2
Extension, E (mm)	5	7.5	12.5	22	25	30

  a Draw a graph of the data.

  b Identify an outlier in the data.

  c Ignoring the outlier, is the force proportional to the extension?

  Discussion Can the scientist say that, based on her results, the force is proportional to the extension? Explain your answer.

Topic links: Scales, Similar triangles, Ratio, Area   **Subject links:** Geography (Q1, Q6), Science (Q5)

6 **Real / Problem-solving** As you climb higher above sea level, the temperature decreases. The table shows the decrease in temperature at different heights on Ben Nevis.

Height above sea level (m)	0	300	700	1200
Temperature decrease (°C)	0	1.2	2.8	4.8

a Are height and temperature decrease in direct proportion?

b Write a formula that shows the relationship between height, h, and temperature decrease, T.

The summit of Ben Nevis is 1344 m above sea level. One day the temperature at sea level is 15.7°C.

c What is the temperature at the summit of Ben Nevis?

Q6c hint

Work out the temperature decrease at 1344 m, subtract it from 15.7°C.

7 Here are the results from some school science experiments. Decide if the variables are directly proportional, inversely proportional or neither.

a

P	0.6	2.4	12
A	30	7.5	1.5

b

c	15.6	34.2	58.8
r	2.6	5.7	9.8

c

t	2	3.5	4.8
V	16 000	11 500	8 500

8 For each sector, write in terms of π
  i the sector area
  ii the arc length.

Q8 hint

'In terms of π' means that your answer should be $\square\pi$.

a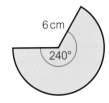

b

9 Work out the radius of each sector.

a

b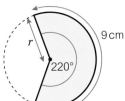

c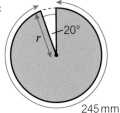

Q9 hint

Write down the formula for the length of an arc. Rearrange to make r the subject.

10 Work out the value of θ.
Write your answer as a fraction in its simplest form.

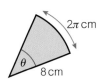

11 The area of the sector is given. Find the missing angle or length.

a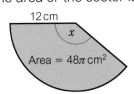

b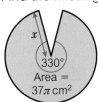

12 Work out the area of the shaded region.

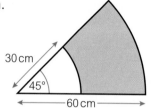

30 cm
45°
60 cm

Q12 hint

Work out the whole area and subtract.

30 cm
45°

  13 This circular company logo has a diameter of 4 m.

Each sector has a central angle of 20°.
Work out the area of the logo painted yellow.

  14 **Problem-solving** Here is a plan of a discus circle and field.

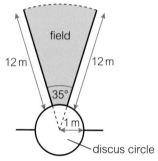

field

12 m   12 m

35°

1 m

discus circle

a Work out the area of the discus circle.
b Work out the area of the field.

  15 **Problem-solving** The diagram shows a **chord** AB and a shaded **segment**.

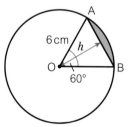

A
6 cm h
O
60°
B

a What is the area of the sector shown?
b What type of triangle is triangle AOB?
The height, h, of the triangle is 5.2 cm.
c Work out the area of the triangle.
d Work out the area of the segment.

Q15 Literacy hint

A **chord** is a line that joins two points on the circumference of a circle.
A **segment** is the area between the chord and the arc joining the two points.

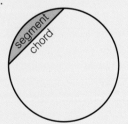

segment
chord

  16 Here is the net of a cone. Calculate the surface area.

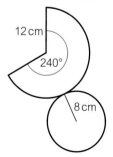

12 cm
240°
8 cm

17 **Real / Modelling** The graph shows the value of a car over a period of time.

a Use the graph to copy and complete the table.

Age, A (years)	1	2	4	6
Value of car, V (£)				

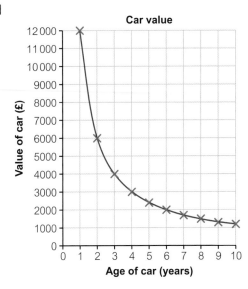

Car value

b Is the value of the car inversely proportional to the age of the car?

c Work out the value of the car after 11 years. Round your answer to the nearest pound.

Discussion Is this a useful model for a 20-year-old car? A 50-year-old car?

18 y is proportional to the square of x.
When $y = 5$, $x = 16$.
a What is the value of y when $x = 40$?
b What is the value of x when $y = 3$?

19 y varies as the square of x.
When $y = 4$, $x = 25$.
a What is the value of y when $x = 50$?
b What is the value of x when $y = 6.5$?
Give your answers to 2 decimal places.

Q18b hint

x will have two possible values.

20 a Match the statement with the correct equation.

A y is proportional to the square of x	**i** $y = kx$
B y is inversely proportional to the cube of x	**ii** $y = \dfrac{k}{x^3}$
C y is inversely proportional to x	**iii** $y = kx^2$
D y is proportional to x	**iv** $y = \dfrac{k}{x^2}$
	v $y = \dfrac{k}{x}$

b Write a statement for the extra card.

21 **Finance** The interest, I, earned on an investment is directly proportional to the amount invested, A, and the time, t, of the investment in years.
When £4000 is invested for 3 years, the interest earned is £720.
a Work out the value of k, the constant of proportionality.
Work out the interest earned when £3000 is invested for
b 7 years
c 6 months.

22 Reflect Think of a problem in everyday life involving proportion or circles. How will the maths you have learned in this unit help you to solve such problems? Compare your response with a partner's.

Master
P100

Check
P109

Strengthen
P111

Extend
P115

TEST

5 Unit test

Log how you did on your
Student Progression Chart.

 1 The distance an aeroplane travels is proportional to the journey time.
An aeroplane travels 240 km in 30 minutes.
How far does it travel in 55 minutes?

2 For each statement
   i are the two quantities in direct proportion?
   ii write a formula to model each situation.
  a The cost, C, in pence of x cereal bars at 59p each.
  b The cost, C, of hiring a van for x hours at £12 per hour and a £14 hiring fee.

3 The table shows the results of a science experiment.

d	2	3	5.5
h	9	13.5	24.75

  a Draw a graph of this data, with d on the horizontal axis.
  b Is d directly proportional to h?

4 The values of x and y are in direct proportion.
Work out the values of a and b.

x	y
15	90
a	75
23	b

 5 The table shows the extension of a spring when different masses are added.

Extension, e (mm)	8	12	28
Mass, m (g)	200	300	700

  a Are mass and extension in direct proportion?
  b Write a formula that shows the relationship between mass, m and extension, e.

 6 x is proportional to y. When $x = 5$, $y = 2.85$.
  a Write a formula connecting x and y.
  b What is the value of y when $x = 13$?
  c What is the value of x when $y = 16.53$?

 7 A car salesman's commission is in direct proportion to the value of the sales he makes.
He is paid £7840 commission because he makes sales of £196 000.
  a Work out the commission on £325 000 of sales.
  b He earns £17 500 of commission. Work out the value of his sales.

 8 t is proportional to the square of r. When $r = 6$, $t = 468$.
  a Write a formula connecting t and r.
  b What is the value of t when $r = 11$?

9 For this set of data, is q inversely proportional to p?

p	5	7.5	10	12.5
q	10	7	5.5	4.6

10 The diagram shows part of a circle.
Work out
  a the length of the arc AB
  b the area of the sector.

11 Work out the radius of the shaded sector.

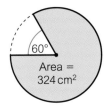

Area = 324 cm²

12 y is inversely proportional to x.
When $x = 4.8$, $y = 7.2$.
  a Work out the value of x when $y = 2.4$.
  b Work out the value of y when $x = 12.8$.

Challenge

13 In a scale drawing the lengths drawn are directly proportional to the real-life lengths. The diagram shows a scale drawing of the ground floor of a house.

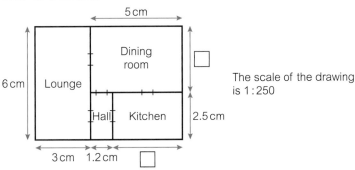

The scale of the drawing is 1 : 250

  a Work out the area of each room in square metres.
The upstairs has three bedrooms, a bathroom and a landing area above the hall.
  b Make a possible scale drawing of the upstairs.

14 This logo is made up of 8 sectors.
The blue sectors each have angle 20° and the orange sectors each have angle 30°. All the sectors have radius 1.5 cm.
The red circle has diameter 0.5 cm.
  a Work out the areas of blue, orange and red in the logo.
  b Make up your own logo that combines shapes, including sectors of circles. Calculate the area of your logo.

15 Reflect The questions in this test involve multiplicative reasoning.
Make a list of other topics that use multiplicative reasoning.

> **Q15 hint**
> Think about the maths you learned in Year 7, Year 8 or earlier this year.

Reflect

MASTER

| Check P132 | Strengthen P134 | Extend P139 | Test P143 |

6.1 Graphs of quadratic functions

You will learn to:
- Understand and draw graphs of quadratic functions
- Identify quadratic graphs and their features
- Solve problems using quadratic graphs.

CONFIDENCE

Why learn this?
The path of a basketball can be modelled using a quadratic function.

Fluency
Describe the transformations that map A to B.

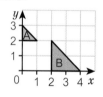

Explore
What is the best way to throw a basketball into the net?

Exercise 6.1

1 Copy and complete this table of values for $y = x^2$.

x	−4	−3	−2	−1	0	1	2	3	4
y									

Key point

A **quadratic function** contains a term in x^2 but no higher power of x. $y = x^2$, $y = 5x^2$, $y = x^2 + 5$ and $y = x^2 + 3x + 2$ are all quadratic. The graph of a quadratic function is called a **parabola**.

2 Work out the value of $2x^2$ when

    a $x = 4$ **b** $x = -3$ **c** $x = -1$

3 Work out the value of $x^2 - 5$ when

    a $x = 4$ **b** $x = -2$ **c** $x = 0$

4 **a** Draw an x-axis from −4 to 4 and a y-axis from −30 to 30. Plot the coordinates from your table of values for $y = x^2$ in Q1. Join the points with a smooth curve. Label your graph $y = x^2$.

    b Describe the symmetry of your graph.

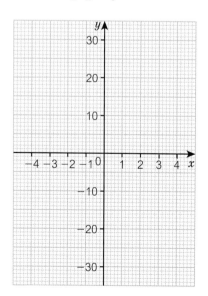

Q4b hint

What is the equation of the line of symmetry?

Warm up

Topic links: Symmetry, Transformations

Subject links: Science (Q10)

5 Reasoning

  a Copy and complete this table of values for the quadratic function
    $y = x^2 + 10$.

x	−4	−3	−2	−1	0	1	2	3	4
y									

  b Plot the graph of $y = x^2 + 10$ on the same axes as Q4.
    Label your graph with its equation.

  c What is the same about the two graphs?

  d What is different about the two graphs?

  e Predict what the graph of $y = x^2 − 10$ looks like. Plot the graph on
    the same axes as Q4 to test your prediction.

  Discussion What will the graphs of $y = x^2 + 5$ and $y = x^2 − 5$ look like?
  How does the graph of $y = x^2$ change when you add or subtract a
  constant?

Q5e hint

You could use a graph-plotting package.

Q5 Literacy hint

A **constant** is a value that doesn't change.

6 Reasoning

  a Draw an x-axis from −4 to 4 and a y-axis from 0 to 50.

  b Copy and complete this table of values for the quadratic
    function $y = 2x^2$.

x	−4	−3	−2	−1	0	1	2	3	4
y									

  c Plot the graphs of these quadratic functions on the same axes.
    i $y = x^2$ **ii** $y = 2x^2$ **iii** $y = \frac{1}{2}x^2$

  d What is the same about the three graphs?

  e What is different about the three graphs?

  Discussion How does the graph of $y = x^2$ change when you multiply
  x^2 by a number greater than 1? Less than 1?

7 Reasoning

  a Copy and complete this table of values for the quadratic
    function $y = 2x^2 + 10$.

x	−4	−3	−2	−1	0	1	2	3	4
$2x^2$		18							
+10	+ 10	+ 10	+ 10	+ 10	+ 10	+ 10	+ 10	+ 10	+ 10
y		28							

  b Plot the graph of $y = 2x^2 + 10$.

  c Describe how adding 10 changes the graph of the function $y = 2x^2$.

  d Describe how multiplying x^2 by 2 and adding 10 changes the
    graph of the function $y = x^2$.

  Discussion What will the graph of $y = 2x^2 − 10$ look like?
  What will the graph of $y = 3x^2 + 10$ look like?

Q7 Strategy hint

Don't draw the axes until you know the largest and smallest values of y.

Investigation   **Reasoning**

  a Plot the graphs of $y = x^2$ and $y = −x^2$ on the same axes. What do you notice?

  b Plot the graphs of $y = 3x^2$ and $y = −3x^2$ on the same axes. What do you notice?

  c **i** Predict the shape of the graph $y = −2x^2$. (Look at the graph of $y = 2x^2$ you drew in Q6.)

      ii Plot the graphs of $y = −2x^2$ and $y = 2x^2$ on the same axes to check your prediction.

8 Look at your graphs in this lesson.
Write the coordinates of their **turning points** and say if they are **maximum** or **minimum**.
Discussion For a quadratic graph how can you tell what the coordinates of the turning point are by looking at its equation?

9 Match each graph to its function.

i $y = x^2$ **ii** $y = -x^2 + 10$ **iii** $y = 2x^2$

iv $y = 2x^2 - 10$ **v** $y = -x^2$ **vi** $y = -2x^2$

A 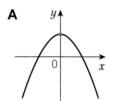 **B** 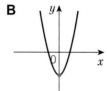 **C**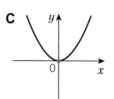

D 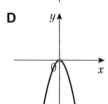 **E** 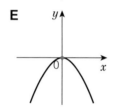 **F**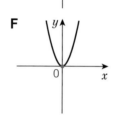

10 **Modelling / Real / Problem-solving** A machine launches tennis balls at a speed of 50 ft/s and between 19° and 45° to the ground.
The graphs show the paths of a ball launched at the minimum and maximum angles.

a What is the maximum height of a ball launched at 45°?

b A ball is launched at 19°. How far from the machine will it be at a height of 2 ft?

c Giovanni can reach a ball at a height of 8 ft. A ball is launched at 45°. How close can he be to the machine to hit the ball?

d A tennis court net has a height of 3 ft in the middle. What is the furthest the tennis ball machine can be from the net so that all of the balls clear the net?

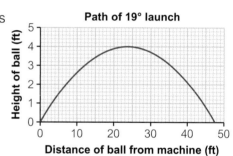

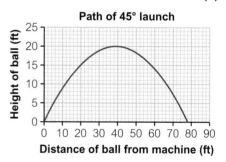

11 **Explore** What is the best way to throw a basketball into the net? Is it easier to explore this question now you have completed the lesson?
What further information do you need to be able to answer this?

12 **Reflect** Frank and Zoe are discussing Q9. Frank says, 'First I looked at the shape of the parabola and decided whether the **coefficient** of x^2 would be positive or negative.'
Zoe says, 'First I looked at the y-intercept of the parabola so I knew whether there would be a constant term.'
Did you use Frank or Zoe's method to answer Q9?
What other information did you need to think about?

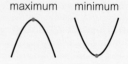

Q12 Literacy hint

The **coefficient** of a term is the number in front of it. In $3x^2$, the coefficient of x^2 is 3.

Explore

Reflect

6.2 Solving quadratic equations

You will learn to:
- Use quadratic graphs to solve equations.

Why learn this?
The time it takes for a javelin to reach the ground can be estimated by solving a quadratic equation.

Fluency
Match the function to its graph.

$y = 2$ $\quad$ $y = 2x^2$ $\quad$ $y = x^2 + 2$

Explore
How long does it take for a catapulted rock to reach the ground?

Exercise 6.2

1 Factorise these quadratic expressions.

  a $x^2 - 4x$

  b $3x^2 + 6x$

  c $x^2 + 2x + 1$

2 Solve these equations.

  a $x^2 = 49$

  b $x^2 = 81$

  c $x^2 + 5 = 30$

3 Solve these equations by factorising.

  a $x^2 + 4x + 3 = 0$

  b $x^2 - 5x - 5 = 0$

  c $x^2 - 5x + 6 = 0$

 4 a On graph paper, plot the graph of $y = x^2$ from $x = -4$ to 4.

  b Use your graph to **estimate** the x-coordinates when $y = 12$. Write your answers to 1 decimal place.

  c Use your calculator to check your estimates.

  d Use your graph to estimate solutions to the equation $x^2 = 5$. Check your answers on your calculator.

> **Key point**
>
> You can use a graph to **estimate** solutions to an equation.

5 a Plot the graph of $y = 3x^2$ from $x = -3$ to 3.

  b Use your graph to estimate the solutions to $3x^2 = 20$.

6 a Plot the graph of $y = x^2 - 10$ from $x = -4$ to 4.

  b Use your graph to estimate the solutions to $x^2 - 10 = 3$.

  c The graph of $y = x^2 - 10$ crosses the x-axis at two points. Write the quadratic equation that has these two solutions.

> **Q6c hint**
>
> What is the y-coordinate of every point on the x-axis?

Warm up

7 **Reasoning**

   a Plot the graph of $y = x^2 - 6x + 5$ from $x = -1$ to 7.

   b Use your graph to solve $x^2 - 6x + 5 = 0$.

   c Factorise $x^2 - 6x + 5$.

   Discussion What does the factorised form tell you about where the graph crosses the x-axis?

Q7 hint

Use a table of values or graph-plotting package.

8 The sketch shows the graph of $y = x^2 - 7x + 10$.

   a Factorise $x^2 - 7x + 10$.

   b Solve $x^2 - 7x + 10 = 0$.

   c Write down the points where the graph crosses the x-axis.

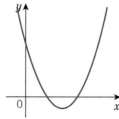

Q7c hint

$x^2 - 6x + 5 = (x - \square)(x - \square)$

Key point

The graph crosses the x-axis when $y = 0$.

9 **a** Plot the graph of $y = x^2 - 4x$.

   b Use your graph to solve $x^2 - 4x = 0$.

   c Factorise $x^2 - 4x$.

   d Explain how the factorisation shows where the graph crosses the x-axis.

10 **STEM / Reasoning / Modelling** The height h, in metres, of a cricket ball t seconds after it is thrown is $h = 20t - 5t^2$.

   a Copy and complete the table of values.

t	0	1	2	3	4	5
$20t$				60		
$-5t^2$				-45		
h				15		

   b Plot the graph of $h = 20t - 5t^2$.

   c What is the highest point reached by the ball?

   d Use your graph to find how long the ball stayed in the air.

   e Show how to find the answer to part **d** by factorising $20t - 5t^2$.

   f Is the graph a good model for the height of the ball? Explain.

11 **Explore** How long does it take for a catapulted rock to reach the ground?

   Is it easier to explore this question now you have completed the lesson?

   What further information do you need to be able to answer this?

12 **Reflect** In this lesson you solved quadratic equations using graphs. In unit 2 you solved quadratic equations by factorising.

   Which method do you prefer? Why?

   Which method do you think gives a more accurate answer? Explain.

Topic links: Factorisation, Quadratic equations

Subject links: Science (Q10)

Active Learn   Delta 3, Section 6.2

6.3 Graphs of cubic functions

You will learn to:
- Understand and draw graphs of cubic functions
- Identify cubic graphs and their features.

Why learn this?
Structural engineers use cubic functions to design rollercoasters.

Fluency
What are the first five cube numbers?
What is
- 10^3
- $\sqrt[3]{64}$
- 3×2^3?

Explore
What can a cubic function tell you about a rollercoaster?

Exercise 6.3

1 Copy and complete this table of values for $y = x^3$.

x	−3	−2	−1	0	1	2	3
y							

2 Match each equation to its graph.

  i $y = -x^2$ **ii** $y = 2x^2$ **iii** $y = x^2 + 2$ **iv** $y = -2x^2 - 2$

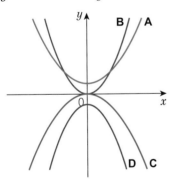

3 a On graph paper, plot the graph of the **cubic function** $y = x^3$ using your table of values from Q1.
Draw an x-axis from −3 to 3 and a y-axis from −60 to 60.
Label your graph $y = x^3$.
  b Describe the symmetry of your graph.
  Discussion What happens at the point (0, 0)?

4 Reasoning a Plot the graph of $y = 2x^3$ on the same axes as Q3.
  b Plot the graph of $y = \frac{1}{2}x^3$ on the same axes.
  c What is the same about the two graphs?
  d What is different about the two graphs?
  Discussion What will the graphs of $y = 3x^3$ and $y = \frac{1}{4}x^3$ look like?

Key point

A **cubic function** contains a term in x^3 but no higher power of x.
$y = x^3$, $y = 2x^3$, $y = -x^3$ and $y = x^3 + 5x$ are all cubic.

Q4 hint

Use a table of values or a graph-plotting package.

5 Problem-solving / Modelling The diagram shows a packing box for cube-shaped soaps of side x cm.

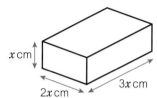

x cm
$2x$ cm
$3x$ cm

a Write a formula for the volume y, in cm³, of the box.

b Draw an x-axis from 0 to 5 and y-axis from 0 to 800. Plot the graph of your formula.

c The volume of a box is 500 cm³. Estimate the side length of a block of soap.

Q5c hint

Draw the line $y = 500$.

6 Reasoning

a Make a table of values for the cubic function $y = -x^3$.

b Plot the graph of $y = -x^3$.

c What is the same about the graphs of $y = -x^3$ and $y = x^3$?

d What is different about the graphs of $y = -x^3$ and $y = x^3$?

e What transformation maps $y = x^3$ to $y = -x^3$?

Discussion Is there only one answer to part **e**?

Q6 hint

Use the same x-values as in Q1.

7 a Problem-solving / Reasoning Plot the graph of $y = x^2$. Draw axes with x from 0 to 4 and y from 0 to 80.

b Use your graph to estimate the square root of 7.

c i On the same axes, plot the graph of $y = x^3$.

ii Use your graph to estimate the cube root of 50.

d The two graphs intersect at two points. What are the points of intersection?

e Copy and complete these statements using $<$, $>$ or $=$.

$x^2 \square x^3$ for $x = 0$

$x^2 \square x^3$ for $0 < x < 1$

$x^2 \square x^3$ for $x = 1$

$x^2 \square x^3$ for $x > 1$

Discussion How do your answers to part **e** change when $x < 0$?

Q7e Strategy hint

Look at the points for which one graph is greater than the other.

Investigation   Reasoning

a Draw suitable graphs to show when x^3 is bigger than $10x^2$. Write your answer using an inequality.

b Repeat part **a** to show when x^3 is bigger than $20x^2$.

c Predict when x^3 is bigger than $30x^2$. Check your prediction by drawing a graph.

d When is x^3 bigger than nx^2, where n is a positive number? Write your answer as an inequality.

Part a hint

Use a graphical package. Calculate values of y when $x = 0, 5, 10, 15, ...$

Topic links: Square and cube roots, Inequalities, Solving problems using algebra

8 a Plot the graph of $y = 2x^3$.
  b Use your graph to estimate the solution to $2x^3 = 10$, to 1 decimal place.
  c Use a calculator to check your answer.

9 Problem-solving The diagram shows the graph of $y = x^3 - 6x$.

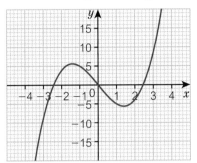

a Write the coordinates of the
   i local minimum
   ii local maximum.

b Use the graph to solve the equations
   i $x^3 - 6x = 7$
   ii $x^3 - 6x = 0$.

c Use your answer to part **b i** to find the values of x where $x^3 - 6x \geqslant 7$.

d n is an integer. Two of the solutions of the cubic equation $x^3 - 6x = n$ lie between 0 and 2. Use the graph to find a possible value of n.

Discussion Do you think this cubic graph has reflection symmetry? Rotational symmetry? How could you check?

10 Explore What can a cubic function tell you about a rollercoaster? Is it easier to explore this question now you have completed the lesson? What further information do you need to be able to answer this?

11 Reflect Owen says, 'A linear equation always has one solution. A quadratic equation always has two solutions. A cubic equation always has three solutions.'
Think back to what you know about graphs and equations.
Do you agree with Owen?
Use examples to help explain your answer.

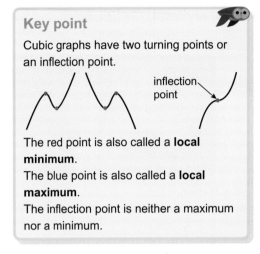

Key point
Cubic graphs have two turning points or an inflection point.

inflection point

The red point is also called a **local minimum**.
The blue point is also called a **local maximum**.
The inflection point is neither a maximum nor a minimum.

Q9c hint
Use the same method as in part **b**.

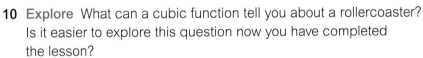

Explore

Reflect

Active Learn   Delta 3, Section 6.3

6.4 STEM: Graphs of reciprocal functions

CONFIDENCE

You will learn to:
- Identify and draw graphs of reciprocal functions
- Solve problems using reciprocal graphs.

Why learn this?
Scientists use reciprocal functions to calculate the gravitational force on a satellite to place it in orbit around the Earth.

Fluency
What is the reciprocal of
- 2
- 10
- $\frac{1}{4}$
- 0.5
- 0.01?

Explore
How far from Earth do you need to travel to halve your weight?

Exercise 6.4: Graphs of reciprocal functions

Warm up

1 Copy and complete this table of values for $y = \frac{1}{x}$

x	−4	−3	−2	−1	−0.5	−0.25	0.25	0.5	1	2	3	4
y												

2 Work out the values of $\frac{1}{x}$ when

   a $x = 2$ **b** $x = 10$ **c** $x = 0.1$ **d** $x = -10$

> **Key point**
>
> A **reciprocal function** has a power of x in the denominator.
>
> $y = \frac{1}{x}$, $y = \frac{2}{x}$, $y = \frac{1}{x^2}$ and $y = \frac{16}{x^3}$
>
> are all reciprocals.

3 a Plot the graph of the **reciprocal function** $y = \frac{1}{x}$
     Use your table of values from Q1.
     Join the points using two smooth curves.
  b What transformation takes one curve to the other?
  c Use your graph to estimate

     i $\frac{1}{1.6}$ **ii** $\frac{1}{-2.5}$

     Check your answer using the reciprocal key $\boxed{x^{-1}}$ or $\boxed{\frac{1}{x}}$ on your calculator.

Discussion Why can't you plot the reciprocal of 0?

> **Q3a hint**
>
> Draw a curve for the positive values of x. Draw a separate curve for the negative values of x.

4 a Copy and complete this table of values for $y = \frac{1}{x^2}$

x	−3	−2	−1	−0.8	−0.5	−0.4	0.4	0.5	0.8	1	2	3
y									1.5625			

  b Plot a graph of the function. Join the points using two smooth curves.
  c What transformation takes one curve to the other?
  Discussion What is the same about this graph and the graph in Q3? What is different?
  d Use your graph to estimate the solutions of the equation $\frac{1}{x^2} = 3$.
     Check your answers using a calculator.

> **Q4d hint**
>
> Find the points on your graph where $y = 3$.

5 **STEM / Real** The graph shows the relationship between the pressure P, in **bar**, and volume V, in cm^3, of gas in a petrol-engine cylinder.

Q5 Literacy hint

Bar is a measure of air pressure. The pressure of air at sea level is 1 bar.

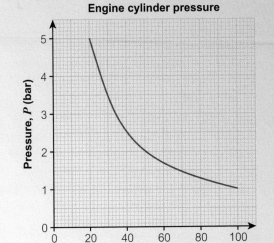

Engine cylinder pressure

a Copy and complete this table of values.

Volume, V (cm^3)	20	40	50	100
Pressure, P (bar)				

b i For each pair of values, work out the product PV.
  What do you notice?

  ii Write an equation connecting P and V and show that P is the reciprocal of V.

c Copy and complete each sentence.
  i P is _____ proportional to V.
  ii The constant of proportionality is ☐.
  iii The pressure P increases as the volume V _____

d Use your equation to find
  i P when $V = 10$
  ii V when $P = 1.25$.

6 **STEM / Reasoning** The gravitational force F, in newtons, between two spherical meteorites whose centres are d km apart is $F = \dfrac{400}{d^2}$

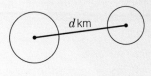

a Copy and complete this table of values.

Distance, d (km)	2	4	6	8	10
Force, F (newtons)					

b Plot the graph of $F = \dfrac{400}{d^2}$

Q6b hint

F depends on d, so plot d on the x-axis and F on the y-axis.

c Use your graph to estimate
  i the gravitational force when $d = 7$ km
  ii the distance between the centres of the two meteorites when $F = 50$ newtons.

d Emma says that the gravitational force would be 0 if the meteorites were millions of km apart. Is she correct?
  Explain your answer.

Worked example

Sketch the graph of the reciprocal function $y = -\dfrac{2}{x^2}$.

x	−10	−0.1	0.1	10
y	−0.02	−200	−200	−0.02

Work out y for a small and a large positive value of x, and for a small and a large negative value of x.

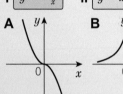

The lines are curved just like for $y = \dfrac{1}{x^2}$ in Q4.

Literacy hint

A **sketch** of a graph shows its shape and some key points. It doesn't have to be accurately plotted.

7 Sketch the graph of each reciprocal function.

   a $y = -\dfrac{1}{x}$ **b** $y = \dfrac{5}{x}$

8 Match each function to its graph.

  i $y = -\dfrac{1}{x}$ **ii** $y = x^2 + 2$ **iii** $y = \dfrac{1}{x^2}$ **iv** $y = -2x^2$ **v** $y = -x^3$

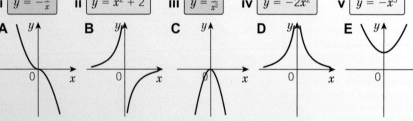

9 **STEM / Reasoning** The body produces a chemical called noradrenaline. After being released into the bloodstream, its effectiveness halves every 2 minutes, starting at 100%.

  a Copy and complete the table.
  b Plot the graph of E against t.

Time, t (minutes)	0	2	4	6	8	10
Effectiveness, E (%)	100					

  c Use your graph to estimate
    i the effectiveness after 3 minutes
    ii the time taken for the effectiveness to reduce by 90%.

  d Henna says this is the graph of $E = \dfrac{100}{t}$

    Plot the reciprocal graph on the same axes, from $t = 1$ to 10. Is she correct? Explain.

10 **Explore** How far from Earth do you need to travel to halve your weight?
    Is it easier to explore this question now you have completed the lesson?
    What further information do you need to be able to answer this?

11 **Reflect** Look back at the work you have done on reciprocal graphs. Write, in your own words, an explanation of why there are no solutions to the equation $\dfrac{10}{x} = 0$.

Explore

Reflect

6 Check up

Log how you did on your Student Progression Chart.

Quadratic graphs

1 a Copy and complete this table of values for $y = x^2 - 4$.

x	−3	−2	−1	0	1	2	3
y							

b Plot the graph of $y = x^2 - 4$.

2 The diagram shows the graph of $y = 2x^2 - 5$.

a Describe the symmetry of the graph.

b Write the coordinates of the turning point.
Is it a maximum or minimum?

c Use the graph to estimate the solutions to
  i $2x^2 - 5 = 10$
  ii $2x^2 - 5 = 0$

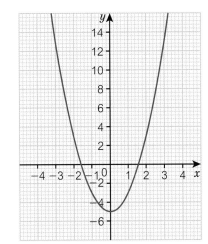

3 The sketch shows the graph of $y = x^2 - 8x + 7$.

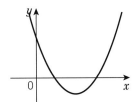

a Factorise $x^2 - 8x + 7$.

b Write down the points where the graph crosses the x-axis.

Cubic graphs

4 Sketch the graph of $y = -x^3$ on axes like these.

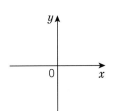

5 Match each graph to its function.

i $y = x^3$ **ii** $y = -2x^2$ **iii** $y = -2x^3$ **iv** $y = x^2 - 5$ **v** $y = 2x^2 + 5$

A 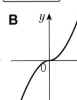   **B**   **C**   **D**   **E**

6 Laurence bought some company shares.
The graph shows the share price, P pence,
after t months.
  a Estimate the coordinates of
    i the local maximum
    ii the local minimum.
  b Explain what happened between these two points.
  c When was the share price three times what Laurence paid?

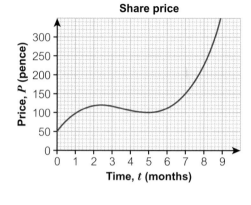

Share price

Graphs of reciprocal functions

7 A tin of paint can cover a rectangle of length x metres and width
y metres. The graph shows the relationship between x and y.
  a What is the width of the rectangle when the length is 30 m?
  b What is the length of the rectangle when the width is 10 m?
  c What is the area of the rectangle?
  d Write an equation linking x and y.

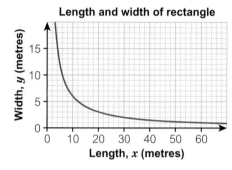

Length and width of rectangle

8 Sketch the graph of the reciprocal function $y = -\dfrac{1}{x}$ on axes like
these.

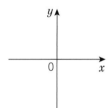

9 How sure are you of your answers? Were you mostly

  😞 Just guessing   😐 Feeling doubtful   😊 Confident

**What next? Use your results to decide whether to strengthen or
extend your learning.**

Challenge

10 a Copy and complete the table of values for the quadratic function
$y = (x - 3)^2$.

x	0	1	2	3	4	5	6	7	8
y	9								

  b Plot the graph of $y = (x - 3)^2$.
  c What are the coordinates of the turning point?
  d Find the coordinates of the turning point for each quadratic
  function.
    i $y = (x - 1)^2$ **ii** $y = (x + 6)^2$
  e Write a quadratic function whose graph has a turning point at
    i $(5, 0)$ **ii** $(-2, 0)$.

Reflect

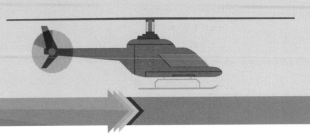

6 Strengthen

You will:
• Strengthen your understanding with practice.

Quadratic graphs

1 a Copy and complete this table of values for the function $y = 3x^2$.

x	−4	−3	−2	−1	0	1	2	3	4
x^2	16								
$y = 3x^2$	48								

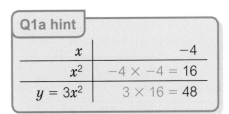

Q1a hint

x	−4
x^2	−4 × −4 = 16
$y = 3x^2$	3 × 16 = 48

b Use your table to copy and complete each pair of coordinates.

(−4, 48), (−3, □), (−2, □)

c Draw these axes on graph paper and plot the graph of the function $y = 3x^2$.

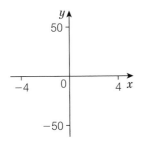

d What are the coordinates of the turning point of the graph?

e Is the turning point a minimum or maximum point?

Q1d hint

The turning point of the graph is also the lowest point.

(□, □)

2 a Use your table in Q1 to complete this table of values for the function $y = -3x^2$.

x	−4	−3	−2	−1	0	1	2	3	4
$3x^2$	48								
$y = -3x^2$	−48								

b Plot the graph of $y = -3x^2$ on the same axes as in Q1.

c What are the coordinates of the turning point of the graph?

d What transformation maps the graph of $y = 3x^2$ to the graph of $y = -3x^2$?

Q2b hint

Use your table to write down pairs of coordinates on the graph of the function $y = -3x^2$.

Q2d hint

Could you
• reflect it
• rotate it about a point
• translate it?

3 The diagram shows the graphs of the functions

  i $y = x^2$ **ii** $y = 2x^2$ **iii** $y = 4x^2$

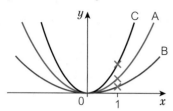

The point when $x = 1$ has been marked on each graph.

a For each function, work out the value of y when $x = 1$.

b Use your answers to match each function to its graph, A, B or C.

4 a Reasoning Copy and complete this table of values for the function $y = x^2 + 5$.

x	−4	−3	−2	−1	0	1	2	3	4
x^2	16								
$y = x^2 + 5$	21								

b Copy the axes in Q1. Plot the points and join them with a smooth curve. Label your graph $y = x^2 + 5$.

c **i** What are the coordinates of the minimum point?

  ii How can you tell the coordinates of the minimum point by looking at the function $y = x^2 + 5$?

d What are the coordinates of the minimum points of

  i $y = x^2 + 10$ **ii** $y = x^2 + 15$ **iii** $y = x^2 - 10$?

e Plot the graphs of each function in part **d** on your axes.

f Copy and complete this sentence to describe how you can transform $y = x^2 + 10$ into the graph of $y = x^2 + 15$:

  Translate $y = x^2 + 10$ _____ _____ units.

g Describe the transformation that maps

  i the graph of $y = x^2 + 5$ to the graph of $y = x^2 + 15$

  ii the graph of $y = x^2 + 5$ to the graph of $y = x^2 - 10$.

Q4f hint

Compare the two graphs. Does the graph move up or down? By how many units?

5 a Plot the graph of the function $y = 3x^2 + 10$ for $x = -4$ to 4.

b **i** What are the coordinates of the minimum point of the graph?

  ii How can you tell the coordinates by looking at the function?

c What would be the coordinates of the minimum point of the graphs of

  i $y = 3x^2 + 15$ **ii** $y = 3x^2 - 10$?

Q5a hint

Use a table of values to find some points to plot. Draw a pair of axes on graph paper that reach the largest and smallest values of y.

6 Match each function to its graph.

  i $y = x^2$ **ii** $y = 3x^2 + 10$ **iii** $y = -3x^2$ **iv** $y = x^2 + 5$

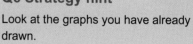

Q6 Strategy hint

Look at the graphs you have already drawn.

Subject links: Science (Quadratic graphs Q7, Cubic graphs Q2, Graphs of reciprocal functions Q2, Enrichment Q1)

135

7 STEM / Reasoning The graph shows the height, h m, of an arrow t seconds after it was thrown.
The height, h, can be found using the formula
$h = 40t - 5t^2$.

a i What are the coordinates of the maximum point of the graph?
  ii What can you say about the arrow at this point?
b How long was the arrow in the air?
c The point marked with a cross shows when the arrow was 60 m high.
  i Use the graph to read the value of t when $h = 60$.
  ii Check that $h = 60$ and your value of t satisfy the equation $h = 40t - 5t^2$.
d Use your graph to find the other solution of the equation in part **c**.

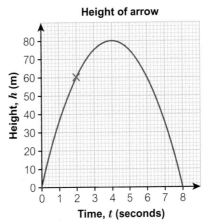

Height of arrow

Height, h (m) / *Time, t (seconds)*

Q7c ii hint

Substitute your values into the equation.

8 a Copy and complete the table of values for the function $y = x^2 + x - 2$.

x	-4	-3	-2	-1	0	1	2	3	4
x^2	16								
$y = x^2 + x - 2$	10								

b Plot the graph $y = x^2 + x - 2$.
c Copy and complete this sentence:
  The graph crosses the x-axis at $x =$ ___ and $x =$ ____
d Factorise the quadratic expression $x^2 + x - 2$.
e What do you notice about your answers to parts **c** and **d**?

Q8d hint

$x^2 + x - 2 = (x + \square)(x - \square)$

Cubic graphs

1 a Copy and complete this table of values for the function $y = 3x^3$.

x	-3	-2	-1	0	1	2	3
x^3	-27						
$y = 3x^3$	-81						

b Use your table to copy and complete each pair of coordinates on the graph of $y = 3x^3$.
  $(-3, -81), (-2, \square), (-1, \square)$
c Draw these axes on graph paper and plot the graph of the function $y = 3x^3$.
d i Use your graph to estimate y when $x = 2.5$.
  ii Substitute $x = 2.5$ into the function $y = 3x^3$ to work out the exact value of y.
  iii How accurate is your graph?
    How could you draw it more accurately?
e i Draw a horizontal line through 20 on the y-axis.
  ii Read the x-coordinate of the point where $y = 20$.
    At this point, $3x^3 = 20$.
  iii Substitute your x-coordinate into $3x^2$.
    Is your answer close to 20?
f Use your graph to estimate solutions to these equations.
  i $3x^3 = 60$
  ii $3x^3 = -20$
  iii $3x^3 = -60$

Q1a hint

x	-3
x^3	$-3 \times -3 \times -3 = -27$
$3x^3$	$3 \times -27 = -81$

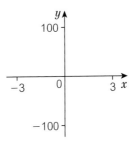

2 STEM The mass of air, A grams, in a ball of radius x cm is given by the formula $A = 0.1x^3$.

a Copy and complete this table of values. Use the x^3 key of your calculator.

x	0	2	4	6	8	10
x^3				216		
$A = 0.1x^3$				21.6		

Q2a hint

x	6
x^3	$6 \times 6 \times 6 = 216$
$A = 0.1x^3$	$0.1 \times 216 = 21.6$

b Continue these on graph paper and plot the graph of the function $A = 0.1x^3$.

c Use your graph to estimate the mass of air in a similar ball with radius 9.2 cm.

d Another ball contains 30 g of air. Estimate its radius.

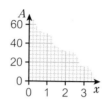

3 Two of these graphs are not cubic. Which two? Explain how you know.

Q3 Strategy hint

Look at the shapes of the graphs.
What shape are quadratic graphs?
What shape are cubic graphs?

A 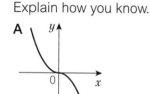 **B** 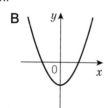 **C**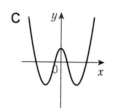

D 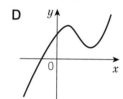 **E**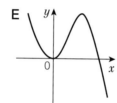

Graphs of reciprocal functions

1 a Copy and complete this table of values for $y = \dfrac{1}{x}$

x	−2	−1	−0.4	−0.2	−0.1	0.1	0.2	0.4	1	2
y		−2.5								

Q1a hint

Use the reciprocal key
$\frac{1}{x}$ or x^{-1} of your calculator.

b Draw these axes on graph paper.

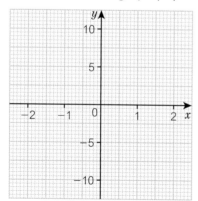

c Use your table of values to plot the graph of the function $y = \dfrac{1}{x}$

Q1c hint

Plot the coordinates from your table.
Join them to make two smooth curves.

2 STEM The graph shows the power density P, units, emitted by a wi-fi router at a distance of d metres.

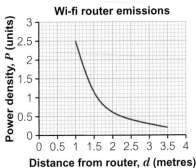

Wi-fi router emissions

Power density, P (units) vs *Distance from router, d (metres)*

a Estimate the power density at a distance of 1.5 m.

b Safety guidelines suggest that a person should not be exposed to a power density above 1 unit. Estimate the recommended minimum distance between a router and a person.

c The formula connecting the power density, P, and the distance d is
$$P = \frac{2.5}{d^2}$$
Use the formula to calculate P when $d = 0.5$ m.

d Use the formula to check your estimate to part **a**.

Q2c hint

Substitute $d = 0.5$ into the formula
$$P = \frac{2.5}{d^2}$$

Enrichment

1 STEM The time, t seconds, it takes a pendulum L cm long to swing forwards and back once is the period. The formula is
$$t = \frac{\sqrt{L}}{25}$$

L cm

a Copy and complete the table of values.

Period, t (seconds)					
Length, L (cm)	0	1	4	16	25

b Use graph paper to plot the graph of $t = \dfrac{\sqrt{L}}{25}$

c Use your graph to estimate the length of a pendulum with period 0.5 seconds.

d A pendulum has a length of 30 cm. Estimate its period.

e Make a pendulum of length 30 cm. Use a stopwatch to time how long it takes to swing back and forth 10 times. Estimate the period. Compare your answer with part **d**.

Q1b hint

The time depends on the length of the pendulum, so plot time on the y-axis.

2 Reflect Copy and complete these sentences about these strengthen lessons.

I found Questions _____ easiest. They were on _____ (list the topics).

I found Questions _____ most difficult. I still need help with _____ (list the topics).

Reflect

6 Extend

You will:
- Extend your understanding with problem-solving.

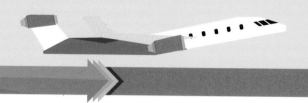

 1 The approximate area, A cm², of a circle with radius r cm is given by the formula $A = 3.14r^2$.

   a Copy and complete the table of values.

Radius, r (cm)	0	2	4	6	8	10
Area, A (cm²)						

   b Use graph paper to plot the graph of $A = 3.14r^2$.
   c Use your graph to estimate
      i the area of a circle with radius 7 cm
      ii the radius of a circle with area 100 cm².

2 **Real / Problem-solving** The length, s ft, of a car skid mark can be estimated using the formula $s = 0.05v^2$, where v mph is the speed of the car when the brakes are applied.

   a Make a table of values for $v = 0$ to 60.
   b Use graph paper to plot the graph of $s = 0.05v^2$.
   c A car driver saw a deer in the road and skidded to a stop. The skid mark was 95 ft long. Estimate the speed of the car when the brakes were applied.
   d It takes approximately 1.4 seconds for a driver to react before braking.
      i Estimate the distance the car travelled before the driver applied the brakes in part **c**.
      ii Estimate the distance the car travelled from the time the driver saw the deer.

> **Q2d i hint**
>
> Convert the speed in miles per hour to feet per second.

 3 The volume, V cm³, of a sphere of radius r cm is given by $V = \frac{4}{3}\pi r^3$.

   a Use graph paper to plot the graph of V for $r = 0$ to 3.
   b Use your graph to estimate
      i the volume of a sphere with radius 1.6 cm
      ii the radius of a sphere with volume 20 cm³.

> **Q3a hint**
>
> Make a table using at least 5 values of r between 0 and 3.

4 **STEM / Reasoning** The table shows the relative risk of 16–20 year old males causing a fatal accident after drinking alcohol.

Blood alcohol concentration, x (%)	0	0.02	0.04	0.06	0.08	0.10
Relative risk, y	0	0.6	5.1	17.3	41.0	80.0

   a Plot the graph of y against x. Join the points with a smooth curve.
   b Dan thinks the graph is quadratic with an equation $y = 8000x^2$.
     Luca thinks the graph is cubic with equation $y = 80\,000x^3$.
     Who do you think is correct? Explain your answer.

> **Q4b Strategy hint**
>
> Substitute a few values of x into each equation.

Subject links: Science (Q2, Q4, Q8, Q10, Q13), Design and technology (Q7, Q12)

5 Match each function to its graph.

i $y = -2x^2$ ii $y = x^3$ iii $y = -2x^3$ iv $y = x^2 + 2$

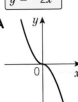
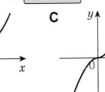
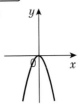

A   B   C   D

6 a Describe the transformation that maps the graph of $y = x^2$
   onto the graph of $y = x^2 + 10$.
  b Describe the transformation that maps the graph of $y = x^2$
   onto the graph of $y = -x^2$.
  c Describe the transformation that maps the graph of $y = x^3$
   onto the graph of $y = -x^3$.
  d Describe the transformation that maps the graph of
   i $y = 2x^2$ onto the graph of $y = 2x^2 - 5$
   ii $y = x^2 + 10$ onto the graph of $y = -x^2 - 10$.

Q6 hint

Use the correct term for the transformations (reflection, rotation, translation or enlargement) and give accurate descriptions.

Q6d hint

Use a graph-plotting package to check your answers.

7 **Problem-solving** The diagram shows a Georgian window
  y m wide and x m high.
  The ratio of height to width of a Georgian window is $x : 1$,
  where x is the positive root of the equation $x^2 - x - 1 = 0$.
  a Plot a table of values for $y = x^2 - x - 1$, for x values
   0, 0.5, 1, 1.5, 2, 2.5, 3.
  b Use your answers to plot the graph of $y = x^2 - x - 1$.
  c Use your graph to solve the equation $x^2 - x - 1 = 0$, giving your
   answers correct to 1 decimal place.
  d A Georgian window has a height of 2 m. Work out its width.

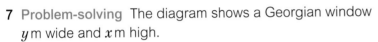
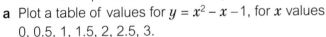

8 **Problem-solving** Tara catapulted a toy
  paratrooper from the top of a cliff.
  The height, h m, of the toy above sea level
  after t seconds is given by the formula
  $h = 25t - 5t^2 + 50$.
  a Make a table of values for $t = 0$ to 8.
  b Plot the graph of h against t.
  c Use your graph to estimate
   i the maximum height of the toy
   ii the time it took to reach the ground.

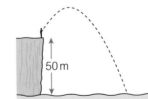

50 m

9 **Problem-solving** The perimeter of this rectangle is 20 cm.

x | Perimeter = 20 cm

Q9 Strategy hint

Write an expression for the length of the rectangle.

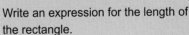

  a Find a formula for the area A of the rectangle in terms of x.
  b Plot the graph of A for $x = 0$ to 10.
  c Use your graph to estimate
   i the maximum possible area of the rectangle
   ii the dimensions of the rectangle when the area is 15 cm^2.

10 **STEM / Problem-solving** The diagram shows a lamp with a parabolic mirror.

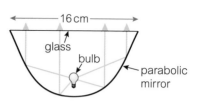

The bulb is placed at the focal point of the parabolic mirror so that the rays of light leaving the lamp are parallel.
 a Draw the mirror by plotting the quadratic function
  $y = 0.1x^2 + 2.5$ between $x = -8$ and 8.
 b The mirror is 16 cm wide. Work out the depth of the mirror.
 c The distance of the focal point, F, from any point, P, on the parabola is the same as the y-coordinate of P.
  i Mark any point P on your parabola.
  ii Find the y-coordinate of P.
  iii Use compasses to mark the position the focal point F.
  iv How far is the bulb from the bottom of the lamp?
 d A ray of light from the bulb bounces off the mirror at the point $Q(x, y)$. Work out the distance the light travels from the bulb to the glass.

11 a Factorise the expression $x^2 - 16$ using the difference of two squares.
 b Use your factorisation to sketch the graph of $y = x^2 - 16$.
 c On your sketch, mark
  i the point where the graph crosses the y-axis
  ii the coordinates of the turning point.
 d Sketch the graph of $y = x^2 - 25$.
 e Sketch the graph of $y = x^2 - a^2$, where a is any positive number.

Q11e hint

What is the value of y when $x = 0$?

12 **Problem-solving** A 3D printer is programmed to make plastic cuboids with this shape.

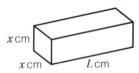

A cuboid with volume 100 cm³ is printed.
 a Write an equation connecting L and x.
 b Show that L is a reciprocal function of x.
 c Plot the graph of L for $x = 1$ to 10.
 d Use your graph to estimate the value of
  i L when $x = 2.5$ ii x when $L = 50$.

13 **STEM / Modelling** The table shows the moisture content, $M\%$, of some seeds after they had been drying for t days.

Time, t (days)	1	2	3	4	5	8	10	12
Moisture content, M (%)	18.5	11	5.5	4	3.5	2.5	1.5	1.5

 a Plot a scatter graph for the data.
 b A researcher thinks that the moisture content is inversely proportional to the drying time. If she is correct, then $Mt = k$ for some constant number k.
  i Use the table of values to estimate the value of k.
  ii Using your value of k from part i, plot the graph of $M = \dfrac{k}{t}$ on the same axes as your scatter graph.
  iii Is your new graph a good model for the data? Explain your answer.

Q13b i hint

Calculate k for all of the table entries. Work out the average.

14 a Reasoning Draw axes with x from -2 to 6 and y from -5 to 5.

  b Plot the graph of the straight line $y = x - 2$.

  c The function $y = \dfrac{1}{x - 2}$ is the reciprocal of the function $y = x - 2$.

Q14c hint

x	-2	-1	0	1	1.5	1.8	2.2	2.5	3	4	5	6
$x - 2$												
$y = \dfrac{1}{x-2}$												

   i Plot the graph of $y = \dfrac{1}{x - 2}$ on the same axes.

   ii Draw the line $x = 2$ using a dotted line.

   iii Explain what happens to y as x gets closer to 2.

  d The diagrams show the graphs of some functions.

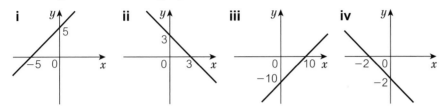

  Sketch the graph of the reciprocal of each function.

15 Match each equation to its graph.

   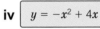

i $y = \dfrac{1}{-x - 4}$ **ii** $y = -\dfrac{1}{x^2}$ **iii** $y = \dfrac{1}{x + 4}$ **iv** $y = -x^2 + 4x$ **v** $y = \dfrac{1}{x - 4}$

16 Reflect Copy and complete these sentences about these extend lessons.

I found Questions _____ easiest. They were on _____ (list the topics).

I found Questions _____ most difficult. I still need help with _____ (list the topics)

6 Unit test

Log how you did on your Student Progression Chart.

1 a Copy and complete this table of values for the function $y = 2x^2 + 5$.

x	−3	−2	−1	0	1	2	3
y							

b Plot the graph of $y = 2x^2 + 5$.

2 The diagram shows the graph of $y = -x^2 + 10$.

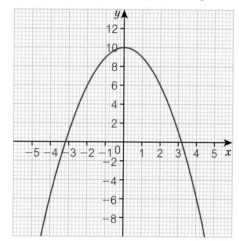

a Describe the symmetry of the graph.

b What are the coordinates of the turning point?

c Is it a maximum or a minimum?

d Use the graph to estimate the solutions to the equation $-x^2 + 10 = 5$.

 3 The diagram shows the graph of the function $y = -2x^3$.

a What transformation takes the right-hand side of the graph to the left-hand side?

b Use the graph to estimate the solution to these equations.

   i $-2x^3 = 20$

   ii $-2x^3 = -10$

c Calculate the value of y when $x = -4.5$.

4 The approximate frequency, y MHz, of a radio wave with wavelength x metres is given by the formula $y = \dfrac{300}{x}$

a Copy and complete the table of values for the function $y = \dfrac{300}{x}$

x	1	2	3	4	5	6
y						

b Plot the graph of $y = \dfrac{300}{x}$

c Use your graph to estimate the solution to $\dfrac{300}{x} = 250$.

5 a Factorise $x^2 - 2x - 3$.

b Which graph is the graph of the function $y = x^2 - 2x - 3$?
Explain your answer.

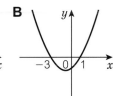

6 Match each graph to its function.

i $y = x^2 + 2$　**ii** $y = x^3$　**iii** $y = \frac{1}{x}$　**iv** $y = -x^2 + 2$　**v** $y = \frac{1}{x^2}$

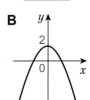

7 Sketch the graph of the reciprocal function

$y = -\dfrac{1}{x^2}$ using a copy of these axes.

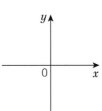

Challenge

8 Each of these points lies on one of the graphs.

(−2, −1)　　(−1, 2)　　(2, −4)　　(−1, 1)　　(1, −2)　　(−1, −1)

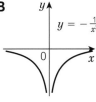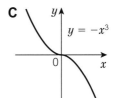

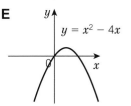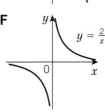

Match each point to its graph.

9 Reflect Use what you have learned about graphs so far to write an
equation that could fit each of these graphs.

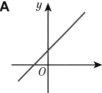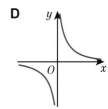

7.1 Rates of change

You will learn to:
- Solve problems involving rates of change
- Convert units with compound measures.

CONFIDENCE

Why learn this?
British speed limits are given in miles per hour (mph) but many countries use kilometres per hour (km/h). Converting between them is useful when travelling abroad.

Fluency
Rearrange the formula $s = \dfrac{d}{t}$ to make
- d the subject
- t the subject.

Explore
What is the speed limit on French motorways in mph?

Exercise 7.1

Warm up

1 This distance–time graph shows a hiker's journey.

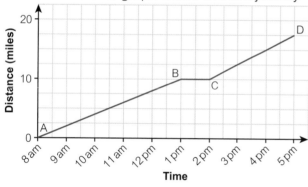

Calculate the hiker's average speed in miles per hour (mph) from
a A to B   **b** B to C   **c** C to D.

> **Key point**
> When compound measures involve dividing by a unit of time, they are called **rates of change**. Speed is the rate of change of distance with time.

2 Write these times in hours and minutes.
a $2\frac{1}{4}$ hours   **b** 0.75 hours   **c** 1.5 hours   **d** 3.2 hours

3 Work out the average speed for each journey.
a A car travels 200 km in 5 hours.
b An athlete runs 400 m in 64 seconds.
c An aeroplane travels 2475 miles in $4\frac{1}{2}$ hours.
d A swimmer completes a 50 m length in 40 seconds.

> **Q3 hint**
> Most objects do not travel at a constant speed. You usually calculate **average speed** over a whole journey:
> $$\text{average speed} = \frac{\text{distance travelled}}{\text{time taken}}$$

4 An arrow flies 15 m to a target at an average speed of 60 **m/s**.
Find the time taken for it to reach the target.

5 A jockey completes a 2.4-mile course at an average speed of 32 mph.
Calculate the length of time it takes him
a in hours as a decimal   **b** in minutes and seconds.

> **Q4 Literacy hint**
> **m/s** means 'metres per second'.

Topic links: Real-life graphs

6 Real An aeroplane descends at a constant rate of 200 feet per minute. How long does it take the aircraft to descend from an altitude of 18 000 feet to an altitude of 10 000 feet?

7 Real / Problem-solving Joanne drives 90 miles to visit friends. She plans to travel at an average speed of 55 mph and wants to arrive by 1 pm. Calculate the latest time Joanne should leave.

8 Problem-solving The Channel Tunnel is 31.4 miles long. The speed limit for trains in the tunnel is 160 km/h. Work out the time taken for a train travelling at the speed limit to complete its journey through the tunnel.

> **Q8 hint**
>
> 5 miles = 8 km

Worked example

Convert 72 km/h to m/s.

$72 \times 1000 = 72\,000$

$72\,\text{km/h} = 72\,000\,\text{m/h}$

$72\,000 \div 3600 = 20$

$72\,000\,\text{m/h} = 20\,\text{m/s}$

> Start by converting 72 km into m. You now have the speed in metres per hour.

> There are $60 \times 60 = 3600$ seconds in 1 hour. Divide the speed in metres per hour by 3600 to find the speed in metres per second.

> **Key point**
>
> To convert between compound measures, convert each unit one at a time.

9 Convert 45 km/h into m/s.

10 The peregrine falcon can reach speeds of up to 90 m/s when diving. Convert this speed into km/h.

11 Problem-solving / Reasoning Amir's remote-controlled car has a maximum speed of 32 km/h. A world-class athlete can run 200 m in 19.6 seconds. Amir says his car could beat the sprinter in a 200 m race. Is he correct? Show your working to explain.

12 This distance–time graph shows trips taken by three different cyclists.
  a Which cyclist travelled at the fastest speed?
  b Which cyclist had the highest average speed for the entire journey?
  A fourth cyclist completes the same trip as cyclist C, starting and finishing at the same time. She travels at a constant speed for the whole journey.
  c Calculate her constant speed, giving your answer correct to 1 decimal place.

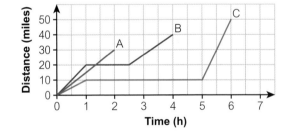

13 Explore What is the speed limit on French motorways in mph? What have you learned in this lesson to help you explore this question? What further information do you need?

14 Reflect Saz says, 'When I'm converting between compound measures I look at the units to help decide whether to multiply or divide. m/s (metres per second) is a bit like a fraction $\frac{m}{s}$ so I multiply by the length measure and divide by the time measure.'
Did you use a method similar to Saz's to help?
What other methods do you use when working with compound measures?

7.2 Density and pressure

You will learn to:
- Calculate density and pressure
- Solve problems involving compound measures.

Why learn this?
Meteorologists examine air pressure so they can predict a storm.

Fluency
$v = u + at$
- Calculate v when $u = 5$, $a = 2$ and $t = 10$.
- Calculate u when $v = 100$, $a = 5$ and $t = 4$.

Explore
How do snow shoes reduce your chance of sinking into deep snow?

CONFIDENCE

Exercise 7.2

1 Work out the volume of this triangular prism.

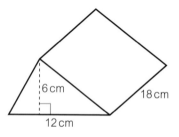

6 cm
18 cm
12 cm

2 Convert

    a 4 cm^2 into mm^2 **b** 600 cm^2 into m^2

    c 0.3 m^3 into cm^3 **d** $750 \text{ m}l$ into cm^3

3 Make x the subject of each equation.

    a $y = 10x$ **b** $3y = 2 - x$

    c $y = \dfrac{5}{x}$ **d** $2(x + 1) = 4$

> **Q2 hint**
>
>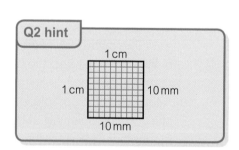
>
> 1 cm
> 1 cm
> 10 mm
> 10 mm

4 **STEM / Real** As part of a science experiment, Kiki measures the mass and volume of samples of four different metals. She records her results in this table.

Metal	Volume (cm³)	Mass (g)
Titanium	16	72
Zinc	200	1427
Silver	42	441
Tin	1500	10920

Calculate the **density** of each substance, giving your answers in g/cm^3 correct to 1 decimal place.

> **Key point**
>
> **Density** is a compound measure. Density measures the mass per unit of volume. Density is often measured in grams per cubic centimetre (g/cm^3) and kilograms per cubic metre (kg/m^3). The Greek letter ρ (*rho*) is used to represent density.
>
> $$\text{density } (\rho) = \frac{\text{mass}}{\text{volume}}$$

Warm up

Topic links: Fractions, decimals and percentages   **Subject links:** Science (Q4, Q5, Q8–14)

Worked example

Sandalwood has a density of 900 kg/m³. Calculate the volume of a piece of sandalwood with a mass of 7560 kg.

$$volume = \frac{mass}{density}$$

$$= \frac{7560}{900}$$

$$= 8.4\,m^3$$

> Rearrange the formula density = $\frac{mass}{volume}$ to make volume the subject.

> The unit of density is kg/m³ and the unit of mass is kg, so the unit of volume is m³.

5 STEM The table shows the densities of three common metal alloys.

Metal alloy	Density, ρ (kg/m³)
Brass	8400
Steel	7820
Sterling silver	10400

Calculate
a the volume of 50 kg of brass
b the mass of 1.3 m³ of steel
c the mass of 4 cm³ of sterling silver
d the volume of 75 g of brass.

> **Q5c hint**
> The density is given in kg/m³ so you need to convert cm³ to m³.

6 Problem-solving 250 ml of cooking oil has a mass of 230 g. Calculate the density of cooking oil in g/cm³.

7 Problem-solving / Modelling The floor of this room is covered with rubber tiles with a density of 1200 kg/m³. The tiles are 5 mm thick. Estimate the total mass of the rubber tiles.

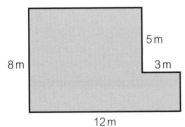

8 STEM / Problem-solving An electrical solder is made by combining 15 g of tin with 85 g of lead. Tin has a density of 7.3 g/cm³ and lead has a density of 11.3 g/cm³. Calculate the density of the solder.

9 STEM The density of the metal mercury is 13500 kg/m³. Convert this density into g/cm³.

10 A force of 65 N is applied to an area of 12 cm². Calculate the **pressure**. Give your answer to 1 decimal place.

11 Real At a depth of 10 m, water has a pressure of 9.8 N/cm². Calculate the force applied to a diving mask with a surface area of 320 cm².

> **Key point**
> **Pressure** is a compound measure. Pressure is the force applied over a given area. The most common units of pressure are newtons per square centimetre (N/cm²) and newtons per square metre (N/m²).
> $$pressure = \frac{force}{area} \qquad P = \frac{F}{A}$$

12 **Problem-solving** Calculate the force needed to produce a pressure of $520\,N/m^2$ on an area of $250\,cm^2$.

Q12 Strategy hint
Make sure all the area measures are in the same units.

13 **Modelling / Real** A roofer uses a board to reduce the pressure applied to a roof he is working on. The roofer has a weight of $880\,N$, and wants the maximum pressure applied to the roof to be $500\,N/m^2$. Calculate the minimum area of board he should use to distribute his weight.

14 **STEM / Problem-solving** Objects that are less dense than their surroundings float. The density of water at $4°C$ is $1\,g/cm^3$.

   a Decide which of these objects will float in a bowl of water with a temperature of $4°C$.

	Object	Mass
A	Wood 2 cm, 5 cm, 1 cm	7 g
B	Plutonium 1 cm, 1 cm, 1 cm	19.8 g
C	Polystyrene 20 cm, 2 cm, 5 cm	2 g
D	Iron 5 cm, 2 cm, 2 cm	160 g

   b The density of mercury is $13.6\,g/cm^3$. Which of the objects will float in mercury?

   Discussion Do your answers change when the volume of the object is increased?

15 **Explore** How do snow shoes reduce your chance of sinking into deep snow?
   Look back at the maths you have learned in this lesson. How can you use it to answer this question?

16 **Reflect** Dale says, 'A compound measure combines two different measures. A rate of change is a type of compound measure that describes exactly how one quantity changes in relation to time.'
   Dale begins this table to explain:

Compound measure	Example
Speed – measure of distance and time	20 miles per hour

   Copy Dale's table and add more examples of compound measures. Highlight those that are rates of change.

7.3 Upper and lower bounds

You will learn to:
- Understand the effect of rounding
- Find upper and lower bounds.

Why learn this?
You need to know the margin of error in your measurements if you are ordering new windows for a house.

Fluency
Work out
- 7000 − 50
- 0.9 + 0.05
- 20 − 0.5
- 0.036 − 0.0005

Explore
How accurate should measures be when
- cooking
- building a house
- calculating a country's GDP?

CONFIDENCE

Warm up

Exercise 7.3

1 Round 253.0992 to
  a the nearest 100
  b the nearest 10
  c 1 decimal place
  d 2 decimal places.

2 The length of this roll of tape has been rounded to 1 decimal place. Which of the lengths in the cloud could be the actual length of the tape?

Length 4.2 m

4.1m 4.13 m
4 m 4.17 m 4.22 m
4.25 m 4.209 m

> **Key point**
> When a measurement is rounded, the actual value could be bigger or smaller than the rounded value. The biggest possible actual value is called the **upper bound**. The smallest possible actual value is called the **lower bound**.

Worked example

A piece of paper is 21 cm wide, correct to the nearest cm. Calculate the **upper** and **lower bound** for the width of the piece of paper.

Upper bound = 21.5 cm — Any number less than 21.5 is rounded to 21.
Lower bound = 20.5 cm — Any number greater than 20.5 is rounded to 21.

Discussion If you round 21.5 cm to the nearest whole number you get 22 cm. Why is this value still used as the upper bound?

3 Write down the upper and lower bounds for each measurement.
  a The Mariana Trench in the Pacific Ocean is 11 km deep, to the nearest km.
  b The Moon orbits the Earth every 27 days, to the nearest day.
  c The mass of a tennis ball is 56.7 g, to 1 decimal place.
  d The height of the Eiffel Tower is 300 metres, to the nearest 10 m.

4 There were 65 000 people at a football match, rounded to the nearest thousand. Write down the upper and lower bounds for the number of people at the football match.

> **Key point**
> The upper bound is half a measure greater than the rounded value. The lower bound is half a measure less than the rounded value.

> **Q4 hint**
> The number of people is a discrete measurement. This means it must be a whole number. Work out the largest possible whole number that rounds to 65 000, to the nearest thousand.

5 Problem-solving A carton contains 500 ml of smoothie, correct to the nearest 10 ml. The carton costs £3.20. Calculate
  a the greatest possible cost per ml
  b the least possible cost per ml.
  Give your answers in pence.

6 Nisha uses a computer program to record her reaction time. She measures it as 0.26 seconds, to 2 decimal places. Copy and complete this inequality to show the upper and lower bounds of her reaction time.
    $\square \leqslant t < \square$
  Discussion Why do you need to use different inequality signs for the lower and upper bounds?

Key point
You can use inequalities to show upper and lower bounds for continuous measurements like time, length or mass.

7 STEM Paul measures the duration, t seconds, of a chemical reaction and records his result as
    $70.05 \leqslant t < 70.15$
  What degree of accuracy was Paul using for his measurement?

8 Copy and complete this table.

Measurement	Degree of accuracy	Actual value
6.3 seconds	1 decimal place	6.3 ± 0.05 seconds
5800 m	nearest 100 m	5800 ± □ m
0.09 km	2 decimal places	0.09 ± □ km
8.0 kg	1 decimal place	□ ± □ kg

Q8 Literacy hint
The symbol ± means 'plus or minus'. You can use it to show the **absolute error** in a measurement.

9 A box of nails contains between 115 and 125 nails. Write this in the form □ ± □

10 Problem-solving A recipe makes 800 g of cake mix, correct to the nearest 10 g. The mixture is divided equally between 4 cake tins. Calculate the maximum **absolute error** for the amount of cake mix in each tin.

Key point
The **absolute error** is the maximum difference between the measured value and the actual value.

11 Real A section of fencing is 180 cm long, to the nearest 10 cm. 8 sections of fencing are joined together.
  a Write down the upper and lower bounds for one piece of the fencing.
  b Work out the upper and lower bounds for the total length of the fencing.
  c Work out the absolute error for the total length of the fencing.
  Discussion What effect does multiplying or dividing a measurement by a whole number have on upper and lower bounds and absolute error?

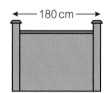

12 Explore How accurate should measures be when
  • cooking
  • building a house
  • calculating a country's GDP?
  Choose some sensible numbers to help you explore this situation. Then use what you've learned in this lesson to help you answer the question.

13 Reflect In this lesson you have shown rounding errors in lots of different ways. Make a list of the different ways you can show the actual values of a rounded number. What are the advantages and disadvantages of each method?

Topic links: Rounding, Decimals, Inequalities

Subject links: Science (Q6, Q7), Cookery (Q10)

Active Learn Delta 3, Section 7.3

Explore

Reflect

7.4 Calculating with bounds

You will learn to:
- Calculate the lower and upper bounds of areas and volumes
- Calculate the lower and upper bounds of compound measures.

Why learn this?
Understanding the margin of error in calculations allows divers to make sure they don't run out of air.

Fluency
$a = 4.7$, $b = 0.9$ and $c = 5.5$
Work out
- $a + 2b$
- $\dfrac{bc}{a}$
- $b^2 - 2ac$

Explore
How many songs can you fit onto your phone or MP3 player?

Exercise 7.4

1 Write down the upper and lower bounds for each measurement.
  a A swimming pool is 25 m long, to the nearest m.
  b A glass contains 170 m*l* of milk, correct to the nearest 10 m*l*.
  c Elena's reaction time is 0.20 seconds, correct to 2 decimal places.

 2 Work out the area of each shape.

a
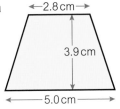

2.8 cm
3.9 cm
5.0 cm

b
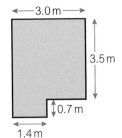

3.0 m
3.5 m
0.7 m
1.4 m

3 A bus travels 4.2 miles in 12 minutes. Calculate its average speed. Give your answer in miles per hour.

 4 The dimensions of this rectangle have been measured correct to 1 decimal place.
  a Write down the upper and lower bounds for the length of the rectangle.
  b Write down the upper and lower bounds for the width of the rectangle.
  c Calculate the upper bound for the area of the rectangle.
  d Calculate the lower bound for the area of the rectangle.

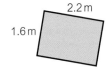

2.2 m
1.6 m

Q4c hint

To work out the largest possible area, use the largest possible length and width.

 5 The dimensions of this rectangle are correct to the nearest whole number. Calculate
  a the upper bound for the area of the rectangle
  b the lower bound for the area of the rectangle.

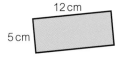

12 cm
5 cm

Warm up

A ball bearing has a mass of 89 g and a volume of 11 cm³. Both values are correct to the nearest whole number.

a Copy and complete this table.

	Lower bound	Upper bound
Mass (g)		
Volume (cm³)		

b Use the values in your table to calculate **four** different values for the actual density of the ball bearing. Give your answers correct to 2 decimal places.

c Which bound should you use for each measurement to obtain
  i the largest possible density   ii the smallest possible density?

Worked example

An athlete completes a 400 m course in 84 seconds.
Both measurements are correct to the nearest whole number.
Calculate the upper and lower bounds for the athlete's average speed. Give your answers in m/s correct to 2 decimal places.

	Lower bound	Upper bound
Distance (m)	399.5	400.5
Time (s)	83.5	84.5

Write down the upper and lower bounds for each measurement.

$$\text{Average speed} = \frac{\text{distance}}{\text{time}}$$

$$\text{Upper bound for average speed} = \frac{400.5}{83.5} = 4.80 \text{ m/s}$$

To find the upper bound, divide the largest possible distance by the smallest possible time.

$$\text{Lower bound for average speed} = \frac{399.5}{84.5} = 4.73 \text{ m/s}$$

To find the lower bound, divide the smallest possible distance by the largest possible time.

6 These values are all correct to 1 decimal place.

$p = 6.2$ $q = 4.0$ $r = 1.5$

Find the greatest and least possible values of

a $p - q$ b $\dfrac{q}{r}$

c $\dfrac{p + q}{r}$ d $2q^2 - p$

7 A force of 12.5 N is applied over an area of 6.2 cm².
Both measurements are correct to 1 decimal place.
Calculate
a the upper bound for the pressure applied by the force
b the lower bound for the pressure applied by the force.
Give your answers correct to 2 decimal places.

8 A boat travels 35 km at an average speed of 18 km/h.
Both measurements are correct to the nearest whole number.
Calculate

a the **greatest possible value** for the time taken

b the **least possible value** for the time taken.

Give your answers correct to 1 decimal place.

Key point

Greatest possible value is the same as **upper bound**.
Least possible value is the same as **lower bound**.

Topic links: Rounding, Decimals, Formulae   **Subject links:** Science (Q7, Q10)

9 The dimensions of this trapezium are correct to the nearest 10 mm.
  a Calculate the upper and lower bounds for the area of the trapezium, correct to the nearest mm.
  b Work out the absolute error for the area of the trapezium. Give your answer in the form $\square \pm \square$ mm, correct to the nearest mm.

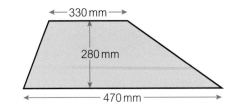

10 **Problem-solving** The density of iron is 7900 kg/m^3, correct to the nearest 100 kg/m^3. A block of iron has a mass of 2420 kg, correct to the nearest 10 kg. Calculate the greatest possible volume of the block. Give your answer in m^3 to 2 decimal places.

11 **Problem-solving** The lengths given in this diagram are accurate to the nearest cm. Find the greatest and least possible values for each length.
  a AD   **b** BC   **c** CD

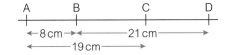

12 **Problem-solving** The area of a rectangular field is given as 380 m^2 to the nearest 10 m^2. The length of one side is 25 m to the nearest m. Find the upper and lower bounds for the length of the other side.

13 **Problem-solving / Real** This is a plan of a section of a park. The measurements are correct to the nearest whole number. The park-keeper has enough petrol to mow 800 m^2 of grass. Does he definitely have enough petrol to mow this section of the park? Show all of your working to support your answer.

Q13 Strategy hint
You need to find the maximum possible area. Be careful – you shouldn't just use the upper bound for every measurement.

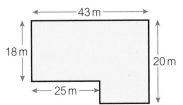

14 **Explore** How many songs can you fit onto your phone or MP3 player?
Look back at the maths you have learned in this lesson. How can you use it to answer this question? What other information do you need?

15 **Reflect** Ingrid says, 'During this lesson I kept saying "This number needs to be as big as possible. This number needs to be as small as possible."'
Did you find you repeated phrases to yourself to help answer questions? Was it the same phrase as Ingrid's?
What other strategies did you use to answer these questions?

7.5 STEM: Accurate measures in real life

You will learn to:
- Use upper and lower bounds to solve complex problems.

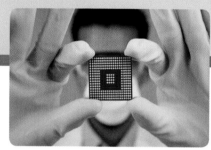

Why learn this?
Accuracy is important when manufacturing products that involve lots of different parts.

Fluency
- $1\,cm^2 = \square\,mm^2$
- $1\,m^2 = \square\,cm^2$
- $1\,km^2 = \square\,m^2$

Explore
How can you be certain that you have enough petrol for a journey?

CONFIDENCE

Exercise 7.5: Real-life measures

Warm up

1 The dimensions of this triangle are given to the nearest metre.
Work out the upper and lower bounds for the area of the triangle.

10 m

13 m

2 These values are all correct to 1 decimal place.
$x = 4.4 \qquad y = 10.5 \qquad z = 0.8$
Find the greatest and least possible values of

a $x + y$ **b** $2z + y$ **c** xy **d** $\dfrac{2\pi x}{z}$

> **Q2d hint**
> Leave your answer in terms of π

3 STEM A wooden joist is made of 25 identical sheets of wood glued together. Each sheet is 3.5 mm thick, correct to 1 decimal place.
Calculate the upper and lower bounds for the total thickness of the joist.

 4 STEM / Problem-solving Cases for computer hard drives are stamped out of sheet metal. The metal comes in rolls that are 60 metres long. Each case requires 26 cm of the roll, correct to the nearest cm. Calculate the upper and lower bounds for the number of cases that can be made from one roll of metal.

> **Key point**
> To answer a problem involving upper and lower bounds you might need to consider the **best-case** scenario or **worst-case** scenario.

 5 STEM / Reasoning In a 'pop' rivet, a metal rod with diameter x is inserted into a metal head with opening diameter y. A company plans to design a rivet with $x = 2.38$ mm, correct to 2 decimal places, and $y = 2.4$ mm, correct to 1 decimal place.
Explain why this is not a suitable design for the rivet.

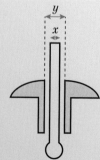

Topic links: Rounding, Area and volume   **Subject links:** Science (Q6, Q10), Design and technology (Q3–5, Q7, Q11)

6 **STEM / Problem-solving** A company manufactures steel ball bearings in three different sizes. The density of the steel used for the ball bearings is 7.9 g/cm³.

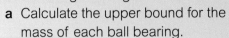

A Radius = 28 mm B Radius = 40 mm C Radius = 50 mm Measurements correct to nearest mm.

a Calculate the upper bound for the mass of each ball bearing.

In one day the company manufactures 10 000 of each size of ball bearing. The ball bearings are shipped on lorries with a maximum weight loading of 18 000 kg.

b How many lorries will the company need to be sure it can transport the entire day's production?

> **Q6 hint**
> Volume of a sphere = $\dfrac{4\pi r^3}{3}$

7 **STEM / Reasoning** A factory estimates that 11 g of solder, to the nearest gram, is needed to manufacture 1 MP3 player.

a Calculate the upper bound of the amount of solder needed to manufacture 2500 MP3 players. Give your answer in kg correct to 2 decimal places.

The factory buys 4 rolls of solder weighing 7.5 kg, correct to 1 decimal place.

b Calculate the lower bound for the amount of solder the factory buys.

c Does the factory definitely have enough solder to manufacture 2500 MP3 players? Explain.

8 **Problem-solving** A cargo ship uses 43 gallons of fuel per mile. It has 230 000 gallons of fuel in the tank, correct to the nearest 10 000 gallons. The distance from Tokyo to San Francisco is 5200 miles, to the nearest 100 miles. Does the cargo ship definitely have enough fuel to complete this journey? Show working to support your answer.

> **Q8 Strategy hint**
> Draw a table showing the upper and lower bounds for each rounded measurement.
> Consider the worst-case scenario: largest distance and smallest amount of fuel.

9 **Real** A loaded lorry can travel 8 miles, to the nearest mile, on one gallon of diesel. The driving distance from Leeds to Southampton is 240 miles, to the nearest 10 miles. A driver has 33 gallons of diesel in the tank. Can he definitely complete the journey from Leeds to Southampton?

10 **STEM / Problem-solving** A service lift has a maximum loading of 4200 kg, correct to the nearest 100 kg. How many boxes weighing 80 kg, correct to the nearest 10 kg, can safely be loaded onto the lift? Show working to support your answer.

> **Q10 hint**
> You need to consider the worst-case scenario. This means you should use the lower bound for the maximum loading, and the upper bound for the weight of each box.

11 **STEM / Problem-solving** A shipping company wants to pack boxes onto a pallet. Each box is a cube with a side length of 0.8 m, correct to 1 decimal place. The dimensions of the pallet are shown on the diagram, correct to the nearest metre. Work out the maximum and minimum number of boxes the company could pack on the pallet.

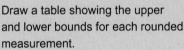

4 m

2 m

12 **Explore** How can you be certain that you have enough petrol for a journey?
Look back at the maths you have learned in this lesson.
How can you use it to answer this question?

13 **Reflect** In this lesson you have worked with accurate measures in science, technology and engineering contexts. Why is it important to know about the level of accuracy in these contexts? In what other contexts is understanding accuracy of measures important?

Explore

Reflect

Master
P145

CHECK

Strengthen
P159

Extend
P163

Test
P167

7 Check up

Log how you did on your
Student Progression Chart.

Compound measures

1 A car completes a 225-mile journey in 6 hours. Calculate its average
speed in mph.

2 A marathon runner completes a 42 km course at an average speed of
7 km/h. Calculate the time taken to complete the course.

3 Convert 24 km/h into m/s.

4 The diagram shows a gold bar.

7.2 cm   2.5 cm
4.0 cm

    a Calculate the volume of the gold bar.

Gold has a density of 19.3 g/cm³.

    b Calculate the mass of the gold bar in kg.

Upper and lower bounds

5 An egg weighs 60 g correct to the nearest gram.
Write down the upper and lower bounds for the mass of the egg.

6 The statue of the Angel of the North is 20 m tall, to the nearest metre.
Copy and complete this inequality for the height of the statue.
    $\square \leqslant$ height $< \square$

7 A plant seedling is 11.9 cm tall, to 1 decimal place.
Write the absolute error of its height in the form $11.9 \pm \square$ cm.

8 The measurements on this triangle are correct to the nearest 10 cm.

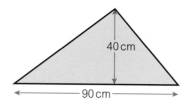
40 cm
90 cm

Calculate
    a the lower bound for the area of the triangle
    b the upper bound for the area of the triangle.

Accuracy and problem-solving

9 A sprinter runs for 26 seconds, to the nearest second.
She runs 200 m, to the nearest 10 m.

a Copy and complete this table.

	Lower bound	Upper bound
Distance (m)		
Time (s)		

b Work out the upper bound for the average speed.

10 A ruby has a volume of 6.5 cm^3 and a mass of 25.2 g.
Both measurements are correct to 1 decimal place.

a Write down the lower bound for the mass of the ruby.

b Write down the upper bound for the volume of the ruby.

c Calculate the least possible value for the density of the ruby.

11 A £1 coin has a thickness of 3.15 mm, correct to 2 decimal places.
Calculate the upper and lower bounds for the thickness of 5 £1 coins stacked together.

12 Christina is mixing paint in a bucket with a capacity of 4.5 litres, correct to 1 decimal place. She adds 1.5 litres of red paint, 2.3 litres of blue paint, and 0.6 litres of white paint. All three measurements are correct to 1 decimal place.

a Write down the lower bound for the capacity of the bucket.

b Work out the upper bound for the total amount of paint added.

c Is there any possibility that the bucket will overflow?
Give a reason for your answer.

13 **How sure are you of your answers? Were you mostly**
Just guessing **Feeling doubtful** **Confident**
What next? Use your results to decide whether to strengthen or extend your learning.

Reflect

Challenge

14 An old-fashioned shower has a flow rate of 9.5 litres per minute.
A water-saving shower has a flow rate of 6.1 litres per minute.
Estimate how much water a person will save in one year using the water-saving shower.
What assumptions have you made?

7 Strengthen

You will:
- Strengthen your understanding with practice.

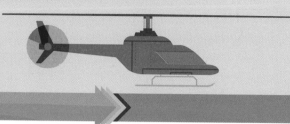

Compound measures

1 Find the average speed for each journey. Give units with your answers.
  a A runner finishing a 12-mile course in 4 hours
  b A train travelling 360 miles in 5 hours
  c A pedestrian walking 4 miles in 1 hour and 20 minutes

> **Q1 hint**
>
> You can use the formula triangle for speed. The position of the variables tells you whether to multiply or divide.
>
>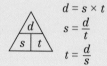
>
> $d = s \times t$
> $s = \dfrac{d}{t}$
> $t = \dfrac{d}{s}$

2 A swimmer completes a 400 m race at an average speed of 0.8 m/s. Calculate the time taken in minutes and seconds.

3 A car travels 100 miles at a constant speed of 40 miles per hour. Calculate the time taken in hours and minutes.

4 A satellite travelling at a constant speed travels 480 km in 1 minute. Calculate its speed in km/h.

> **Q4 hint**
>
> Work out how far the satellite travels in 1 hour.

5 **Real** The motorway speed limit in Italy is 130 km/h. Karl is driving at a speed of 40 m/s. Is Karl speeding?

6 Calculate the density of each material. Give units with your answers.
  a An iron girder with a volume of $0.6\,\text{m}^3$ and mass of 4188 kg
  b A platinum bracelet with a volume of $3.5\,\text{cm}^3$ and a mass of 74.9 g

> **Q6 hint**
>
> You can use the formula triangle for density.
>
>
>
> mass = density × volume
> density = $\dfrac{\text{mass}}{\text{volume}}$
> volume = $\dfrac{\text{mass}}{\text{density}}$

7 **Problem-solving** This diagram shows a skateboard ramp. It is made of solid concrete with a density of $2400\,\text{kg/m}^3$. Calculate the mass of the skateboard ramp.

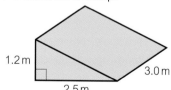

1.2 m   3.0 m   2.5 m

> **Q7 hint**
>
> Start by working out the volume of the prism using the formula
> volume of prism
> = length × area of cross-section

8 **STEM** The density of lead is $11.3\,\text{g/cm}^3$. Convert this density into kg/cm^3.

9 **STEM** An aeroplane window has an area of $990\,\text{cm}^2$. The force acting on the window due to the pressurized air in the cabin is 5148 N. Calculate the pressure on the window in N/cm^2.

> **Q9 hint**
>
> This is the formula triangle for pressure.
>
>

Subject links: Science (Compound measures Q6–9, Accuracy and problem-solving (Q3, Q5), Cookery (Accuracy and problem-solving Q8)

Upper and lower bounds

1 A bucket contains 3 litres of water, correct to the nearest litre. Which of the following statements are true? Give reasons for your answers.
  A The actual amount of water in the bucket could be 3.2 litres.
  B The upper bound for the amount of water in the bucket is 3.4 litres.
  C The lower bound for the amount of water in the bucket is 2.5 litres.

2 Write down the upper and lower bounds for each measurement.
  a The London Eye is 135 m high, correct to the nearest m.

> **Q2a hint**
>
> All of the highlighted values round to 135 to the nearest whole number:

  b The age of the Earth is 4.54 billion years, to 2 decimal places.
  c A cheetah can run at 70 mph, correct to the nearest 10 mph.
  d The radioactive isotope Radon 222 has a half-life of 3.8 days, to 1 decimal place.

3 The population of the UK in 2014 was 64.1 million, to 1 decimal place. Write down the upper and lower bounds for the population of the UK in 2014.

> **Q3 hint**
>
> The number given is to 1 decimal place, so the upper and lower bounds will have 2 decimal places.

4 This is the label on a box of screws. Calculate the upper and lower bounds for the cost per screw. Give your answer in pence, correct to 2 decimal places.

> **£4.99**
>
> Number of screws
> 250 ± 10

5 Samantha measured the capacity of a glass as 250 ml to the nearest 10 ml. Copy and complete this statement showing the absolute error in her measurement:
  Actual capacity = 250 ± ☐ ml

> **Q5 hint**
>
> How much bigger or smaller could the capacity be?

> **Q6 Strategy hint**
>
> To find the upper bound and lower bound of a calculation use these rules:
>
> | | Type of calculation | | | |
> |---|---|---|---|---|
> | | **+** | **−** | **×** | **÷** |
> | Upper bound | UB + UB | UB − LB | UB × UB | UB ÷ LB |
> | Lower bound | LB + LB | LB − UB | LB × LB | LB ÷ UB |

6 **Problem-solving** Both the dimensions in this rectangle are correct to 1 decimal place.

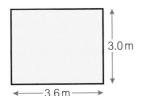

3.0 m

3.6 m

  a Write down the upper bound for each measurement.
  b Calculate the maximum possible area of the rectangle.

7 Problem-solving The dimensions of this triangle are correct to the nearest mm.

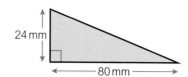

24 mm

80 mm

Calculate the upper and lower bounds for the area of the triangle.

Accuracy and problem-solving

1 A rabbit runs 250 metres, to the nearest 10 metres, in 55 seconds, to the nearest second. Find the upper bound for its average speed. Give your answer correct to 2 decimal places.

2 These values are correct to 1 decimal place.

$x = 6.3$ $y = 9.1$ $z = 12.5$

Work out the greatest and least possible values for

a $x + y$ **b** $z - y$ **c** $\dfrac{x}{y}$ **d** $xy - z$

3 A wooden paperweight has a mass of 250 g correct to the nearest 10 g. It has a volume of 370 cm³, correct to the nearest 10 cm³. Calculate the greatest and least possible values for the density of the wood used to make the paperweight.

4 Dhevan has a 25 m coil of electrical wire. He cuts off 7 m of wire. Both measurements are correct to the nearest metre. Calculate the upper bound for the amount of wire remaining.

5 Modelling A tennis ball has a mass of 57 g to the nearest gram. During a tennis tournament 32 000 balls are used. Find the upper and lower bounds for the total mass of all the tennis balls used during the tournament. Give your answers in kg.

6 Modelling A path is made from 12 square paving stones laid end to end. Each paving stone has a side of length 0.6 m, correct to 1 decimal place. Calculate

a the largest possible actual length of the path

b the smallest possible actual length of the path.

7 Problem-solving / Real Amy is going on holiday. She has one piece of baggage that weighs 11 kg and two pieces of baggage that each weigh 4 kg, correct to the nearest kg. The airline has a weight limit of 20 kg. Amy says that because 11 + 4 + 4 is 19 she will definitely be within the weight limit.
Work out the upper bound of the total weight of Amy's luggage to explain why she is wrong.

Q1 hint

$$s = \frac{d}{t}$$

Use the upper bound for the distance, and the lower bound for the time.

Q2d hint

To find the greatest possible value for $xy - z$, use the upper bounds for x and y and the lower bound for z.

8 Problem-solving Diya uses this recipe to make fruit punch.

> ### Fruit punch
> 600 ml orange juice
> 400 ml pineapple juice
> 200 ml grape juice
> 750 ml lemonade

She measures her ingredients correct to the nearest 10 ml.
Diya's punch bowl has a capacity of 2 litres, correct to the nearest 100 ml.
Will Diya's punch definitely fit into her punch bowl? Show working to support your answer.

Q8 Strategy hint

Convert the capacity of the bowl into ml, then write down its upper and lower bounds. Make sure you show your working and write a final answer.

Enrichment

1 STEM / Problem-solving This table shows the densities of six different metals.

Metal or alloy	Density, ρ (g/cm³)
Aluminium	2.7
Cadmium	8.6
Lead	11.3
Magnesium	1.7
Tin	7.4
Tungsten	19.2

Each of these solid cuboids is made from one of the six metals.
Work out which metal is used for each cuboid.

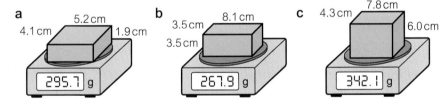

a 5.2 cm 4.1 cm 1.9 cm 295.7 g

b 3.5 cm 8.1 cm 3.5 cm 267.9 g

c 4.3 cm 7.8 cm 6.0 cm 342.1 g

2 STEM The weight of an object is the force due to gravity.
On Earth, weight = mass × 9.8.
A backpack has a mass of 20 kg.
a Work out the weight of the backpack on Earth.
b On Mars, weight = mass × 3.7.
Work out the weight of the backpack on Mars.

Q2b Literacy hint

Weight has a force, so it is measured in newtons.

3 Reflect These strengthen lessons suggested using number lines and formula triangles to help you answer questions.
• Look back at the question with a number line. Did it help you? Explain why.
• Look back at the questions with formula triangles. Did they help you? Explain why.
• In what other subjects have you used triangles to help with formulae?

7 Extend

You will:
- Extend your understanding with problem-solving.

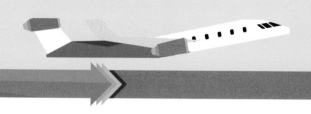

1 Reasoning

  a A circle has a radius of 120 mm, correct to the nearest 10 mm. Calculate the upper and lower bounds for the area of the circle.

  b Another circle has a diameter of 240 mm, correct to the nearest 10 mm. Calculate the upper and lower bounds for the area of this circle.

  c Darrel says, 'The diameter of each circle is the same, but the upper and lower bounds for the area are different.' Write a sentence to explain why.

2 A football pitch must be between 100 yards and 130 yards long, and between 50 yards and 100 yards wide. Write both of these measurements in the form ☐ ± ☐ yards.

> **Q2 hint**
>
> The first number is half-way between the minimum and maximum values.

3 The upper and lower bounds for the weight, x kg, of an elephant are given as $4950 \leqslant x < 5050$.
Work out the degree of accuracy that the elephant was weighed to.

4 Reasoning An oven thermometer records the temperature as 177°C, correct to the nearest °C. Jamie says that the actual temperature, T °C, must be in the range $176.5 \leqslant T \leqslant 177.49$. Is Jamie correct? Give a reason for your answer.

5 Real A skydiver falls at a constant speed of 55 m/s from an altitude of 3700 m. She must open her parachute at least 500 m above the ground. How long can she wait before opening her parachute?

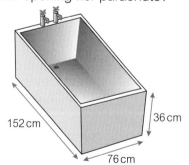

6 Modelling / Problem-solving
This bathtub is filled from a tap with a flow rate of 18 litres per minute. Model the bathtub as a cuboid and estimate the length of time it will take to fill three-quarters of the bathtub.

152 cm   36 cm   76 cm

> **Q6 hint**
>
> 1 litre = ☐ cm³

7 Modelling This bowling ball weighs 16 lb and has a radius of 10.8 cm. Estimate the density of the resin used to make the bowling ball.
Give your answer in g/cm³ to 1 decimal place.

Discussion What assumptions do you have to make as part of your estimate?

10.8 cm

> **Q7 hint**
>
> 2.2 lb ≈ 1 kg

Subject links: Science (Q9, Q11, Q14, Q16)

8 Problem-solving The diagram shows a running track made up of two straight 100 m sections and two semicircular sections with diameter 64 m.

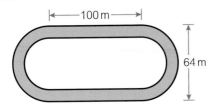

Emma runs around the track at an average speed of 7.2 m/s.
Calculate the length of time taken for her to complete 4 laps.

9 Problem-solving / Reasoning The diagram shows a 900 ml flask containing 350 ml of oil. An iron bar of mass 4.2 kg is placed into the flask. The density of iron is 7.9 g/cm³. Will the flask overflow? Explain your answer.

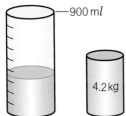

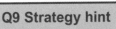

Q9 Strategy hint

Work out the volume of the iron bar. It will displace the same volume of oil when placed in the flask.

10 Modelling / Problem-solving The diagram shows a cone-shaped candle. The candle is made of wax with a density of 0.9 g/cm³. When burning, the candle consumes 2 g of wax per minute. Estimate the length of time it will take for the candle to burn half of its mass.

Q10 hint

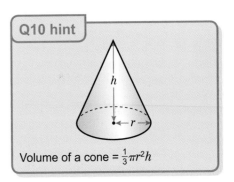

Volume of a cone = $\frac{1}{3}\pi r^2 h$

11 Problem-solving / STEM This solid metal block has a density of 8500 kg/m³.

  a Calculate the mass of the block.

  b Calculate the weight of the block in newtons.

  c The block is upright. Calculate the pressure exerted by the block on the ground.

The block is rotated so one of its longer faces rests on the ground.

  d Calculate the pressure exerted by the block on the ground in this position.

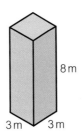

Q11 Literacy hint

The weight of an object is the force due to gravity.
On Earth, weight = mass × 9.8.

12 The measurements on this triangle are correct to the nearest 10 cm.

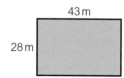

6.2 m   4.3 m

Find the upper and lower bounds for

a the perimeter of the triangle

b the area of the triangle.

13 Reasoning Danni and Ian use a metre wheel to measure a rectangular playground. They record these dimensions, correct to the nearest metre.

43 m

28 m

Ian writes down the area as 1204 m². Danni says, 'The measurements are too inaccurate to give the area correct to the nearest m².'

a Calculate the upper and lower bounds for the area of the playground.

b Do you think Danni is correct? Give a reason for your answer.

Discussion What would be a suitable degree of accuracy to give the area of the playground to?

14 Problem-solving A gold nugget has a mass of 2.4 kg. The density of gold is 19.3 g/cm³. Both values are correct to 1 decimal place. The nugget is melted down and formed into a cube. Calculate the upper and lower bounds for the side length of the cube.

15 Problem-solving Blackpool Tower is 158 m tall to the nearest metre. Baked bean tins are 11 cm tall to the nearest cm. If you stacked 1500 baked bean tins on top of each other, would they definitely reach the top of the tower?

16 Problem-solving Julia uses the formula $s = ut + \frac{1}{2}at^2$ to calculate distance. She measures these quantities correct to 1 decimal place.

$u = 12.2$ $t = 2.0$ $a = 9.8$

Calculate the least possible value of s.

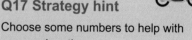

> **Q16 Strategy hint**
> Decide whether to use the upper or lower bound of each variable. You have to use the same choice for t in both places in the formua.

17 Reasoning Identical boxes are loaded onto a lorry. Paula says that if the mass of each box is correct to the nearest kg, then the total mass of the loaded boxes will be correct to the nearest kg. Explain why she is incorrect.

> **Q17 Strategy hint**
> Choose some numbers to help with your explanation.

18 A bag of sugar has a mass of 500 g, to the nearest 10 g.

a Write the absolute error for the mass of the bag in the form 500 g ± ☐

b Calculate the absolute error for the mass of 8 bags of sugar.

One bag of sugar is divided equally between 8 bowls.

c Calculate the absolute error for the mass of sugar in each bowl.

Amrita and Ben want to work out the thickness of a 2p coin. They are both going to measure thicknesses to the nearest mm. Amrita measures one 2p coin and records a thickness of 2 mm. Ben measures a stack of fifteen 2p coins and records a thickness of 28 mm.

1 Write down the upper and lower bounds for the actual thickness of Amrita's coin.

2 Use Ben's measurement to estimate the thickness of one 2p coin.

3 Show working to explain why Ben's method of measuring thickness is more accurate than Amrita's.

4 What could you do to get a more accurate measurement? Try it.

19 Reasoning a, b, c and d are all rounded values. Avnee wants to find the upper bound of $\dfrac{a - b}{c - d}$

For each value used in the expression, write down whether she should use the upper bound or the lower bound.

 20 Problem-solving A rectangular pencil case has sides of length 6.2 cm and 8.5 cm, both correct to 1 decimal place. A pencil is 10 cm long, correct to the nearest cm. Will this pencil definitely fit into the pencil case? Show working to support your answer.

21 Problem-solving A section of fencing is made from 20 posts placed next to each other. Each post is 28 cm wide, correct to the nearest cm, and 1.4 m tall, correct to 1 decimal place. One litre of varnish will cover an area of 14 m². Arya has 600 ml of varnish, correct to the nearest 10 ml. Does Arya definitely have enough varnish to cover the entire section of fencing? Explain.

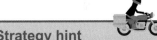
Q21 Strategy hint
Consider the worst-case scenario:
- when the fence posts are as large as possible
- when Arya has as little varnish as possible.

22 In a fairground game, players have to throw a circular hoop over a square wooden block. The hoop has a diameter of 15 cm and the block has a side length of 10 cm. Both measurements are correct to the nearest centimetre. Will the hoop definitely fit over the wooden block? Explain.

23 Reflect Look back at the questions in these extend lessons.
- Write down the question that was the easiest to answer. What made it easy?
- Write down the question that was the most difficult to answer. What made it most difficult?
- Look again at the question you found most difficult. What could you do to make this type of question easier to answer?

Q23 hint
Ask your classmates how they answered this question. Do they have some hints for you?

Reflect

7 Unit test

Log how you did on your Student Progression Chart.

1 The mass of a letter is 52 g to the nearest gram. Write down
  a the upper bound for the mass of the letter
  b the lower bound for the mass of the letter.

2 The mass of a block of cheese is 400 g, to the nearest 10 g.
  Write this in the form □ g ⩽ mass < □ g.

3 A box of matches contains between 46 and 56 matches.
  Write this in the form □ ± □

4 A runner completes a 12-mile course in 1 hour and 36 minutes.
  Calculate his average speed in miles per hour.

5 A speedboat travels 75 km at an average speed of 30 km/h.
  Calculate the time taken in hours and minutes.

6 Convert 5 m/s into km/h.

7 This triangular prism has a mass of 5.2 kg.
  Calculate the density of the material
  used to make the triangular prism.
  Give your answer in g/cm^3 correct
  to 1 decimal place.

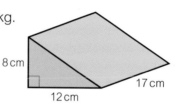

8 The point of a nail is a circle with radius 0.5 mm. The nail is hit with a
  force of 150 N. Calculate the pressure exerted by the point of the nail.
  Give your answer in N/cm^2, correct to the nearest 1000 N/cm^2.

9 The length and width of this rectangle
  have been measured correct to
  1 decimal place. Calculate the lower
  bound for the area of the rectangle.

10 This diagram shows a square of paper. Another square has been cut
   out of the corner. Both measurements are correct to the nearest cm.
   Calculate the upper bound for the area of paper remaining.

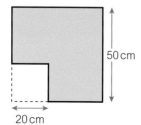

11 A skier travels 85 m in 7 seconds. Both measurements are correct to the nearest whole number. Calculate the upper bound for the average speed of the skier. Give your answer in m/s correct to 2 decimal places.

12 A length of bunting is made by joining together 6 identical flags. Each flag has a length of 40 cm, correct to the nearest 10 cm. Calculate the lower bound for the length of the bunting.

13 A blank CD can store 80 minutes of music, correct to the nearest 10 minutes. Jo estimates that her songs are 3 minutes long to the nearest minute. Can Jo definitely fit 21 songs onto one CD? Explain.

Challenge

14 The diagram shows the dimensions of the Statue of Liberty in New York. All the dimensions are correct to the nearest metre. Work out the maximum possible value of

  a the height of the whole statue from A to D

  b the distance BC from the head of the statue to its feet

  c the distance CD from the top of the head to the top of the torch

  d the ratio of the height of the statue BD to the height of the plinth AB.

15 **Reflect** The title of this unit is 'Accuracy and measures'.
Look back at the questions in this unit.
- Make a list of all the ways you have used accuracy.
- Make a list of all the different types of measures you have used.
- Compare your list with those of your classmates.

Reflect

8.1 Simultaneous equations

You will learn to:
- Solve a pair of simultaneous equations.

Why learn this?
You can solve two equations together to work out the cheapest phone deal.

Fluency
Write an expression for the cost of
- 3 cups of tea at £x each
- 4 cups of coffee at £y each
- 3 teas and 4 coffees.

Explore
Is it better for a business to pay £55 per callout for computer repairs or pay £100 per year and then £38 per callout?

CONFIDENCE

Exercise 8.1

Warm up

1 **Modelling** Write an equation for each of these.
   a 3 bags of soil and 1 plant weigh 75 kg altogether.
   Use x for the weight of a bag of soil and y for the weight of a plant.
   b It costs $44 for 2 adults and 2 children to attend a football game.
   Use x for the price of an adult ticket and y for the price of a child's ticket.
   c 3 boxes of cereal and 2 litres of milk cost £10.49.
   Use x for the cost of a box of cereal and y for the price of a litre of milk.

2 For the equation $2x - 5y = 25$, work out
   a x, when $y = 1$ **b** x, when $y = 4$
   c y, when $x = 5$ **d** y, when $x = 12$

Literacy hint
Solve means work out the values for x and y.

Worked example

Solve the **simultaneous equations** $y = 3x$ and $5x + y = 46$.

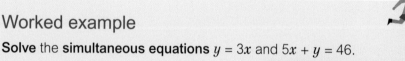

$$5x + y = 46 \quad (1)$$
$$y = 3x \quad (2)$$

Write one equation above the other with the equals sign lined up. Number them (1) and (2).

$$5x + 3x = 46 \quad (1)$$
$$8x = 46$$

Substitute $y = 3$ into equation (1).

$$x = 5.75$$

Simplify and solve.

$$y = 3 \times 5.75$$
$$y = 17.25$$

Substitute the value of x into one equation. Choose the simpler one to solve.

Check:
$$5x + y = 46 \quad (1)$$
$$5 \times 5.75 + 17.25 = 46 \checkmark$$

Check the values in the other equation.

Key point
You can solve two **simultaneous equations** to find the values of two variables.

3 Solve these pairs of simultaneous equations.

    a $3x + y = 15$ **b** $5x + y = 60$ **c** $2x + y = 17$

          $y = 2x$ $y = 3x$ $y = 2x$

    d $x + 3y = 22$ **e** $2x + y = 32$

          $\frac{1}{2}x = y$ $y = 4x$

> **Q3e hint**
>
> Leave your answer as a simplified fraction.

4 **Problem-solving / Modelling** 4 oranges and 1 watermelon cost £6.30. The cost of 1 watermelon is 5 times the cost of 1 orange.

    a How much does 1 orange cost?

    b How much does 1 watermelon cost?

5 **Problem-solving / Modelling** A concert venue holds 720 people with 15 standing rows and 10 seated rows. Each standing row holds twice the number of people as a seated row.

    a How many people are in each standing row?

    b How many people are in each seated row?

6 **Problem-solving / Modelling** It costs 1 adult and 3 children £17.50 to go to the cinema. A child ticket costs half the price of an adult ticket.

    a What is the price of a child ticket?

    b What is the price of an adult ticket?

 7 At the school play, students sold programmes for £4.50 and ice creams for £1.50. They sold twice as many ice creams as programmes. Altogether they made £322.50.

How many programmes and how many ice creams did the students sell?

Worked example

Solve the simultaneous equations $5x + y = 43$ and $x - y = 5$.

$5x + y = 43$ (1)   Write one equation above the other with equals signs lined up. Number them.

$x - y = 5$ (2)

$6x + 0 = 48$ (1) + (2)

$x = 8$ Add equations (1) and (2) together to cancel y. Solve for x.

$8 - y = 5$

$y = 3$ Substitute $x = 8$ into one equation to work out y.

Check:

$5x + y = 43$ (1)   Substitute both values into the other equation to check.

$5 \times 8 + 3 = 43$ ✓

8 Solve these pairs of simultaneous equations.

    a $4x + y = 17$ **b** $3x + y = 20$ **c** $4x - y = 19$

        $3x - y = 11$ $2x - y = 0$ $5x + y = 53$

    d $5y - x = 16$ **e** $6x + 2y = 51$ **f** $2x - 5y = 0$

        $3y + x = 12$ $x - 2y = 5$ $2x + 5y = 20$

Discussion This method of solving simultaneous equations is called the elimination method. Why do you think this is?

9 **Real / Modelling** A boat travels downstream at 6.5 miles per hour. The same boat travels back upstream at 3.5 miles per hour. The speed of the boat in still water is x mph. The speed of the current is y mph.

Downstream: Speed of boat = $x + y$

Upstream: Speed of boat = $x - y$

a Work out the speed of the boat in still water.

b Work out the speed of the current.

10 **Problem-solving / Modelling** The sum of two numbers is 19. The difference between the two numbers is 7. Use a and b to represent the numbers.

a Write two equations linking a and b.

b Solve the simultaneous equations.

11 Solve these pairs of simultaneous equations.

a $7x + y = 45$
$4x + y = 27$

b $5x + 2y = 41$
$3x + 2y = 27$

c $3x + 9y = 66$
$3x + 3y = 30$

d $2x + 7y = 17$
$6x + 7y = 37$

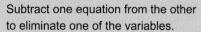

Q11 Strategy hint
Subtract one equation from the other to eliminate one of the variables.

12 **Real** A bike rental company charges a **flat fee** plus an hourly rate. Emma rented a bike for 4 hours and paid £18. Louise rented a bike for 7 hours and paid £25.50.

a How much was the cost per hour to rent a bike?

b How much was the flat fee to rent a bike?

c Michael rents a bike for 2 hours. How much does it cost?

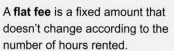

Q12 Literacy hint
A **flat fee** is a fixed amount that doesn't change according to the number of hours rented.

13 **Real** At a water park, 2 adults and 2 children pay £21 for entry. A different group of 2 adults and 5 children pay £30. Work out the cost for 1 adult and the cost for 1 child.

14 **Explore** Is it better for a business to pay £55 per callout for computer repairs or pay £100 per year and then £38 per callout? Is it easier to explore this question now you have completed the lesson? What further information do you need to be able to answer this?

15 **Reflect** In this lesson you have solved simultaneous equations in two different ways:
• substitution
• elimination.

a Write, in your own words, the difference between the two methods.

b Write down a pair of simultaneous equations that can be solved using
• substitution
• elimination.

 Delta 3, Section 8.1

8.2 Using $y = mx + c$

You will learn to:
- Rearrange equations of graphs to find the gradient and y-intercept
- Find the equation of the line between two points.

Why learn this?
The marketing manager of a furniture shop might analyse gradients of graphs of sales figures to predict future trends.

Fluency
What is the equation of this line?

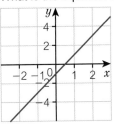

Explore
How do you know which supermarket is increasing their sales the fastest?

Exercise 8.2

1 Draw the graph of $x + 2y = 6$.
Use a coordinate grid from -10 to $+10$ on both axes.

2 a Without drawing the graphs, sort these equations into pairs of parallel lines.

   A $y = \frac{1}{4}x - 1$ **B** $y = -4x + 7$ **C** $y = 4x + 1$

      D $y = -4x + 1$ **E** $y = 4x - 5$ **F** $y = \frac{1}{4}x + 7$

   b Which equations in part **a** give lines that intercept the y-axis in the same place?

   c Write down two pairs of perpendicular lines from part **b**.

3 Make x the subject.

   a $y = x - 9$ **b** $y = 5x$ **c** $y = \frac{1}{3}x$

   d $y = -\dfrac{3x}{4}$ **e** $y = 8 - \dfrac{2x}{5}$ **f** $y = 2(x - 3)$

4 a Draw the graph of $5x + 2y = 10$.
   b Use your graph to write down the gradient and y-intercept.
   c Write the equation of the line as $y = mx + c$.
   d Rearrange $5x + 2y = 10$ to make y the subject.
     What do you notice?

   Discussion How can you find the gradient and y-intercept of the line $3x + y = 7$?

5 Which of these equations are equivalent?
   A $y = 3 - 2x$ **B** $y - 2x = 3$ **C** $y + 2x = 3$
   D $y = 3x - 2$ **E** $y = 2x + 3$ **F** $y - 3x = 2$

Q5 hint
Rearrange the equation to make y the subject.

Warm up

6 a Write each equation in the form $y = mx + c$.

  i $y - 4x = 9$ **ii** $2y - 7x = 3$ **iii** $3y + 11x = 9$ **iv** $\frac{1}{2}y + 4x = 5$

  b Which line has the steepest gradient?

Key point

To compare two lines, write their equations in the form $y = mx + c$.

7 Decide if each pair of lines have the same y-intercept?

  a $y - 4 = 7x$ and $y + 3x = 4$

  b $4x - 2y = 7$ and $y = 4x + 7$

  c $x + y = -1$ and $3x + 5y = -5$

  d $-3x + 6y = 12$ and $10 + 7x = 5y$

8 Decide if each pair of lines are parallel, perpendicular or neither.

  a $y = 3x + 7$ and $3y = 9x - 4$

  b $y = 2x + 5$ and $y = -\frac{1}{2}x + 7$

  c $2y = 3x + 8$ and $3y = 2x + 9$

  d $x = y - 7$ and $5x - 5y = 7$

  e $-x = 4 + y$ and $3x - 4y = 1$

Investigation   Problem-solving

1 Work out the gradients of $3x + 2y = 10$ and $2x - 3y = 6$.
2 Show that the two lines are perpendicular.
3 Repeat steps **1** and **2** for $8x - 10y = 20$ and $10x + 8y = 12$.
4 Write down the equation of a line perpendicular to
  a $5x - 4y = 12$ **b** $2y - 8x = 14$

Worked example

Find the equation of the line that passes through points A(4, 2) and B(9, 17).

$y = mx + c$

At A, $x = 4$ and $y = 2$

$2 = m \times 4 + c$

$2 = 4m + c$

> Points A and B lie on the line, so their coordinates satisfy the equation of the line. Substitute the x- and y-values from point A into $y = mx + c$ and write an equation for the line.

At B, $x = 9$ and $y = 17$.

$17 = m \times 9 + c$

$17 = 9m + c$

> Substitute the x- and y-values from point B into $y = mx + c$.

$2 = 4m + c$ (1)

$17 = 9m + c$ (2)

$15 = 5m$ (2) − (1)

$m = 3$

> Solve the simultaneous equations to find m and c. To eliminate c, subtract equation (1) from equation (2).

$2 = 4 \times 3 + c$

$c = -10$

> Substitute $m = 3$ into equation (1).

Equation of line is $y = 3x - 10$.

> Substitute the values of m and c into $y = mx + c$.

Topic links: Straight-line graphs

9 Find the equation of the line that passes through points C(3, 2) and D(6, 8).

10 Find the equation of the line that passes through points E(8, 3) and F(1, −4).

11 Real / Modelling There is a linear relationship between the price P charged by a cleaning company and the number of hours h spent cleaning. The company charges £60 for 2 hours of cleaning and £99 for 5 hours of cleaning.

   a Copy and complete.

      Two points on the graph $P = mh + c$ are (2, ☐) and (☐, 99).

   b Work out the equation of the line.

   c What does the gradient represent?

   d What does the y-intercept represent?

> **Key point**
>
> A linear relationship can be expressed in the form $y = mx + b$ or $P = mh + c$.

12 Real / Modelling There is a linear relationship between the value V of a car and its age a.
A 5-year-old car is worth £14 000.
The same car is worth £11 400 2 years later.

   a Work out an equation in the form $V = ma + c$.

   b What was the value of the car when it was new?

> **Q12b hint**
>
> What is the age of a new car?

13 Explore How do you know which supermarket is increasing their sales the fastest?
Is it easier to explore this question now you have completed the lesson?
What further information do you need to be able to answer this?

14 Reflect Write down, in your own words, as many facts about straight-line graphs as you can. Compare your facts with your classmates' facts.
Use these words:

   parallel

   perpendicular

   equation

   y-intercept

   gradient

Explore

Reflect

8.3 More simultaneous equations

You will learn to:
- Solve more complex simultaneous equations.

CONFIDENCE

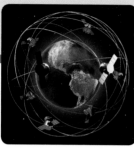

Why learn this?
Most real-life situations require more complex simultaneous equations to model them.

Fluency
Would you add or subtract to solve these pairs of simultaneous equations to solve them?
- $2x + y = 21$ and $5x - y = 9$
- $7y + 3x = 15$ and $7y + 2x = 31$
- $4x + y = 16$ and $6x + y = 11$
- $8y - 3x = 42$ and $3y - 3x = 17$

Explore
In what year will the population of India equal the population of China?

Exercise 8.3

Warm up

1 Solve these pairs of simultaneous equations.

  a $2x + y = 9$ **b** $4x + 3y = 32$
     $3x - y = 6$ $2x + 3y = 28$

2 Multiply each term in the equation $2x + 3y = 6$

  a by 2   **b** by 3   **c** by −2

> **Q2 hint**
> $\Box x + \Box y = \Box$

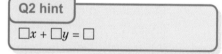

Worked example

Solve the simultaneous equations $3x + y = 18$ and $x + 2y = 11$.

$3x + y = 18$ (1)
$x + 2y = 11$ (2)

> First write the equations one under the other and label them (1) and (2).
> Adding or subtracting will not eliminate either x or y.

$6x + 2y = 36$ (3)
$x + 2y = 11$

> Multiply equation (1) so it has the same y-coefficient as equation (2).

$5x + 0 = 25$ (3) − (2)

$x = 5$

> Subtract one equation from the other.

$3 \times 5 + y = 18$

> Substitute $x = 5$ into equation (1).

$y = 3$

$5 + 2 \times 3 = 11$ ✓

> Check $x = 5$ and $y = 3$ work in equation (2).

Solution is $x = 5$ and $y = 3$

Discussion Does it matter whether you eliminate x or y first?

3 **Reasoning** Archie wants to solve this pair of simultaneous equations.

$$7x + y = 53 \quad (1)$$
$$x + 2y = 28 \quad (2)$$

  a What could he multiply equation (1) by?

  b What could he multiply equation (2) by?

  c Use your answer to part **a** or part **b** to solve the equations.

4 Solve these pairs of simultaneous equations.

  a $3x + y = 25$
    $x + 5y = 27$

  b $4x - y = 3$
    $x + 2y = 21$

  c $x - 6y = -28$
    $5x - y = 5$

  d $x - 2y = 6$
    $11x + y = 89$

Q4 hint

Multiply one of the equations.
Do you need to add or subtract?

5 **Real / Modelling** Two different groups watch a cricket match.

  Group 1: 5 adults and 1 child pay £117.

  Group 2: 1 adult and 3 children pay £43.

  a Write an equation that models group 1.

  b Write an equation that models group 2.

  c Solve the simultaneous equations to work out the cost for

    i 1 adult

    ii 1 child.

6 **Real / Modelling** At a theme park, Ryan goes on the big dipper once and the dodgems 5 times. This costs him £10.50. Jodi goes on the big dipper 7 times and the dodgems once. She pays £22.50.
Work out the cost for one ride on

  a the big dipper

  b the dodgems.

Q6 hint

First set up a pair of simultaneous
equations using the information.

7 **Real / Modelling** A job is divided up into day shifts and night shifts.
The job will take 62 hours in total.
Workers can choose between two plans.

  Plan A: 9 day shifts and 1 night shift.

  Plan B: 1 day shift and 7 night shifts.

  Both plans have exactly the right amount of time for the job.

  How long is

  a a day shift

  b a night shift?

8 Solve these pairs of simultaneous equations.

  a $5x + y = 15$
    $3x + 4y = 26$

  b $3x - y = 18$
    $4x + 2y = 44$

  c $5x - 3y = -6$
    $x + 2y = 17$

  d $9x + 2y = 31$
    $4x - 4y = -40$

9 **Real / Modelling** Two branches of the same company have the same pay structure. Managers are paid £x annually and staff are paid £y annually.

Branch A has 3 managers and 19 staff.
Their total annual wages come to £513500.

Branch B has 1 manager and 5 staff.
Their total annual wages comes to £142500.

Work out the annual wage of a manager and a staff member.

10 **Real / Modelling** Jeff is on an exercise plan.
On day 1, he runs for 30 minutes and then cycles for 20 minutes.
He burns 390 calories.
On day 2, he runs for 40 minutes and then cycles for 10 minutes.
He burns 420 calories.
How many calories does Jeff burn by
a running for 1 minute
b cycling for 1 minute?

11 **Finance** Mohana and Amit both own shares in the same two companies.
Mohana owns 7 shares in company A and 16 shares in company B.
The value of her investment is £106.77.
Amit owns 21 shares in company A and 12 shares in company B.
The value of his investment is £118.35.
What is the value of 1 share in company A and 1 share in company B?

12 **Explore** In what year will the population of India equal the population of China?
Is it easier to explore this question now you have completed the lesson?
What further information do you need to be able to answer this?

13 **Reflect** In this lesson you have solved lots of simultaneous equations from word problems.
What did you find most difficult about these questions?
What did you find easiest?
Write yourself a hint to help you with this sort of problem in the future.

8.4 Graphs and simultaneous equations

You will learn to:
- Solve simultaneous equations by drawing graphs.

CONFIDENCE

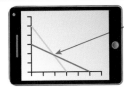

best solution

Why learn this?
Businesses use graphs of equations to find the best solution.

Fluency
$y = x^2 - 6x$
Find y when
- $x = 8$
- $x = 2$
- $x = 6$
- $x = \frac{1}{2}$

Explore
How can you throw two balls across a park and make sure they collide?

Exercise 8.4

Warm up

1 a Copy and complete the table of values for $y = x^2$.

x	−2	−1	0	1	2
y					

b Draw the graph of $y = x^2$ from $x = -2$ to 2.

2 Solve each quadratic equation.

a $x^2 + 6x + 8 = 0$ **b** $x^2 - 3x - 18 = 0$

3 a Plot the graphs of $x - 3y = 4$ and $2x + y = 10$.

b Write down the coordinates of the **points of intersection**.

> **Key point**
>
> The point where two (or more) lines cross is called the **point of intersection**.

Investigation   Problem-solving

1 Solve this pair of simultaneous equations using algebra.

$2x - y = 7$
$x + 2y = 11$

2 Plot the two lines on a coordinate grid.

3 Write down the coordinates of the point of intersection.

Discussion What do you notice about your answers to parts **1** and **3**?

4 Repeat steps **1–3** with these equations.

$4x - y = 5$
$6x + y = 15$

5 Graph this pair of equations.

$3x - 5y = 12$
$3x - 5y = 6$

Discussion What do you notice about the graphs in part **5**?

> **Key point**
>
> You can find the solution to a pair of simultaneous equations by
> - drawing the lines on a coordinate grid
> - finding the point of intersection.

4 Draw graphs to solve these pairs of simultaneous equations.

a $4x - y = 12$
$x + y = 8$

b $2x + y = 14$
$3x - y = 11$

Q4 hint

You could use a graph-plotting package.

5 **Real / Problem-solving** Suhal buys a total of 24 books from a charity shop. Hardbacks cost £2 and paperbacks cost £1.50. He spends £43.50.
Let x represent the number of hardbacks.
Let y represent the number of paperbacks.

a $x + y = \square$

b $2x + 1.5\square = \square$

c On the same set of axes, draw graphs of the equations in parts **a** and **b**.

d How many of each book does Suhal buy?

6 **Real / Modelling** Two families visit a theme park.
The entrance costs are:
Family A: 3 adults and 2 children cost £46.
Family B: 2 adults and 5 children cost £54.50.

a Write down two equations to model these situations.

b Draw a graph to model the simultaneous equations in part **a**.

c Write down the cost of an adult ticket and the cost of a child ticket.

Discussion How accurate are your answers?

7 **Real / Problem-solving / Modelling** 20-second advert slots on television cost £x and 30-second slots cost £y.
During a commercial break, five 20-second adverts and one 30-second advert cost £16 500. Two 20-second adverts and three 30-second adverts cost £17 000.

a Draw a graph to model these situations.

b Work out the cost of one 20-second advert and one 30-second advert.

8 **Real / Problem-solving / Modelling** At a barbecue, in the afternoon 15 burgers and 12 drinks are sold for a total of £84.
In the evening 56 burgers and 48 drinks are sold for a total of £320.

a Draw a graph to model this situation.

b Estimate the cost of 1 burger and 1 drink.

9 Here is a graph of two equations.

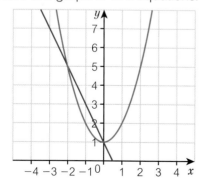

Solve the simultaneous equations.

Topic links: Straight-line graphs

10 For each pair of equations

    i $y = -3x + 5$ and $y = x^2 + 7$

    ii $y = 2x + 3$ and $y = x^2 - 1$

  a plot their graphs

  b write down the coordinates of the point of intersection.

  Discussion What are the solutions to $x^2 + 7 = -3x + 5$?

Q10 hint

First make a table of values from $x = -5$ to $x = 5$.

11 Work out the point of intersection algebraically.

  a $y = x^2 - 6$ and $y = 2x$

  b $y = x^2 - 5$ and $y = 3x$

  c $y = 3x^2$ and $y = 2x + 11$

  d $y = x^2 - 8$ and $y = 2x$

  e $y = 4x^2$ and $y = 2x + 7$

Q11a hint

$y = x^2 - 6$ and $y = 2x$
They both equal y so they equal each other.
$x^2 - 6 = 2x$

12 **Reasoning** Adam is trying to solve this pair of simultaneous equations:

$2y - 6x = 2$ and $y - 3x = 8$

Draw graphs to show why there are no solutions.

13 **Reasoning / Problem-solving** This is the graph of $y = x^2 + 2$.

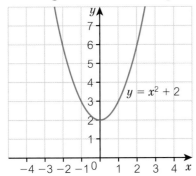

  a Write down the equation of a line that will never intersect $y = x^2 + 2$.

  b Show algebraically that the two graphs will not cross.

14 **Explore** How can you throw two balls across a park and make sure they collide?
Is it easier to explore this question now you have completed the lesson?
What further information do you need to be able to answer this?

15 **Reflect** In this unit you have solved simultaneous equations using algebra and using graphs. Which do prefer? Why?
Compare your preferences with those of your classmates.

Explore

Reflect

MASTER

Check
P184

Strengthen
P186

Extend
P190

Test
P195

8.5 Solving inequalities

You will learn to:
- Solve inequalities by graphing straight lines
- Solve inequalities that involve quadratic graphs.

Why learn this?
Companies use models to work out how to maximise their profits in different situations.

Fluency
What values of x satisfy
- $x > 4$
- $x \leqslant -3$
- $-2 \leqslant x < 5$?

Explore
When is the optimal time to upgrade your phone?

CONFIDENCE

Warm up

Exercise 8.5

1 Draw these graphs. Use a coordinate grid from -10 to $+10$ on both axes.

  a $y = 4x - 1$

  b $2y + x = 8$

  c What are the coordinates of the point where the two lines meet?

2 $x = 4$ and $y = 7$. Choose $<$, $>$ or $=$ to make each statement correct.

  a $5x + 2y \ \square \ 35$

  b $6y - 3x \ \square \ 30$

  c $-2x + 4y \ \square \ 19$

  d $-4x - 5y \ \square \ -40$

Worked example

Show the region $x \leqslant 4$, $y < 2$ on a coordinate grid.

Show clearly the region that **satisfies** both these inequalities.

Literacy hint

When a region **satisfies** an inequality, all the points in it work in the inequality.

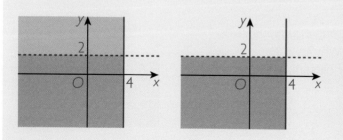

Draw the line $x = 4$.
x can be less than or equal to 4 so use a solid line.
Shade the part of the grid where all x-values are **less than 4**.
Draw the line $y = 2$.
y is strictly less than 2, so use a dashed line.
Shade the part of the grid where all y-values are **less than 2**.
The region that satisfies both inequalities is where all points have x-coordinate $\leqslant 4$ and y-coordinate < 2.
This is where the regions overlap.

3 On a coordinate grid, show the region given by $x > -3$ and $y \leqslant 4$.
Show clearly the region that satisfies both these inequalities.

4 Write down the inequalities that describe each shaded region.

a
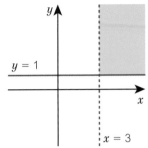

b
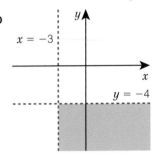

c
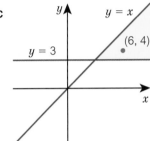

Q4c hint

At the point (6, 4) is $y > x$ or $y < x$?

5 a Plot the line $y = 2x + 3$
b Substitute $x = 0$ and $y = 0$ into $y \geqslant 2x + 3$.
c Does the point (0, 0) satisfy the inequality?
d Shade the region of your graph that satisfies the inequality $y \geqslant 2x + 3$.

Q5d hint

If (0, 0) satisfies the inequality, shade that side of the line.
Otherwise, shade the other side of the line.

6 Draw the line $x - 3y = 12$.
Shade the region of your graph that satisfies the inequality $x - 3y \geqslant 12$.

Q6 hint

Choose a point on one side of your line. Check if it satisfies the inequality.

7 a Write the three inequalities that define each region.

A
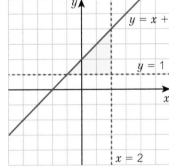

B
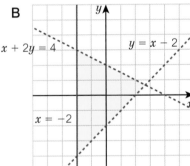

b Does the point (0, 2) satisfy the inequalities in graph A?
c Does the point (2, 1) satisfy the inequalities in graph B?

Investigation   Problem-solving

1 Draw a coordinate grid with axes from −10 to +10.
2 Plot the points (1, 2), (1, 6), (5, 6) and (5, 2) and join them together. What shape is formed?
3 The shape can be formed using four inequalities: $x \geqslant 1$, $y \leqslant 6$, ☐ and ☐.
4 Write down the inequalities that form the rectangle with vertices at (−4, −5), (−4, 3), (7, 3) and (7, −5).
5 What shape is formed by the inequalities $y \leqslant 7$, $y \leqslant 2x + 1$, $y \geqslant 3$, $y \geqslant 2x - 9$?
6 Write down four inequalities that form the shape with vertices (3, 4), (5, 10), (9, 10), (7, 4).

8 a Draw graphs to show the regions satisfied by
$x > 1, y < 5, y \geqslant 3x - 4$.
b Show clearly the region satisfied by all three inequalities.
c Is the point (2, 3) in the region?
d Is the point (3, 2) in the region?
Discussion Mo says that the point (1, 5) is in the region.
Explain why Mo is wrong.

9 A group of adults a and children c are planning a theatre visit.
At most 10 people will be going. Adult tickets cost £14 and child
tickets cost £6. The group has a total of £84 to spend.
a Write down two inequalities to model this situation.
b Jack says that $a \geqslant 0$ and $c \geqslant 0$. Explain why Jack is correct.
c Draw the inequalities on a coordinate grid with a on the horizontal
axis and c on the vertical axis.
d Write down three coordinate pairs that are in the region.
Discussion Which coordinate pair shows the **optimal solution**?

Q9 Literacy hint

The **optimal solution** is the solution
that best fits the situation.

10 a Draw the graph of $y = x^2 + 3$.
b Does the point (0, 0) satisfy $y \geqslant x^2 + 3$?
c Shade all the points where $y \geqslant x^2 + 3$.

11 a Draw the graph of $y = x^2 - 5$.
b On the same axes, draw the graph of $y = 2x + 3$.
c Write down the coordinates of the points of intersection of
$y = x^2 - 5$ and $y = 2x + 3$.
d Shade the region that satisfies $y \geqslant x^2 - 5$ and $y \leqslant 2x + 3$.

12 Explore When is the optimal time to upgrade your phone?
Is it easier to explore this question now you have completed the
lesson?
What further information do you need to be able to answer this?

13 Reflect Liz says, 'To show an inequality like $x < 2$, you just need a
number line, but to show an inequality like $y + 3 < x$, you need a
coordinate grid.'
Write down one more difference and one similarity between the two
types of inequalities.

8 Check up

Log how you did on your Student Progression Chart.

Simultaneous equations

1 Solve these equations.
$$5x + y = 72$$
$$y = 3x$$

2 On a trip to an ice-skating rink, Wendy buys 1 adult ticket and 5 child tickets. This costs her £31.50. Adult tickets are twice the price of child tickets.
  a Write two equations. Use y for price of adult tickets and x for price of child tickets.
  b Work out the cost of
    i 1 adult ticket
    ii 1 child ticket.

3 Solve these equations.
$$8x + y = 51$$
$$x - y = 3$$

4 The sum of two numbers is 21 and their difference is 7.
  Let x and y represent the numbers.
  a Write down two equations to model this situation.
  b Solve the equations to find the values of x and y.

5 Solve these equations.
$$7x + y = 22$$
$$x + y = 4$$

6 A gardener charges a fixed callout fee as well as an hourly rate. He charges £70 for 3 hours' work and £126 for 7 hours' work. Write an equation in the form $y = mx + c$, where y is the charge and x is the time.

7 Solve these equations.
$$8x + y = 42$$
$$x + 5y = 15$$

Graphs

8 a Rearrange each equation in the form $y = mx + c$.
   b Write the gradient and the y-intercept.
      i $y - 3x = -7$
      ii $3x + 2y = 6$
      iii $3y + \frac{1}{2}x = 5$

9 Decide if each pair of lines are parallel, perpendicular or neither.
  a $y = 2x - 5$ and $2y = 4x + 9$
  b $-x = 8 + 2y$ and $5x - 3y = 7$
  c $y = -3x + 6$ and $y = \frac{1}{3}x - 2$

10 Draw graphs to solve these simultaneous equations.
  $4x + y = 8$
  $x - y = 2$

11 Work out the equation of the line joining points A(2, 9) and B(6, 1).

Inequalities

12 Write down the inequalities that define each region.

a 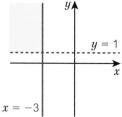 **b** 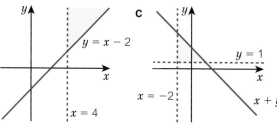 **c**

13 Sketch a graph and shade the region $x \geqslant -2$ and $y < 4$.

14 How sure are you of your answers? Were you mostly

  🙁 Just guessing   😐 Feeling doubtful   🙂 Confident

  What next? Use your results to decide whether to strengthen or extend your learning.

Challenge

15 The following clues reveal the location of some buried treasure on an island.
  Draw a 10 × 10 grid and follow the clues.
  The treasure is *not* in the regions
  a $y > 5$
  b $y < x - 5$
  c $x + y < -6$
  d $y < 2$
  e $2y - x < 10$
  f $x < -4$
  Write a description of the region that contains the treasure.

Q15a hint

The treasure is not in the region $y > 5$.
Draw a dotted line $y = 5$.
Shade the area where $y > 5$.

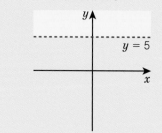

Reflect

Master
P169

Check
P184

STRENGTHEN

Extend
P190

Test
P195

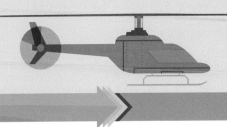

8 Strengthen

You will:
• Strengthen your understanding with practice.

Simultaneous equations

1 Find the values of x and y that satisfy these pairs of equations.

a $4x + y = 24$
$y = 2x$

b $2x + y = 30$
$y = 4x$

c $x + 7y = 66$
$\frac{1}{4}x = y$

d $x + 4y = 18$
$\frac{1}{2}x = y$

 2 Real / Modelling On a trip to the cinema, Ian buys 1 adult ticket and 5 child tickets. This costs him £28. Adult tickets cost 3 times as much as child tickets.

    a Write an equation that shows what Ian paid.

    b Write an equation that shows the relationship between adult and child tickets.

    c Use your equations to find the cost of 1 adult and 1 child ticket.

3 Real / Modelling On a trip to the zoo, a group spends £99 on 3 adult tickets and 5 child tickets.
Adult tickets are twice the price of child tickets.
What is the price of 1 adult ticket and 1 child ticket?

4 $8x + y = 49$ and $3x - y = 6$

    a Add the two equations together.

    b What happens to the value of y? Explain.

    c Solve your equation to work out x.

    d Using the value of x, find the value of y.

5 Find the values of x and y that satisfy these pairs of equations.

    a $6x + y = 34$ and $4x - y = 16$

    b $5x + y = 44$ and $3x - y = 12$

6 Modelling Two numbers have a sum of 46 and a difference of 20.

    a Write two equations to model this situation.

    b Solve the simultaneous equations to work out the two numbers.

7 $5x + 2y = 58$ and $3x + 2y = 42$ are a pair of simultaneous equations.

    a Subtract one equation from the other.

    b What happens to the value of y? Explain.

    c Solve your equation to work out x.

    d Using the value of x, find the value of y.

Q1a hint

$4x + y = 24$
$y = 2x$ so $4x + 2x = 24$

Q1c hint

$\frac{1}{4}x = y$, so $x = \square$

Q2a hint

Choose two letters to represent the cost of each ticket.

Q4a hint

$\begin{aligned} 8x + y &= 49 \\ + \quad 3x - y &= 6 \end{aligned}$

Q5 hint

Use the same strategy as in Q4. Remember to add all like terms together.

Q6 hint

$x + y = \square$
$x - y = \square$

Q7a hint

$\begin{aligned} 5x + 2y &= 58 \\ - \quad 3x + 2y &= 42 \end{aligned}$

8 Solve these equations.
  a $6x + y = 13$ and $4x + y = 9$
  b $x + 3y = 8$ and $x + 9y = 20$

9 Solve these equations.
  a $4x + y = 28$ and $2x - y = 2$
  b $2x + y = 2$ and $y = -3x$
  c $7x + y = 36$ and $2x + y = 11$

Q9 hint

For each pair of equations, which is the best method? The method used in Q1, Q4 or Q7?

10 A plumber charges a flat fee x plus an hourly rate y.
She charges £101 for 2 hours and £193 for 6 hours.
Work out her flat fee and her hourly rate.

Q10 hint

$x + \square y = 101$
$x + \square y = 193$

11 A fairground charges an entrance fee and then a fee per ride.
Emily goes on 18 rides and pays a total of £15.10.
Nicola goes on 7 rides and pays a total of £10.15.
What is the entrance fee and what is the fee per ride?

Q11 hint

Write £15.10 as 1510p.

12 Mustafa finds the equation of the line between points (1, 3) and (7, 15).
  a Copy and complete:

  At (1, 3), $x = \square$ and $y = \square$.

  Substituted into $y = mx + c$

  $\square = \square m + c$ (1)

  b Write another equation using the point (7, 15).
  Label the equation (2).
  c Solve the simultaneous equations to work out m and c.
  d Write the equation of the line.

13 Work out the equation of the line between:
  a (4, 9) and (6, 17)
  b (3, 10), and (6, 1).

Q13 hint

Substitute each pair of coordinates into $y = mx + c$.

14 Real / Problem-solving 17 units of electricity cost £8.06 and 23 units of electricity cost £9.14
Find a linear equation that connects the cost C and the units u of electricity.

Q14 hint

Two points on the line would be (17, £8.06) and (23, £9.14).
Write £8.06 and £9.14 in pence.

15 Solve these equations.
  a $5x + y = 21$
  $x + 4y = 8$
  Multiply all the terms in the first equation by 4.
  Then subtract one equation from the other and solve.
  b Solve the pair of simultaneous equations in part **a** again. This time multiply all the terms in the second equation by 5. Then subtract one equation from the other and solve.

16 Solve these equations.
  a $6x + y = 28$ **b** $5x - y = 4$ **c** $3x + y = 15$
  $x + 3y = 33$ $x + 3y = 4$ $x - 2y = -9$

Q16 hint

Which is the better method? Adding or subtracting the equations?

17 Real / Problem-solving Six crates and 5 boxes weigh 38.5 kg.
Four crates and 1 box weigh 20.3 kg.
What is the weight of 1 crate and the weight of 1 box?

Q17 hint

First construct a pair of simultaneous equations.

Graphs

1 Write each equation in the form $y = mx + c$.

  a $y - 4x = 5$

  b $y - 3x = 7$

  c $-2x + y = 9$

Q1 hint

Rearrange the equation to make y the subject.

2 a Write each equation in the form $y = mx + c$.

    i $2y - 6x = 8$

    ii $2y + 7x = 5$

    iii $7y + 2x = 5$

    iv $3y - 5x = 7$

    v $\frac{1}{2}y - 2x = 3$

  b Write down the gradient and the y-intercept for each equation.

Q2b hint

In the form $y = mx + c$, m is the gradient and c is the y-intercept.

3 For the equation $3x - 4y = 12$

  a What is the value of x when $y = 0$?

  b Copy and complete: The graph crosses the x-axis at ($\Box$, 0).

  c What is the value of y when $x = 0$?

  d Copy and complete: The graph crosses the y-axis at (0, $\Box$).

  e Draw suitable axes and plot the points in parts **b** and **d**.

  f Draw the graph of $3x - 4y = 12$.

Q3a hint

When $y = 0$, $3x - 4 \times 0 = 12$.
So, $3x = 12$, $x = \Box$.

4 a Draw the graph of $y = x + 2$.

  b On the same axes, draw the graph of $y = 5$.

  c Where the two graphs cross, label this the 'point of intersection'.

  d Write down the coordinates of the point of intersection.

Q4a hint

Follow the method in Q2.

5 Draw graphs to solve these simultaneous equations.

  a $y = 2x + 1$

    $x = 3$

  b $y = x - 4$

    $x + y = 2$

  c $2x - 3y = 6$

    $x + y = 8$

Q5 hint

Plot them on the same coordinate grid. Then write down the coordinates of their point of intersection.

Inequalities

1 a Sketch a coordinate grid and draw the line $y = 3$.

  b On your sketch graph shade the region $y \leqslant 3$.

2 Draw a sketch of the region defined by each inequality.

  a $y < 2$

  b $x \geqslant 4$

  c $y > -2$

  d $x \leqslant -1$

Q1b hint

Mark three points with coordinates where $y \leqslant 3$, e.g. (−1, 0), (0, 2), (1, 1). Shade the region where these points lie.

3 Write down the inequalities that define each region.

a region A

b region B

c region C

d region D

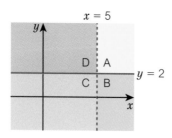

Q3 hint

Put a point in region A. Does it have:

• x coordinate $x > 5$ or $x < 5$
  ($>$ or $<$ because $x = 5$ is a dotted line)

• y coordinate $y \geqslant 2$ or $y \leqslant 2$
  ($\geqslant$ or $\leqslant$ because $y = 2$ is a solid line)?

4 Sketch a graph and show the region $x < -3$ and $y \geqslant 2$.

5 The graph shows the line with equation $y = 2x - 3$.

a Copy the graph.

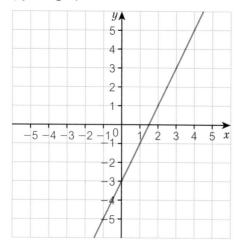

b Shade the region where $y \geqslant 2x - 3$.

Q5b hint

Is $y > 2x - 3$ likely to be above or below the line?

6 **a** Draw the graphs of $y = 3x + 1$ and $3x + 2y = 12$.

b Shade the region where $y \leqslant 3x + 1$.

c Shade the region where $3x + 2y \leqslant 12$.

d Shade the region where $y \leqslant 3x + 1$ and $2x + 3y \leqslant 12$.

Q6a hint

Rearrange in the form $y = mx + c$.

Q6c hint

Is the region $y < 3x + 1$ above or below the line?

Enrichment

1 **a** Write three pairs of simultaneous equations with solutions $x = 3$ and $y = 4$. Solve them to check you are correct.

b Choose any two of your equations in part **a**.
Draw the graphs of the equations and shade a region.
Write the inequalities that define the region.

2 **Reflect** Jazmin says, 'When I don't understand a question with a graph I choose a point on the graph and ask, "What do these coordinates tell me?"'
Neil says, 'When I've solved simultaneous equations I always substitute the solutions into the equations to check.'
Olivia says, 'When I'm stuck on an inequality question I choose some numbers and ask, "Do these satisfy the inequality?"'
Look back at a question you found difficult. Use one of these methods to help you with the question.
Write down what methods you use when you get stuck.

Master
P169

Check
P184

Strengthen
P186

EXTEND

Test
P195

8 Extend

You will:
* Extend your understanding with problem-solving.

1 Find the values of x and y that satisfy these pairs of equations.

   a $8x + y = -24$
           $y = -2x$

   b $4x - y = -20$
          $y = -x$

Q1 hint

Watch out for multiplying and dividing with positives and negatives.

2 Sketch graphs and shade the region where

   a $y \geqslant 2x - 5$ and $y < 7$

   b $4x + 5y < 20$ and $3x - 2y < 18$.

3 Work out the equation of the line between the points
$(-7, -4)$ and $(-3, -18)$.

4 Line AB is perpendicular to line CD.

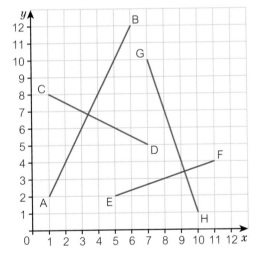

   a Work out the gradient of line AB.

   b Work out the gradient of line CD.

   c Multiply the gradients of the two lines together.
   Line EF is perpendicular to line GH.

   d Repeat parts **a** to **c** for this pair of lines.

   e Copy and complete:
      When two lines are perpendicular, their gradients multiply to □.

5 Decide whether these lines are perpendicular.

   a $y = 5x - 4$ and $5y = x - 1$

   b $3y + 2x = 4$ and $2y - 3x = 6$

   c $y - 4x - 9 = 0$ and $4y = 2 - x$

   d $x = 4$ and $y = 2$

Q5 hint

Rearrange each equation so it is in the form $y = mx + c$.

6 Look at this pair of equations.

$$2x + 2y = 20 \quad (1)$$
$$5x + 3y = 44 \quad (2)$$

  a Explain why $x + y = 10$.
  b What is the value of $3x + 3y$?
  c Use your answer to part **b** to work out the value of $2x$.
  d Find the values of x and y that satisfy the pair of equations.
  e Use a similar method to solve

$$3x + 3y = 36$$
$$2x + 5y = 27$$

7 **Real / Modelling** A camp site charges for entrance and then for each night of camping.
The Walter family paid £343 for 9 nights of camping.
The Ali family paid £235 for 6 nights of camping.
Let x represent the entrance fee and y represent the cost per night.
  a Write down an equation to model the Walter family's charge.
  b Write down an equation to model the Ali family's charge.
  c Work out the cost of one night.
  d Work out the entrance fee.

8 Solve these equations.
  a $7x - 2y = 22$
     $3x + y = 15$
  b $5x + y = 12$
     $11x - 3y = 16$

9 **a** Draw a graph of $y = 2x^2 - 5x - 3$.
  b Draw a graph of $y = 3x - 3$.
  c Shade the region where $y \leqslant 2x^2 - 5x - 3$ and $y \geqslant 3x - 3$.

Q9 hint

Draw a table of values for x from -5 to 5.
Work out each y-value.

10 Draw the following inequalities on the same grid.
  a $y > 2x - 3$
  b $y < \frac{1}{2}x + 3$
  c $x + y > 6$
  d x and y are integers. What is the only point that satisfies all three inequalities?

Q10 hint

Use x- and y-axes from -8 to 8.

11 Write down the inequalities that define each shaded region.

  a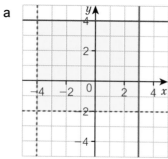
  b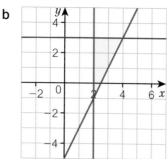
  c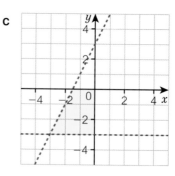

12 **a** On the same axes draw each pair of graphs.
  b Write down the coordinates of the points of intersection.

    i $y = x^2 + 2x - 7$
       $y = 3x - 1$
    ii $y = 2x^2 + x - 1$
        $y = 4x + 1$
    iii $y = 3x^2 + x + 1$
         $y = 2x + 3$

  Discussion Are your answers to part **b** always exact? Explain.
  c Use algebra to solve each pair of simultaneous equations.
  d Does solving algebraically or graphically give more exact answers?

Q11c hint

What line bounds the region to the right? $x = \square$

13 For this pair of simultaneous equations

$$5x + 2y = 23 \quad (1)$$
$$3x + 7y = 37 \quad (2)$$

   a multiply equation (1) by 3. Label it (3)

   b multiply equation (2) by 5. Label it (4)

   c work out equation (4) – equation (3)

   d work out the value of x and y.

Harry suggests starting this question by first multiplying equation (1) by 7 and equation (2) by 2.

Discussion Will Harry's method work? Explain.

14 For this pair of simultaneous equations

$$5x + 4y = 91 \quad (1)$$
$$4x - 3y = 48 \quad (2)$$

   a solve the equations using method A

   b solve the equations using method B.

Method A	Method B
• (1) × 4. Label it (3)	• (1) × 3. Label it (5)
• (2) × 5. Label it (4)	• (2) × 4. Label it (6)
• (3) − (4)	• (5) + (6)

Discussion Which method did you prefer? Why?

15 Find the values of x and y that satisfy these pairs of equations.

   a $4x - 3y = 18$
      $3x + 7y = 32$

   b $2x + 3y = 37$
      $5x - 2y = 7$

   c $8x - 3y = 3$
      $5x + 2y = 29$

   d $3x + 5y = -20$
      $2x - 3y = 12$

> **Q15 hint**
> Use one of the methods from Q14.

16 Real / Modelling 3 adults and 2 children attend an exhibition and pay £70.

5 adults and 3 children attend the same exhibition and pay £113.50.

   a Write two equations to model this situation.

   b Solve the equations to find the price of an adult ticket and the price of a child ticket.

   c A family of 2 adults and 5 children go to the same exhbition. How much do they pay?

> **Q17 hint**
> First, convert the money from pounds to pence.

17 Real / Modelling One week Grace uses her mobile phone to send 17 text messages and make 8 minutes of calls. This costs her £2.07. The next week she sends 28 text messages and makes 24 minutes of calls. This costs her £4.60.

How much does the phone company charge for each text message and each minute of calling?

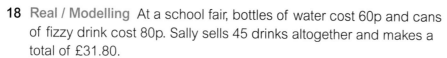

18 **Real / Modelling** At a school fair, bottles of water cost 60p and cans of fizzy drink cost 80p. Sally sells 45 drinks altogether and makes a total of £31.80.
   a Write down an equation to model the number of drinks sold.
   b Write down an equation to model the total money taken.
   c Draw the graphs on suitable axes.
   d How many bottles of water and how many cans of fizzy drink did Sally sell?

19 On the same axes draw the graphs of
   a $2y + 3x = 12$ and $4y + 6x = 24$
   b $2x + 5y = 10$ and $2x + 5y = 20$
   Discussion What do you notice about these lines? How many solutions are there to each pair of simultaneous equations? What happens when algebra is used to solve the simultaneous equations?

> **Key point**
>
> Simultaneous equations can have **no solutions**, **one solution** or **infinitely many solutions**.
>
>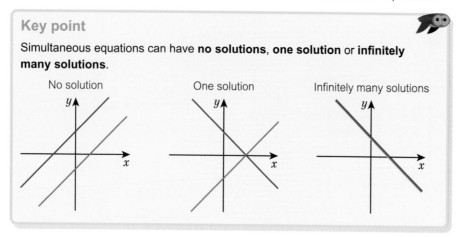
>
> No solution   One solution   Infinitely many solutions

20 **Reasoning** Use algebra to decide whether these pairs of equations have **no solution**, **one solution** or **infinitely many solutions**. If possible, find the values of x and y that satisfy these pairs of equations.
   a $x - y = 3$
      $3x - y = -5$
   b $5x + y = 13$
      $5x - y = 7$
   c $4x + 5y = 20$
      $8x + 10y = 40$
   d $2x - 6y = 4$
      $3x - 9y = 2$
   e $5x + 3y = -9$
      $2x - 4y = 12$

21 **Real / Modelling** At a barbecue, students sell burgers and hot dogs to raise money.
In the morning, they sell 16 burgers and 30 hot dogs for £108.
In the afternoon, they sell 24 burgers and 45 hot dogs for £162.
Work out the cost of 1 burger and the cost of 1 hot dog.

22 **Problem-solving** Use simultaneous equations to work out the value of x and y.

   a
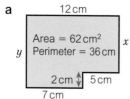

   b
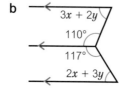

> **Q22 hint**
>
> Use the information to form a pair of simultaneous equations.
> Then solve the equations to find x and y.

23 For each of the following questions
  a write down a pair of simultaneous equations that models the situation
  b solve the equations to find the value of each number.
  i The sum of two numbers is 65. One number is 4 times the value of the other number.
  ii Two numbers have a sum of 8 and a difference of 20.
  iii Two numbers have a sum of 51. One of the numbers is 19 more than the other.

24 **Finance** The difference in value between share A and share B is £27.
  Share A increases threefold and share B increases twofold.
  The difference in value is now £119.
  Work out the value of share A and share B.

25 Solve these simultaneous equations using substitution.

  a $3x + y = 14$
     $y = x + 2$
  b $6x - y = 26$
     $y = x + 2$
  c $3y + 2x = 49$
     $x = y + 7$

Q25a hint

Replace the y term in the first equation with $x + 2$.
You are substituting $x + 2$ for y.

Investigation   Reasoning

1 Show that when $x = 5$ and $y = 0$, $x^2 + y^2 = 25$.
2 Show that when $x = -4$ and $y = 3$, $x^2 + y^2 = 25$.
3 Write down some other pairs of coordinates where $x^2 + y^2 = 25$.
4 Plot the points on coordinate axes and draw the graph of $x^2 + y^2 = 25$.
5 Copy and complete: The graph is a ☐ with a ☐ of 5 and a ☐ at (0, 0).
6 Pick a point within the line. At this point is $x^2 + y^2 < 25$ or is $x^2 + y^2 > 25$?
7 Shade the region where $x^2 + y^2 \leq 25$.
8 Sketch the graph of $x^2 + y^2 = 9$ and shade the region $x^2 + y^2 \geq 9$.

---

26 **Reflect** Copy and complete this sentence in at least three different ways:
  'When I am given a mathematics problem to solve, this is what I do ...'
  Compare your sentences with those of your classmates.

8 Unit test

Log how you did on your Student Progression Chart.

1 Write these equations in the form $y = mx + c$.

a $y - 2x = 11$ **b** $y + \frac{1}{2}x = 7$

2 For each equation write

a the gradient

b the y-intercept.

     i $y = 3x + 7$

     ii $y = \frac{1}{4}x - 1$

3 Find the values of x and y that satisfy these pairs of equations.

a $9x + y = 48$ **b** $x + 5y = 35$

     $y = 3x$ $x = 2y$

4 The sum of two numbers is 9. One of the numbers is 5 times the other. Work out the value of both numbers.

5 Draw graphs to solve this pair of simultaneous equations.

$$y = 3x + 2$$
$$y = 6x - 1$$

6 Find the values of x and y that satisfy these pairs of equations.

a $3x + y = 40$ **b** $7x + 3y = 63$

     $x - y = 8$ $8x - 3y = 27$

7 Work out the equation of the line between points (4, 6) and (8, 18).

8 a Write each of these equations in the form $y = mx + c$.

     i $3y = 2x + 9$

     ii $4y - 10x = 24$

     iii $3y - 2x = 18$

b Which lines have the same gradient?

c Which lines have the same y-intercept?

9 Write down the inequalities that describe each shaded region.

a 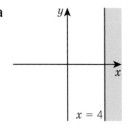   **b** 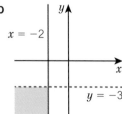   **c** 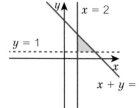   **d**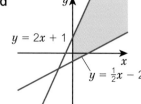

10 a On the same axes, draw the graphs of $2x - 3y = 15$ and $y = -2x + 3$.

b Shade the region that is defined by $2x - 3y \leqslant 15$ and $y \leqslant -2x + 3$.

11 Find the values of x and y that satisfy these pairs of equations.

  a $x + 7y = 66$
    $x + 4y = 39$

  b $6x + 5y = 47$
    $2x + 5y = 39$

12 A fairground charges for entrance and then for each ride.
  Sam went on 14 rides and spent a total of £36.
  Caroline went on 5 rides and spent a total of £22.50.
  Let x represent the cost per ride and y represent the entrance fee.

  a Write an equation for Sam.

  b Write an equation for Caroline.

  c Find the values of x and y that satisfy these pairs of equations.

13 Find the values of x and y that satisfy these pairs of equations.

  a $4x + y = 41$
    $x + 6y = 39$

  b $6x - y = 11$
    $x + 2y = 17$

14 At a school stall, winners could choose between a bouncy ball
  worth 40p and a yo-yo worth 50p. 80 people won and the stall gave
  out £33.50 in prizes.

  a Write an equation that models the number of winners.

  b Write an equation that models the amount of money, in pence,
    given out in prizes.

  c Plot these equations on a coordinate grid with x and y from
    0 to 100.

  d Use your graph to work out how many bouncy balls and how many
    yo-yos were won.

15 a Draw the graphs of $y = x^2 + 3x + 5$ and $y = 4x + 7$ on
    coordinate axes.

  b Write down the coordinates of the points of intersection.

Challenge

16 Use equations and inequalities to describe how this face
  can be drawn on a coordinate grid.

  a Write the equations of the four lines that make the
    outline of the face.

  b Write down four inequalities that describe the mouth.

  c Write down three inequalities that describe the nose.

  d Write down four inequalities that describe the left eye.

  e Write down four inequalities that describe the right eye.

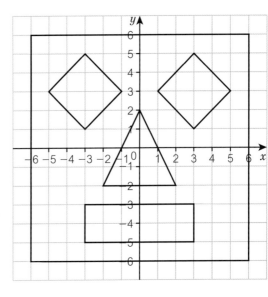

17 Reflect Look back at the questions you answered in this test.

  a Which one are you most confident that you have answered
    correctly? What makes you feel confident?

  b Which one are you least confident that you have answered
    correctly? Why?

  c Discuss the question you feel least confident about with a
    classmate or your teacher. How does discussing it make you feel?

9.1 The tangent ratio

You will learn to:
- Use conventions for naming sides of a right-angled triangle
- Work out the tangent of any angle
- Use the tangent ratio to work out an unknown side of a right-angled triangle.

CONFIDENCE

Why learn this?
Trigonometry is used by engineers to build bridges.

Fluency
In each right-angled triangle, which side is the hypotenuse?

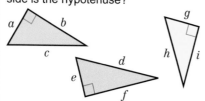

Explore
How does an architect use trigonometry to design the roof of a building?

Exercise 9.1

Warm up

1 Round these numbers to 1 decimal place.

   a 4.56   **b** 8.476

   c 8.476   **d** 0.465

2 Use your calculator to write each fraction as a decimal. Give your answers to 1 decimal place.

   a $\frac{4}{7}$ **b** $\frac{2}{11}$ **c** $\frac{2}{3}$ **d** $\frac{4}{13}$

3 Rearrange each formula to make P the subject.

   a $10 = \frac{P}{2}$ **b** $2 = \frac{P}{3}$

   c $3 = \frac{P}{T}$ **d** $2 = \frac{4}{P}$

4 In each triangle which side is

   a the **hypotenuse**

   b the **opposite** side to angle θ

   c the **adjacent** side to angle θ?

   i   **ii**   **iii**   **iv**   **v**

> **Key point**
>
> The side opposite the chosen angle (angle θ in this diagram) is called the **opposite** side. The side next to θ is called the **adjacent** side.
>
>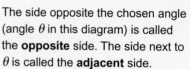

Investigation

1   Draw these triangles accurately using a ruler and protractor.

a
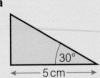
30°
←—5 cm—→

b
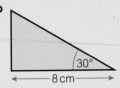
30°
←——8 cm——→

c
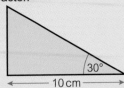
30°
←——— 10 cm ———→

2   Explain why all the triangles are similar.
3   Label the opposite side to 30° 'opp' and the adjacent side to 30° 'adj'.
4   Measure the opposite sides and the adjacent sides.
5   Copy and complete this table.

Triangle	Opposite length	Adjacent length	$\dfrac{\text{opposite}}{\text{adjacent}}$ (1 d.p.)
a			
b			
c			

6   a   What patterns do you notice in your table?
   b   What do you think will happen for other right-angled triangles with an angle of 30°?
   c   Test your hypothesis by drawing some more right-angled triangles with an angle of 30°.
7   Repeat with an angle of 50° instead of 30°.
Discussion   What does this tell you about the ratio of the sides of similar triangles?

5   Use your calculator to find, correct to 1 d.p.
   a   tan 35°   b   tan 54°   c   tan 72°

6   Write **tan θ** as a fraction for each triangle.

a
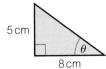
5 cm

θ
8 cm

b
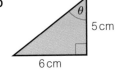
θ
5 cm
6 cm

c

4 cm
θ
6 cm

Discussion   Use your calculator to find tan 90°.
Draw a diagram to explain why this happens.

> **Key point**
>
> The ratio of the opposite side to the adjacent side is called the **tangent** of the angle.
> The tangent of angle θ is written as **tan θ**.
> $$\tan \theta = \frac{\text{opposite}}{\text{adjacent}}$$

Worked example

Use the **tangent** ratio to work out the value of x, correct to 1 d.p.

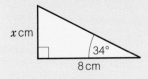
x cm
34°
8 cm

$\tan \theta = \dfrac{\text{opposite}}{\text{adjacent}}$ — Write the tangent ratio.

opposite = x — Identify the opposite and adjacent sides.
adjacent = 8
$\theta = 34°$

$\tan 34° = \dfrac{x}{8}$ — Substitute the sides and angle into the equation.

$8 \times \tan 34° = x$ — Rearrange to make x the subject.
Use your calculator to work out 8 × tan 34°.

$x = 5.4$ cm (to 1 d.p.)

7 Work out the value of x, correct to 1 d.p.

a
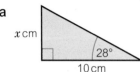
x cm
28°
10 cm

b
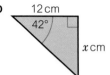
12 cm
42°
x cm

c

36°
x cm
23 cm

d
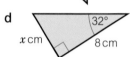
32°
x cm
8 cm

8 Work out the value of x, correct to 1 d.p.

a
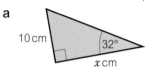
10 cm
32°
x cm

b
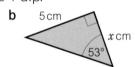
5 cm
x cm
53°

c
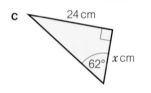
24 cm
62°
x cm

d
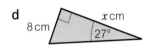
x cm
8 cm
27°

Q8a hint

$\tan \theta = \dfrac{\text{opp}}{\text{adj}}$

$\tan 32° = \dfrac{10}{x}$

Rearrange the formula to make x the subject.

9 Real / Modelling An aircraft is landing.
Its descent makes an angle of 10° with the ground and its horizontal distance from landing is 4000 m.
Calculate the vertical height of the aircraft above the ground.

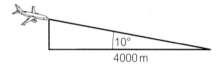
10°
4000 m

10 Problem-solving Calculate the height of this isosceles triangle.

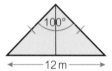
100°
12 m

11 Explore How does an architect use trigonometry to design the roof of a building?
Is it easier to explore this question now you have completed the lesson? What further information do you need to be able to answer this?

12 Reflect Look back at the questions in this lesson.
Which other areas of mathematics do you need to use when working with tangents?

Explore

Reflect

9.2 The sine ratio

You will learn to:
- Work out the sine of any angle
- Use the sine ratio to work out an unknown side of a right-angled triangle.

Why learn this?
Trigonometry is used in cartography – the making of maps.

Fluency
Write these fractions as decimals.
Round each number to 1 d.p.

- $\frac{5}{12}$
- $\frac{4}{11}$
- $\frac{3}{7}$
- $\frac{9}{17}$

Explore
How can you measure the height of a kite from the ground?

Exercise 9.2

1 Copy these triangles.
Label the hypotenuse and the sides opposite and adjacent to angle θ.

a   b   c

2 Rearrange each formula to make H the subject.

   a $5 = \dfrac{H}{3}$ **b** $9 = \dfrac{H}{2}$ **c** $6 = \dfrac{3}{H}$ **d** $3 = \dfrac{9}{H}$

Investigation   **Reasoning**

1 Draw these triangles accurately using a ruler and protractor.

   a   **b**   **c**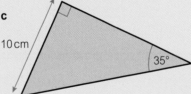

2 Label the hypotenuse.
3 Label the opposite side to 35° 'opp' and the adjacent side to 35° 'adj'.
4 Measure the opposite sides and the hypotenuse.
5 Copy and complete this table.

Triangle	Opposite length	Hypotenuse length	$\dfrac{\text{opposite}}{\text{hypotenuse}}$ (1 d.p.)
a			
b			
c			

6   **a** What patterns do you notice in your table?
    b What do you think will happen for other right-angled triangles with an angle of 35°?
    c Test your hypothesis by drawing some more right-angled triangles with an angle of 35°.
7 Repeat with an angle of 70° rather than 35°.
Discussion What does this tell you about the ratio of the sides of similar triangles?

3 Use your calculator to find, correct to 1 d.p.

   a sin 43°   **b** sin 84°   **c** sin 17°

Q3a hint

On your calculator, enter

4 Write **sin θ** as a fraction for each triangle.

   a 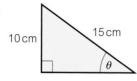   **b**   **c**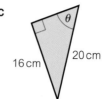

Key point

The ratio of the opposite side to the hypotenuse is called the **sine** of the angle.

The sine of angle θ is written as **sin θ**.

$$\sin \theta = \frac{\text{opposite}}{\text{hypotenuse}}$$

Worked example

Use the **sine** ratio to work out x, correct to 1 d.p.

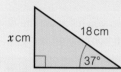

$$\sin \theta = \frac{\text{opposite}}{\text{hypotenuse}}$$ Write the sine ratio.

opposite = x

hypotenuse = 18   Identify the opposite side and hypotenuse.

θ = 37°

$$\sin 37° = \frac{x}{18}$$ Substitute the sides and angle into the equation.

18 × sin 37° = x Rearrange to make x the subject.
Use your calculator to work out 18 × sin 37°.

x = 10.8 cm (to 1 d.p.)

 5 Work out the value of x, correct to 1 d.p.

   a 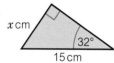   **b**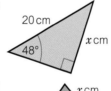

   c   **d**

 6 Work out the value of x, correct to 1 d.p.

   a 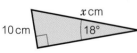   **b**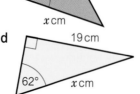

   c   **d**

Q6a hint

$$\sin \theta = \frac{\text{opp}}{\text{hyp}}$$

$$\sin 18° = \frac{10}{x}$$

Rearrange the formula to make x the subject.

7 **Real / Modelling** A skateboard ramp is 50 cm long and makes an angle of 35° with the ground.
Calculate the height of the ramp.

8 **Real / Modelling** A ladder 6 m long is leaning against a wall.
The angle between the ladder and the ground is 72°.
What height does the ladder reach?

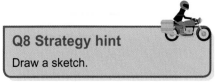

Q8 Strategy hint

Draw a sketch.

9 **Problem-solving** Work out the perimeter of this right-angled triangle.

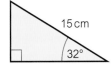

10 **Problem-solving / Reasoning** For each triangle
i decide whether you need to use the tangent or the sine ratio
ii work out the value of y.

a    **b** 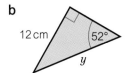   **c**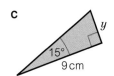

11 **Explore** How can you measure the height of a kite from the ground?
Is it easier to explore this question now you have completed the lesson? What further information do you need to be able to answer this?

12 **Reflect** The hint for Q8 suggested drawing a sketch.
Did the sketch help you?
Explain how.

Explore

Reflect

9.3 The cosine ratio

You will learn to:

- Work out the cosine of any angle
- Use the cosine ratio to work out an unknown side in a right-angled triangle.

CONFIDENCE

Why learn this?
Trigonometry is used by astronomers to find the distance from the Earth to stars.

Fluency
In each right-angled triangle, identify the hypotenuse, and the sides adjacent and opposite to the angle θ.

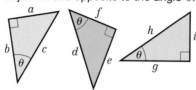

Explore
How can you use the cosine ratio to design a ramp for a skateboard?

Exercise 9.3

Warm up

1 For this triangle, write the fraction
   a $\tan \theta$
   b $\sin \theta$

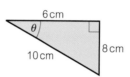

6 cm
8 cm
10 cm

2 Rearrange each formula to make T the subject.

   a $2 = \dfrac{T}{9}$ **b** $3 = \dfrac{T}{4}$ **c** $7 = \dfrac{2}{T}$ **d** $2 = \dfrac{5}{T}$

Investigation   Reasoning

   1 Look at the triangles you drew in the Investigation in lesson 9.2.
   2 Copy and complete this table.

Triangle	Adjacent length	Hypotenuse length	$\dfrac{\text{adjacent}}{\text{hypotenuse}}$ (1 d.p.)
a			
b			
c			

   3 What patterns do you notice in your table?
   4 Repeat for the triangles with a 40° angle.
   Discussion What does this tell you about the ratio of the sides of similar triangles?

---

3 Use your calculator to find, correct to 1 d.p.

   a $\cos 53°$ **b** $\cos 62°$ **c** $\cos 46°$ **d** $\cos 19°$

4 Write **cos θ** as a fraction for each triangle.

   a
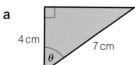
4 cm   7 cm

   b
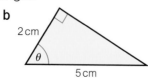
2 cm   5 cm

Key point

The ratio of the adjacent side to the hypotenuse is called the **cosine** of the angle.
The cosine of angle θ is written as **cos θ**.

$$\cos \theta = \frac{\text{adjacent}}{\text{hypotenuse}}$$

Worked example

Use the **cosine** ratio to work out x, correct to 1 d.p.

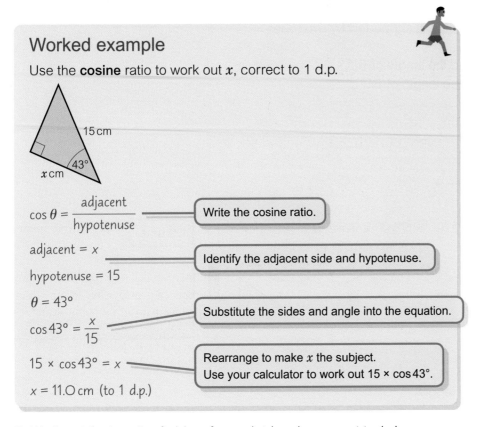

$\cos \theta = \dfrac{\text{adjacent}}{\text{hypotenuse}}$ ——— Write the cosine ratio.

adjacent = x ——— Identify the adjacent side and hypotenuse.

hypotenuse = 15

$\theta = 43°$

$\cos 43° = \dfrac{x}{15}$ ——— Substitute the sides and angle into the equation.

$15 \times \cos 43° = x$ ——— Rearrange to make x the subject.
Use your calculator to work out $15 \times \cos 43°$.

$x = 11.0 \text{ cm}$ (to 1 d.p.)

5 Work out the length of side x for each triangle, correct to 1 d.p.

a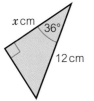

b

c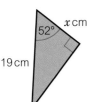

d

6 Calculate the length of side x for each triangle, correct to 1 d.p.

a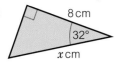
b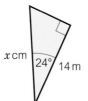
c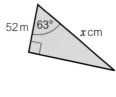

> **Q6a hint**
>
> $\cos \theta = \dfrac{\text{adj}}{\text{hyp}}$
>
> $\cos 32° = \dfrac{8}{x}$
>
> Rearrange the formula to make x the subject.

7 **Problem-solving / Modelling** A roof is made from beams that make an isosceles triangle.
The sloping side of the roof is 8 metres.
The roof makes an angle of 30° with the horizontal.
Calculate the width of the roof.

> **Q7 hint**
>
> $\cos \theta = \dfrac{\text{adj}}{\text{hyp}}$ is true only in a right-angled triangle.

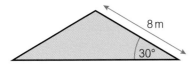

8 Real / Modelling A flagpole, AB, is supported by two ropes, BD and BC.

    a Use the cosine ratio to find the length of BD.

    b Use the sine ratio to find the length of BC.

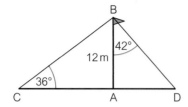

9 Real / Modelling A ship sails for 50 km on a bearing of 130°.

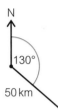

Q9 hint

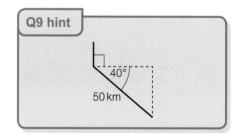

How far east has it travelled?

10 Problem-solving For each triangle

    i decide whether you need to use the tangent, sine or cosine ratio

  ii work out the value of *p*.

a

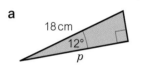

b

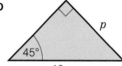

c

11 Explore How can you use the cosine ratio to design a ramp for a skateboard?

Is it easier to explore this question now you have completed the lesson? What further information do you need to be able to answer this?

12 Reflect A mnemonic for remembering sine, cosine and tangent ratios is SOH CAH TOA. Will this help you to remember them?
If not, can you think of another memory aid?

Active Learn   Delta 3, Section 9.3

9.4 Using trigonometry to find angles

You will learn to:
- Use the trigonometric ratios to work out an unknown angle in a right-angled triangle.

Why learn this?
Trigonometry is used by aeroplane pilots to find the angle of descent when landing.

Fluency
What is the inverse of
- +3
- ×4
- ÷5
- −7
- $x^3 + 1$?

Explore
How do pilots use trigonometry to find the angle of descent?

Exercise 9.4

1 For this triangle, find
  a $\sin \theta$
  b $\cos \theta$
  c $\tan \theta$

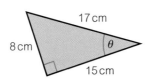

17 cm, 8 cm, θ, 15 cm

2 a Use the sine ratio to work out the value of x.

42°, 17 cm, x cm

  b Use the cosine ratio to work out the value of y.

y cm, 28°, 36 m

  c Use the tangent ratio to work out the value of s.

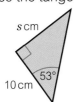

s cm, 10 cm, 53°

Investigation

Problem-solving / Reasoning

In this triangle, $\tan \theta = \frac{4}{5}$.

b, a, θ

1 Write down possible values for a and b.
2 Make an accurate drawing of the triangle using these values.
3 Measure the angle θ to the nearest degree.
4 Draw two more triangles where $\tan \theta = \frac{4}{5}$, and use them to measure θ.

Warm up

Worked example

Use the sine ratio to find the missing angle in this right-angled triangle.

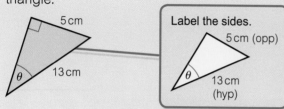

Label the sides.

5 cm (opp)
13 cm (hyp)

Using the sine ratio

$$\sin \theta = \frac{opposite}{hypotenuse}$$

$$\sin \theta = \frac{5}{13}$$

$$\theta = 22.6°$$

You need to find $\sin^{-1} \frac{5}{13}$
Use these buttons on your calculator:

[SHIFT] [sin] [5] [÷] [1] [3] [=]

3 Use the $\cos^{-1}$ function on your calculator to find θ.

  a $\cos \theta = \frac{3}{10}$ **b** $\cos \theta = \frac{3}{7}$ **c** $\cos \theta = 0.42$

4 Use the $\sin^{-1}$ function on your calculator to find θ.

  a $\sin \theta = \frac{7}{10}$ **b** $\sin \theta = \frac{3}{4}$ **c** $\sin \theta = 0.12$

5 Use the $\tan^{-1}$ function on your calculator to find θ.

  a $\tan \theta = \frac{1}{2}$ **b** $\tan \theta = \frac{5}{8}$ **c** $\tan \theta = 0.8$

6 a Use the sine ratio to work out the missing angles.

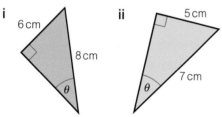

  i 6 cm, 8 cm, θ **ii** 5 cm, 7 cm, θ

  b Use the cosine ratio to work out the missing angles.

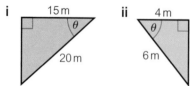

  i 15 m, θ, 20 m   **ii** 4 m, θ, 6 m

Q6b hint

Follow the same method as in the worked example but use the cosine ratio.

  c Use the tangent ratio to find the missing angles.

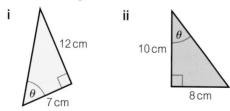

  i 12 cm, θ, 7 cm   **ii** θ, 10 cm, 8 cm

7 Work out the missing angle in each right-angled triangle.

a
4 cm
10 cm θ

b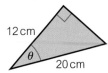
θ
6 cm
8 cm

c
12 cm
θ
20 cm

d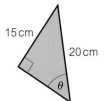
15 cm
20 cm
θ

e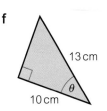
θ 8 cm
15 cm

f
13 cm
θ
10 cm

8 **Real / Problem-solving** Jamie builds a skate ramp with 2 metres of wood.
He wants the vertical height of the ramp to be 1 metre.
What angle does the wood need to make to the ground?

Q8 hint
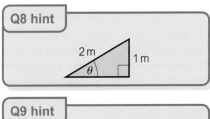
2 m
1 m
θ

9 **Real / Problem-solving** A ship sails 30 km north and 50 km east.
On what bearing has it travelled?

Q9 hint
Write the bearing using three figures.

10 **Problem-solving / Reasoning** Ellie draws this triangle.

Not to scale
θ

She works out tan θ = 1.
What kind of triangle has Ellie drawn? Explain.

11 **Explore** How do pilots use trigonometry to find the angle of descent?
Is it easier to explore this question now you have completed the lesson? What further information do you need to be able to answer this?

12 **Reflect** The inverse of sine is expressed as $\sin^{-1}$.
Think about where you have met the notation $^{-1}$ before.
Did it mean the same thing in that situation?

9.5 Solving problems using trigonometry

You will learn to:
- Use trigonometry to solve problems involving missing lengths and angles.

Why learn this?
Oceanography is the study of the ocean. Scientists use trigonometry to calculate the intensity and height of tides in the ocean.

Fluency
Calculate
- $\cos 56°$
- $\sin^{-1} \frac{3}{4}$
- $\tan^{-1} 0.3$

Round each answer to 1 d.p.

Explore
How can you use trigonometry to calculate the height of a tree?

CONFIDENCE

Warm up

Exercise 9.5

1 Work out the length of the missing side of these triangles.

a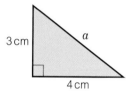

3 cm, a, 4 cm

b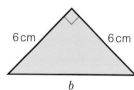

6 cm, 6 cm, b

c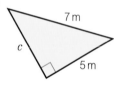

7 m, c, 5 m

d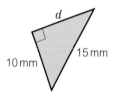

d, 10 mm, 15 mm

2 Work out the value of y.

a

y cm, 21 cm, 48°

b

y cm, 56°, 14 cm

c

18 cm, 51°, y cm

3 Choose the trigonometric ratio and work out x.

a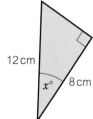

12 cm, 8 cm, $x°$

b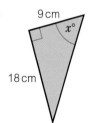

9 cm, $x°$, 18 cm

c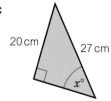

20 cm, 27 cm, $x°$

4 Real / Problem-solving A plane flies for 120 km on a bearing of 070°.
   a How far east has the plane travelled?
   b How far north has it travelled?

5 Real / Problem-solving Fernando is flying a kite.
   The string of the kite makes an angle of 25° with the horizontal.
   The horizontal distance between Fernando and the kite is 30 metres.
   Work out the length of the string of the kite.

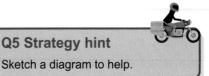

Q5 Strategy hint

Sketch a diagram to help.

6 Problem-solving Work out the area of this isosceles triangle.

7 cm   37°

Q6 hint

You need to find the height of the triangle first.

7 cm   37°

7 Problem-solving Calculate the size of angle θ in this diagram.

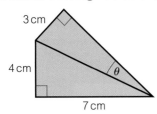

3 cm
4 cm
θ
7 cm

8 Problem-solving Work out the angle between AD and AC.

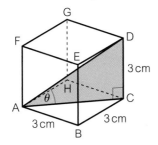

G
F   D
   E   3 cm
θ H
A   C
3 cm   3 cm
B

Investigation   Reasoning

   1 Draw a cube with side length 4 cm.
   2 Work out the angle marked θ.
   3 Compare your answer with Q8.
   4 Repeat for different sized cubes.
   5 What do you notice?
   6 Explain.

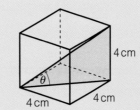

4 cm
θ
4 cm   4 cm

9 Explore How can you use trigonometry to calculate the height of a tree?
   Is it easier to explore this question now you have completed the lesson? What further information do you need to be able to answer this?

10 Reflect Look again at the work you have done in this lesson.
   List all the different mathematical skills you have used.

Explore

Reflect

9.6 Trigonometric graphs

You will learn to:
- Plot and sketch graphs of the trigonometric functions
- Use the trigonometric ratios with any angle from 0 to 360°.

CONFIDENCE

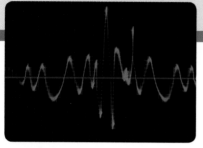

Why learn this?
Trigonometric graphs are used for modelling sound waves and tidal waves.

Fluency
Which trigonometric ratio should you use to work out length a?

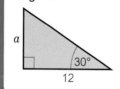

Explore
How can you use the sine curve to show the sound of an ambulance siren?

Exercise 9.6

Warm up

 1 Calculate each of these. Round your answers to 1 d.p.
  a $\sin 80°$ **b** $\cos 60°$ **c** $\tan 50°$

2 a Copy and complete this table of values for $y = 2x^2 - 4x$.

x	−3	−2	−1	0	1	2	3
y							

b Plot the graph of $y = 2x^2 - 4x$.

 3 a Copy and complete this table.

θ	0°	30°	60°	90°	120°	150°	180°	210°	240°	270°	300°	330°	360°
$\sin\theta$													

b Plot the coordinates on a graph with θ on the horizontal axis and $\sin\theta$ on the vertical axis. Join the points with a smooth curve.
c Comment on the symmetry of your graph.

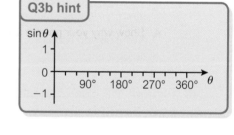
Q3b hint

 4 Extend the θ-axis of your graph from Q3.
  a Plot the point when $\theta = 450°$.
  b Plot the point when $\theta = 540°$.
  Discussion Work out $\sin\theta$ for some larger values of θ using your calculator. What do you notice?

 5 Reasoning / Problem-solving
  a Use this triangle to work out $\sin 45°$.
  b Use your graph from Q3 to work out what other value of θ has this answer.
  c Use the symmetry of the graph to explain why $\sin\theta = \sin(180 - \theta)$.
  Discussion Can you draw a triangle to work out the second value of θ? Explain.

Q5b hint
Draw a line from your value of $\sin 45°$ across to your graph.
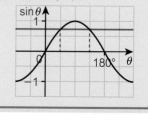

6 Use your graph from Q3 to work out two values of θ when
   a $\sin \theta = 0.5$ **b** $\sin \theta = -0.5$ **c** $\sin \theta = 0$
   d Check your answers using the inverse functions on your calculator.

7 a Copy and complete this table.

θ	0°	30°	60°	90°	120°	150°	180°	210°	240°	270°	300°	330°	360°
$\cos \theta$													

   b Plot the points on similar axes to your graph from Q3. Join the
      points with a smooth curve.
   c Comment on the symmetry of your graph.
   d What is the translation that maps the graph of $\sin \theta$ to the graph of
      $\cos \theta$?

8 Reasoning When $0° \leqslant \theta \leqslant 360°$, for what values of θ is $\cos \theta$:
   a negative   **b** positive?

9 a Copy and complete this table. Round each answer to 1 d.p.

θ	0°	30°	60°	90°	120°	150°	180°	210°	240°	270°	300°	330°	360°
$\tan \theta$													

   b Plot the graph of $\tan \theta$. Use values of θ from 0 to 360° and values
      of $\tan \theta$ from −6 to 6.
   c Describe any patterns that you notice on your graph.

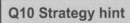
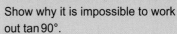

Q10 Strategy hint

Show why it is impossible to work
out $\tan 90°$.

10 Reasoning Draw a right-angled triangle. Use it to explain why
    $\tan 90°$ has no value.

Investigation   **Reasoning**

   1 Complete this table.

θ	$\sin \theta$	$\cos \theta$	$\tan \theta$	$\dfrac{\sin \theta}{\cos \theta}$
40°				
80°				
110°				

   2 What do you notice?
   3 Test your answer by trying three other values for θ.
   4 Show why your pattern always works using this right-angled triangle.

11 Explore How can you use the sine curve to show the sound of an
    ambulance siren?
    Is it easier to explore this question now you have completed
    the lesson? What further information do you need to be able to
    answer this?

12 Reflect Sadaqat says, 'Symmetry is an important concept when
    plotting trigonometric graphs.' Do you think Sadaqat is right?
    Explain your answer.

Explore

Reflect

9 Check up

Log how you did on your Student Progression Chart.

Unknown sides

1 What is

  a the opposite side to angle θ

  b the adjacent side to angle θ

  c the hypotenuse?

2 Write each of these as a fraction.

  a $\sin \theta$

  b $\cos \theta$

  c $\tan \theta$

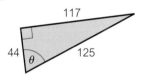

3 Work out the value of x for each right-angled triangle.
The trigonometric function that you need to use is given.

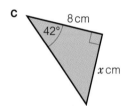

           sine   cosine   tangent

4 Work out the value of y for each right-angled triangle.
You need to decide which function to use.

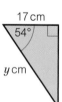

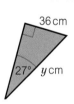

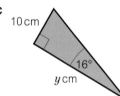

Unknown angles

5 Work out the value of θ for each right-angled triangle.
The trigonometric function that you need to use is given.

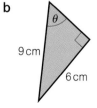

          tangent   sine   cosine

6 Work out angle θ in each triangle.

a

8 cm
θ
5 cm

b 2 cm

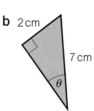

7 cm
θ

Solving problems

7 The length of the diagonal in this rectangle is 12 cm.
The diagonal makes an angle of 28° with the horizontal.
   a Calculate the height of the rectangle.
   b Calculate the width of the rectangle.

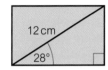

12 cm
28°

8 Work out the length of the base of this isosceles triangle.

18 cm
32°

9 A ship sails 20 km north and then 15 km east.
What is the bearing of the ship from its original position?

15 km
20 km

10 **How sure are you of your answers? Were you mostly**
   🙁 **Just guessing**   😐 **Feeling doubtful**   🙂 **Confident**
   What next? Use your results to decide whether to strengthen or extend your learning.

Challenge

11 Draw a square of side 4 cm.

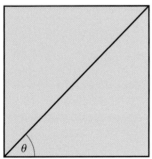

θ

Draw the diagonal.
Calculate tan θ.
Explain why tan θ = 1 for any square.

Reflect

Master
P197

Check
P213

STRENGTHEN

Extend
P219

Test
P223

9 Strengthen

You will:

• Strengthen your understanding with practice.

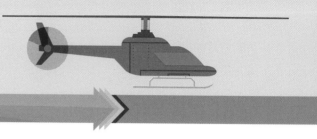

Unknown sides

1 Sketch each triangle and label it with
  a 'opp' on the side opposite to angle θ
  b 'adj' on the adjacent side
  c 'hyp' on the hypotenuse.

  i   **ii**   **iii**

> **Q1 hint**
>
> opposite ⟍ hypotenuse
> θ
> adjacent

2 For each triangle
  a write the tangent ratio.
  b write the sine ratio
  c write the cosine ratio.

  i 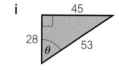 **ii**   **iii**

> **Key point**
>
> The three trigonometric ratios can be remembered using the phrase **SOH CAH TOA**.
>
>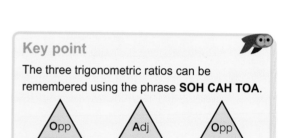

 3 Copy and complete to work out x, correct to 1 d.p.

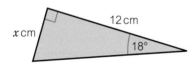

  a Write the tangent ratio.

  $\tan\square = \dfrac{x}{\square}$

  b Rearrange.

  $x = \square \times \tan\square$

  c Use a calculator to work out x.

 4 Copy and complete to work out x, correct to 1 d.p.

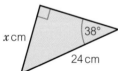

  a Write the sine ratio.

  $\sin\square = \dfrac{x}{\square}$

  b Rearrange.

  $x = \square \times \sin\square$

  c Use a calculator to work out x.

5 Copy and complete to work out x, correct to 1 d.p.

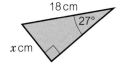

a Write the cosine ratio.

$\cos \square = \dfrac{x}{\square}$

b Rearrange.

$x = \square \times \cos \square$

c Use a calculator to work out x.

6 Follow these steps to work out the value of x.

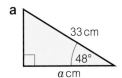

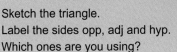
Q6 Strategy hint
Sketch the triangle.
Label the sides opp, adj and hyp.
Which ones are you using?

a Choose the trigonometric ratio you are going to use.

b Write the ratio.

c Rearrange to find x.

d Use your calculator to work out the missing side.

7 Work out the length of each side marked with a letter.

Q7 hint
Follow the same method as in Q6.

a   **b** 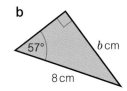 **c**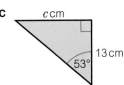

Unknown angles

1 Use the $\sin^{-1}$ function on your calculator to work out θ.

a $\sin \theta = \dfrac{2}{5}$

b $\sin \theta = 0.2$

Q1 hint
Rearrange to make θ the subject.
The inverse of sin is $\sin^{-1}$.
$\theta = \sin^{-1} 0.2$
[SHIFT] [sin] [0] [.] [2] [=]

2 Use the $\cos^{-1}$ function on your calculator to work out θ.

a $\cos \theta = \dfrac{3}{8}$

b $\cos \theta = 0.9$

3 Use the $\tan^{-1}$ function on your calculator to work out θ.

a $\tan \theta = \dfrac{3}{5}$

b $\tan \theta = 0.3$

4 Copy and complete to work out the missing angle, correct to 1 d.p.

a Write the tangent ratio.

$\tan \theta = \dfrac{\square}{\square}$

b Rearrange.

$\theta = \tan^{-1} \dfrac{\square}{\square}$

Q4c hint

Press [SHIFT] [tan]

c Use your calculator to work out θ.

5 Copy and complete to work out the missing angle, correct to 1 d.p.

    a Write the sine ratio.

$$\sin \theta = \frac{\square}{\square}$$

    b Rearrange.

$$\theta = \sin^{-1} \frac{\square}{\square}$$

    c Use your calculator to work out θ.

6 Copy and complete to work out the missing angle, correct to 1 d.p.

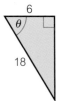

    a Write the cosine ratio.

$$\cos \theta = \frac{\square}{\square}$$

    b Rearrange.

$$\theta = \cos^{-1} \frac{\square}{\square}$$

    c Use your calculator to work out θ.

7 Follow these steps to work out the size of angle θ.

    a Copy the triangle and label the sides that you have been given or need to find.

    b Choose the trigonometric ratio you are going to use.

    c Write the ratio.

    d Rearrange to make θ the subject.

    e Use your calculator to work out the missing angle.

8 Work out the missing angle in each triangle. You need to decide which ratio to use.

> **Q8 hint**
>
> Follow the same method as in Q7.

    a 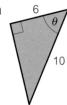   **b**   **c**

Solving problems

1 **Real / Modelling** Peter wants to find the height of a tree.
He is 2 m tall and 12 metres away from the tree.
The angle between his eyeline to the top of the tree and a line parallel
to the ground is 64°.
a Work out which trigonometric ratio Peter needs to use.
b Calculate the height of the tree.

Q1a hint

Draw a sketch of the right-angled triangle. What information have you already been given?

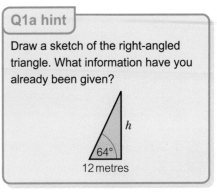

2 **Real / Problem-solving** A ship sails 40 km east and then
60 km north.
What is the bearing of the ship from its original position?

Q2 hint

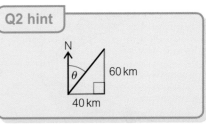

3 **Problem-solving** Work out the height of this isosceles triangle.

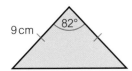

Q3 hint

Split the triangle in half to make a right-angled triangle.

Enrichment

1 **a** Calculate the value of x and y when

i $\sin x = 0.3$ $\cos y = 0.3$
ii $\sin x = 0.6$ $\cos y = 0.6$
iii $\sin x = 0.8$ $\cos y = 0.8$
v $\sin x = 0.9$ $\cos y = 0.9$
b Write down any patterns that you notice.
Explain.

2 **Reflect** Look back at some of the questions in this srengthen section.
What mathematical skills did you need when solving trigonometry
problems?

9 Extend

You will:

• Extend your understanding with problem-solving.

1 Work out the length of the sides marked with letters.

a
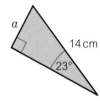
14 cm
23°

b
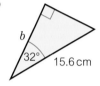
32°
15.6 cm

c

9.7 cm
52°
c

d
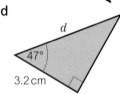
47°
3.2 cm

e

8.2 cm
41°

f
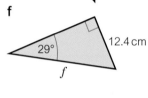
29°
12.4 cm
f

2 Work out the missing angle for each right-angled triangle.

a

7.2
θ
9.6

b
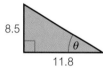
8.5
θ
11.8

c
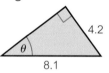
4.2
θ
8.1

3 Real / Problem-solving A children's slide in a park is 5.5 metres long.
It makes an angle of 30° with the ground.

5.5 m
30°

What is the vertical height of the top of the slide?

4 Real / Problem-solving A wheelchair ramp is 2 metres long.
It needs to reach a height of 30 cm.

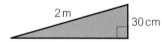
2 m
30 cm

What angle must the ramp make with the ground?

> **Q4 hint**
>
> You must have all measurements in the same units.

5 Real / Problem-solving A ladder is 6 m long and
is leaning against a vertical wall.
In order for it to be safe, the ladder must be
placed between 1.8 m and 2.4 m from the base
of the wall.

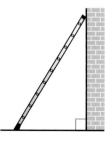

  a What is the largest angle the ladder can
  make with the wall?
  b What is the smallest angle the ladder can
  make with the wall?

6 **Modelling / Problem-solving** A hiker walks 5.4 km north and then turns and walks another 8.9 km east.

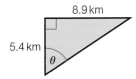

Calculate the hiker's bearing from his original position.

7 **Modelling / Problem-solving** A plane travels 120.2 km east and then 50.7 km north.
Calculate the bearing of the plane from its original position.

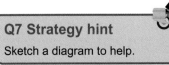

Q7 Strategy hint
Sketch a diagram to help.

8 **Modelling / Problem-solving** A ship leaves port and travels on a bearing of 245° for 40.6 km.
 a How far west has it travelled?
 b How far south has it travelled?

9 **Problem-solving** A right-angled triangle has sides 8 cm, 10 cm and 6 cm. Work out the size of all the angles in the triangle.

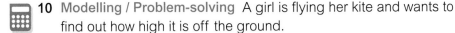

10 **Modelling / Problem-solving** A girl is flying her kite and wants to find out how high it is off the ground.

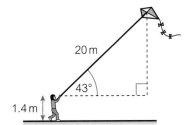

The length of the kite string is 20 m and the angle the string makes with the horizontal is 43°.
The girl is 1.4 metres tall.
How high is the kite off the ground?

11 **Problem-solving** In this triangle BD is perpendicular to AC.

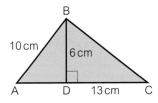

 a Calculate the angle BCD.
 b Calculate the angle BAD.
 c Using your answers to part **a** and **b**, calculate the angle ABC.

12 **Problem-solving** Work out the size of angle θ.

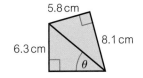

13 In this basketball court the basketball hoop is at the midpoint of AB.

a Work out the distance from D to the basketball hoop.
The hoop is 3.1 m off the ground.
b Work out the angle between D and the top of the hoop.

14 The diagram shows a cube of side length 7 cm.

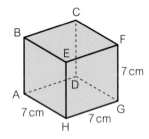

Calculate
a the length AG
b the angle between AG and AF
c the length of the diagonal AF.

15 The diagram shows a square-based pyramid.
The vertex E of the pyramid is over the
centre of the square base and is 5 cm
above the base.
Calculate
a the length AC
b the angle EAC
c the length of AE.

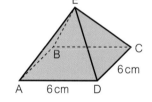

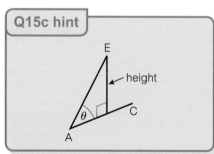

Q15c hint

16 **Modelling / Problem-solving** A balloon is hovering 100 m above
the ground.
The balloon is observed by some people in a car as they look
upwards at an angle of 15°.
30 seconds later, the people in the car had to look up at an angle of
70° to see the balloon.
How fast was the car moving?
Give your answer in m/s and km/h.

Q16 hint

Calculate the horizontal distances
between the balloon and the car to
find out how far the car has travelled.

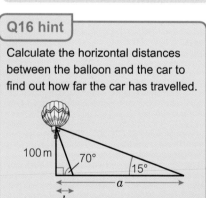

Remember, speed = $\dfrac{\text{distance}}{\text{time}}$

17 A plane travels for 1.5 hours at 120 mph on a bearing of 050°.
It turns and continues for another hour at the same speed on a
bearing of 140°.
At the end of this time, how far away is the plane from its starting point?

18 a Sketch the graph of sin θ for 0° ≤ θ ≤ 360°.
  b From your graph write down the two values of θ where
    sin θ = 0.5.
    Check your answers using the inverse functions on your calculator.

Q17 hint

Draw a diagram to help.

1 Here is an equilateral triangle split into two right-angled triangles.

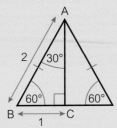

a Work out the length AC. Leave your answer in surd form.

b Copy and complete the trigonometric ratios.

   i $\sin 30° = \dfrac{\square}{\square}$ **ii** $\sin 60° = \dfrac{\sqrt{\square}}{\square}$ **iii** $\cos 30° = \dfrac{\sqrt{\square}}{\square}$

   iv $\cos 60° = \dfrac{\square}{\square}$ **v** $\tan 30° = \dfrac{\square}{\sqrt{\square}}$ **vi** $\tan 60° = \dfrac{\sqrt{\square}}{\square} = \sqrt{\square}$

2 Here is a right-angled triangle.

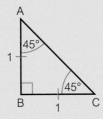

a Find the length of the hypotenuse. Leave your answer in surd form.

b Copy and complete the trigonometric ratios.

   i $\sin 45° = \dfrac{\square}{\sqrt{\square}}$ **ii** $\cos 45° = \dfrac{\square}{\sqrt{\square}}$ **iii** $\tan 45° = \square$

19 Reflect Most of the questions in the extend section included diagrams. How useful is it to have a diagram? Did you sketch diagrams for the questions that didn't already have them?

Reflect

Master
P197

Check
P213

Strengthen
P215

Extend
P219

TEST

9 Unit test

Log how you did on your
Student Progression Chart.

1 Write the ratios as fractions for
this right-angled triangle.
a sin θ
b cos θ
c tan θ

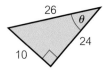

26
θ
24
10

2 Work out the value of x.
The trigonometric function that you will use is given.

a

x cm
42°
35 cm

sine

b
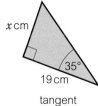
x cm
35°
19 cm

tangent

3 Work out the value of x. You need to decide which function to use.

a
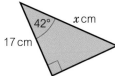
42°
x cm
17 cm

b
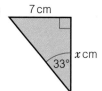
7 cm
33°
x cm

4 Use cosine to work out the size of angle θ.

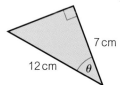
7 cm
12 cm
θ

5 Find the missing angle for each triangle.

a

θ
8 cm
13 cm

b
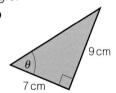
9 cm
θ
7 cm

6 A 5 m ladder leans against a wall at an angle of
56° with the ground.
How far up the wall does the ladder reach?

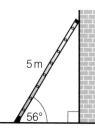
5 m
56°

7 A ship sails 30 km north and then 20 km east.
What is the ship's bearing from its original position?

8 A ramp of 5 m makes an angle of 40° with the ground.
How high is the ramp from the ground?

9 a Work out the height of this isosceles triangle.
  b Work out the length of the base.
  c Work out the area of the triangle.

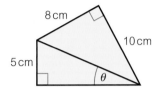

12.4 cm

38°

10 Work out the size of angle θ.

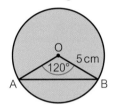

8 cm

10 cm

5 cm

θ

11 The diagram shows a circle with centre O and radius 5 cm.
Find the length of the chord AB.

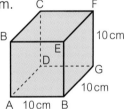

O
5 cm
120°
A   B

12 The diagram shows a cube with side length 10 cm.
Calculate
  a the length AG
  b the angle between AG and AF
  c the length of the diagonal AF.

C   F
B   10 cm
E
D
G
10 cm
A 10 cm B

13 a Sketch the graph of cos θ for 0° ≤ θ ≤ 360°.
  b What are the two values of θ where cos θ = 0.5?
  Check your answers using the inverse functions on your calculator.

Challenge

14 The square and the isosceles triangle have the same area.
Find tan θ.

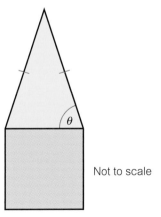

θ

Not to scale

15 Reflect Write down five things you need to remember from your
work in this unit.

10.1 Explain, show and justify

You will learn to:
- Explain, show and justify a mathematical solution.

CONFIDENCE

Why learn this?
A lot of the work mathematicians and scientists do involves justifying why something is true or false.

Fluency
Work out
- 10% of £900
- 5% of £60
- 2.5% of £20

Explore
Are all square numbers positive?

Exercise 10.1

Warm up

1 Decide if these statements are true or false.
   a odd + odd = even
   b odd + even = even
   c odd − even = odd
   d odd − odd = even

2 When $x = 2$, $x^2 = 2x$.
   Does this mean x^2 always equals $2x$?

3 **Reasoning** Angela says, 'The only even prime number is 2.'
   Is she correct? **Explain** your answer.

> **Q3 hint**
>
> A question asking you to **explain** can be answered by starting with:
> 'She is correct/incorrect because ...'

4 **Reasoning** The frequency diagram shows the number of children in 20 households.

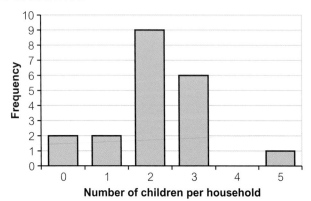

Number of children per household

Charlie says, 'The mean number of children per household must be greater than 1.'
Do you agree with Charlie? Explain.

Topic links: Percentages, Factorising, Algebraic expressions, Expanding brackets, Calculating mean, Upper and lower bounds

5 Reasoning a Work out the area of each shape, in terms of x.

$x + 5$

$x + 2$

x 5

x

2

Key point

Showing working out helps with an explanation.

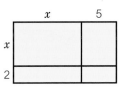

b Use the diagrams and your answer to explain why
$(x + 2)(x + 5) = x^2 + 7x + 10$.

6 Reasoning Annice says, 'To find 10% of a number you divide by 10, therefore to find 5% of a number divide by 5.'
True or false? Show your working to **justify** your answer.

Q6 Strategy hint

A question won't always say 'Show that ...', but sometimes the clearest way to **justify** or explain something is to show working out.

7 Reasoning Are these statements true or false? Justify your answers.
a $2x + 16 = 2(x + 8)$ **b** $(x + 3)^2 = x^2 + 9$
c $(x - 1)(x + 1) = x^2 + 1$ **d** $x^2 + 5 + 6 = (x + 2)(x + 3)$
e $(x - 5)(x + 2) = x^2 - 3x - 7$

8 Reasoning Show that
a $(x + y)(x - y) = x^2 - y^2$
b $2(x + 12) - 3(x + 4) = 12 - x$
c $x^2 - 3x = 2x + x(x - 5)$

Q8 hint

Expand and simplify the expression with brackets.

Investigation   Problem-solving / Reasoning

Here is a 100 square grid.
Shane draws a cross on different parts of the grid.
1 Work out the sum of all the numbers in the cross when the middle value is:
a 23   **b** 57   **c** 79
2 What is the relationship between the sum and the middle value of the cross?
3 This cross has middle value 'x'.
Write down the missing values of the cross in terms of x.

1	2	3	4	5	6	7	8	9	10
11	12	13	14	15	16	17	18	19	20
21	22	23	24	25	26	27	28	29	30
31	32	33	34	35	36	37	38	39	40
41	42	43	44	45	46	47	48	49	50
51	52	53	54	55	56	57	58	59	60
61	62	63	64	65	66	67	68	69	70
71	72	73	74	75	76	77	78	79	80
81	82	83	84	85	86	87	88	89	90
91	92	93	94	95	96	97	98	99	100

4 Use your answer to part **3** to justify your answer to part **2**.

9 Reasoning Jo is designing a watering system for 10 vegetable patches. For each vegetable patch she needs 3.5 m of hose, to the nearest half metre. She buys 35 m of hose, to the nearest 1 m. Will she have enough? Justify your answer.

10 Explore Are all square numbers positive?
Choose some sensible numbers to help you explore this situation. Then use what you've learned in this lesson to help you answer the question.

11 Reflect Look back at the questions in this lesson.
Did you need to revise any topics from previous lessons to answer the questions? If so, has this lesson helped your understanding of those topics?

Explore

Reflect

10.2 MODELLING: Real-life situations

You will learn to:
* Draw graphs to solve mathematical problems.

CONFIDENCE

Why learn this?
Mathematical modelling is used to predict real-life situations.

Fluency
$x + y = 12$ and $x - y = 4$.
What are the values of x and y?

Explore
How is mathematics used to predict currency exchange rates?

Exercise 10.2: Real-life situations

Warm up

1 The number of hours' sleep needed by different animals is listed in the table.

Animal	Number of hours' sleep needed in 24 hours	Average mass (kg)
Human	8	65
Dog	11	20
Cat	12	5
Bat	20	1.5

  a Plot a graph to show the relationship between the hours of sleep needed and mass of different animals.
  b Use your graph to predict how long a 3.5 kg fox spends sleeping.
  Discussion How accurate do you think your answer to part **b** is? Why?

2 **Modelling** A ball is thrown vertically upwards.
The height of the ball over time is recorded.

Time (s)	0	2	4	8	10	12
Height (m)	0	18	32	48	50	49

  a Plot this information on a graph.
  b Use your graph to predict when the ball will return to Earth.

Q2 hint
Time is usually plotted on the x-axis.

3 **STEM / Modelling** The scatter graph shows the amount of the Arctic sea that is covered by ice each year.
  a Copy the graph and draw a line of best fit.
  b Use the line of best fit predict the Arctic sea ice coverage in
    i 2020   **ii** 2040
  Discussion Do you think a straight line is the best way to model this situation?

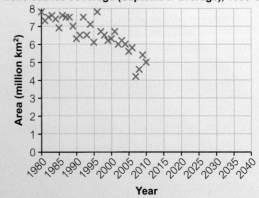

Arctic sea ice coverage (September average), 1980–2040

Topic links: Graphs, Forming equations, Simultaneous equations, Problem-solving

Subject links: Science (Q2, Q3, Q6)

4 Reasoning Two broadband providers offer these packages.

All Talk
£10 monthly +
£3 per GB of data

Flashweb
No monthly charge
£5 per GB of data

a Draw a graph to show the cost of 0–10 GB of data for each company.

b Use your graph to recommend one of the companies to someone who uses 3 GB of data per month.

c What amount of data would cost the same with both companies?

5 Modelling The net of an open box is made by cutting a small square of side length x from each corner of a larger square with side length 20 cm.

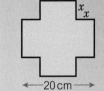

—20 cm—

a Work out the capacity of the box when

   i $x = 1$ cm   **ii** $x = 2$ cm   **iii** $x = 3$ cm

b Use your answers to part **a** to plot a graph with 'side of square' on the x-axis and 'capacity' on the y-axis.

c Use your graph to find the value of x that gives the largest capacity.

d Show that the capacity of the box is equal to $x(20 - 2x)^2$.

6 STEM / Modelling A scientist records the temperature of a liquid that is cooling from 100 °C.
In the first minute the liquid cools by 2 °C.
She assumes that the liquid will continue to cool at a constant rate.

a Write down an equation linking temperature (C) with time (t) in minutes.

b Explain how you worked out your equation.

Discussion Using this model what will the temperature of the liquid be after 50 minutes? Is this a sensible model to use?

7 Problem-solving The area of a warehouse is 480 m². It is split into 24 separate units. Large units are 30 m² and small units are 15 m². A company charges £400 per month to rent large units and £250 per month to rent small units. Work out how many large and small units there should be so the company can maximise its profit. Show your working.

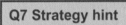

Q7 Strategy hint
Work out the profit for different amounts of large and small units, and use these numbers to plot some coordinates.

8 In a football tournament 4 teams all play each other.
A team scores 5 points for a win and 2 points for a draw.
The table shows the scores.
Work out the results of each match, showing all your working out.

Team	Score
Reds	12
Blues	0
Greens	9
Yellows	7

9 Explore How is mathematics used to predict currency exchange rates?
Is it easier to explore this question now you have completed the lesson?
What further information do you need to be able to answer this?

10 Reflect The questions in this lesson involve mathematical modelling.
How would you explain the idea of modelling to a student who has missed this lesson?

10.3 Proof

You will learn to:
- Identify the difference between giving an example and proving a theory
- Understand how to use mathematical proof

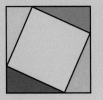

Why learn this?
Proving statements and theories can help you understand why they are true.

Fluency
What is the highest common factor of
- $3n$ and 12
- $15x$ and 25
- $26y$ and 15?

Explore
Pythagoras proved that $c^2 = a^2 + b^2$ in a right-angled triangle. How many triangles would you need to test to *prove* this?

Exercise 10.3

1 Factorise
  a $4n + 8$
  b $5x - 15$
  c $3m - 9$

2 Factorise
  a $x^2 + 2x + 2$
  b $x^2 - 6x + 5$
  c $2x^2 + 12x + 10$

3 n is an integer. Write down an expression in terms of n that is
  a even
  b a multiple of 3
  c a multiple of 5
  d an odd number.

4 Karen says, 'When you have two **consecutive** numbers, one must be odd and one must be even. odd + even = odd, so the sum of two consecutive numbers is always odd.'
Wynona says, '3 + 4 = 7, 36 + 37 = 73 and 120 + 121 = 241.
So the sum of two consecutive numbers is always odd.'
Whose statement is a **proof** and whose is an example?

> **Q4 Literacy hint**
> **Consecutive** means one after the other.

> **Key point**
> A **proof** shows that a statement or theorem is true for all possible occurrences.

Worked example

Prove that the sum of two consecutive numbers is always odd.

$n + (n + 1) = 2n + 1$

> Any two consecutive numbers can be written as n and $n + 1$.

$2n$ must be an even number, so adding 1 will give an odd number.

5 Prove that the sum of three consecutive numbers is always a multiple of 3.

6 Prove that the sum of five consecutive whole numbers is always a multiple of 5.

7 Prove that the product of two consecutive whole numbers is always even.

> **Q5 hint**
> Create, simplify and then factorise an algebraic expression.

Topic links: Forming and solving equations, Factorising, Algebraic expressions

8 Prove that the sum of two consecutive odd numbers is always a multiple of 4.

9 Ariel and Michael have been asked to prove that that the angles in a triangle sum to 180°.
Ariel tears the corners from a triangle and puts them on a straight line to show that the angles on a triangle sum to 180°.

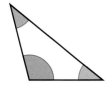

Michael writes this answer:

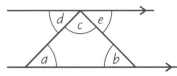

$\angle d + \angle c + \angle e = 180°$ (angles on a straight line)
$\angle d = \angle a$ and $\angle e = \angle b$ (alternate angles)
Therefore: $\angle a + \angle b + \angle c = 180°$

Whose statement is a proof and whose is a demonstration?

10 Prove that the exterior angle of a triangle is equal to the sum of the two non-adjacent interior angles.
$d = b + c$

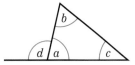

Q10 hint
Use the fact that angles in a triangle sum to 180°.

11 Henry says, 'The sum of three consecutive whole numbers is odd.'
 a Decide if the statement is true or false.
 b If it is true, prove it. If false, give a **counter example**.

Key point
You can disprove a statement by finding an example that shows it is false. This is called a **counter example**.

12 Prove each true statement below. Find a counter example for each false statement.
 a Squaring a number gives an even number.
 b The product of two even numbers is even.
 c The sum of any two odd numbers is even.
 d $x^2 \geqslant 0$ for all values of x.
 e $(x + 1)^2 = x^2 + 1$ for all values of x.
 f A triangle cannot be both isosceles and right-angled.
 g All four-sided shapes have at least one pair of parallel sides.
 h It is impossible to draw a triangle with sides of length 2 cm, 3 cm and 6 cm.

Q12d hint
A proof doesn't have to be algebraic, you can explain in words.

13 Explore Pythagoras proved that $c^2 = a^2 + b^2$ in a right-angled triangle. How many triangles would you need to test to *prove* this?
Look back at the maths you have learned in this lesson.
How can you use it to answer this question?

14 Reflect Cormac says, 'It is easier to disprove something than to prove it.' Do you agree with Cormac?
Explain.

Explore

Reflect

10.4 More proof

You will learn to:
- Present a logical argument using algebra.

Why learn this?
Mathematical theorems need proving before they can be published. There was even a prize for proving Goldbach's Conjecture – it remains unclaimed.

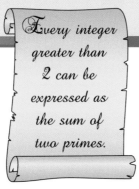

Every integer greater than 2 can be expressed as the sum of two primes.

Fluency
What is a counter example?

Explore
What is the most famous mathematical proof?

Exercise 10.4

1 Work out the size of the angles marked with letters.

a

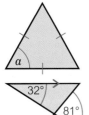

b

32°
81°
b

2 Find a counter example to disprove each statement.
- **a** $x^2 > 0$ for all values of x.
- **b** An isosceles triangle cannot contain an obtuse angle.
- **c** All the terms are odd in the sequence with nth term $3(n - 1)$.

3 Reasoning On a hundred grid T(13) is shown. Tony works out the value of T(13) by adding all the values together.
T(13) = 12 + 13 + 14 + 23 + 33 = 95

1	2	3	4	5	6	7	8	9	10
11	12	13	14	15	16	17	18	19	20
21	22	23	24	25	26	27	28	29	30
31	32	33	34	35	36	37	38	39	40
41	42	43	44	45	46	47	48	49	50
51	52	53	54	55	56	57	58	59	60
61	62	63	64	65	66	67	68	69	70
71	72	73	74	75	76	77	78	79	80
81	82	83	84	85	86	87	88	89	90
91	92	93	94	95	96	97	98	99	100

- **a** Show the value of $T(x) = 5x + 30$ for all values of x.
- **b** For what value of x is it impossible to work out T(x)?

Topic links: Forming and solving equations, Factorising, Algebraic expressions, Sequences, Inequalities, Pythagoras' theorem, Area

4 **Reasoning** A magician uses this trick:

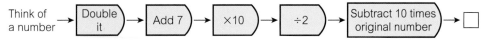
Think of a number → Double it → Add 7 → ×10 → ÷2 → Subtract 10 times original number → □

Is your answer 35?
a Try the trick for several different starting numbers.
b Show why the trick works.

5 **Reasoning** Show that angle $a = 120°$.

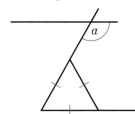

Q5 hint

You must explain each step of working as part of your proof.

6 **Problem-solving / Reasoning** Briana cuts the largest square possible from a circle of paper. The length of the diagonal of the square is 10 cm.
Prove that the remaining paper has area $25\pi - 50$ cm².

Q6 Strategy hint

Sketch a diagram.

7 The nth term of a sequence is $3n^2$. Show that 3000 is not a term in the sequence.

8 Edward states that $\dfrac{10}{b} < 10$ for any value of b.

a Find a counter example to show this is false.
b Rewrite Edward's statement to make it true.

Key point

Sometimes a statement can be true but *only* for particular values.
For example $2x - 1 > 0$ only when $x > \frac{1}{2}$.

9 Complete each statement to make it true.
a $2x + 1$ is an integer when ____
b $\dfrac{n}{2}$ is an integer when n is ____
c $x^2 > 1$ when x is ____
d $(x + 1)(x - 1) > 0$ when x ____

10 Dylan's **hypothesis** is, '$x^2 + 3x + 2$ can always be expressed as the product of two consecutive numbers when x is a positive integer.'
Investigate Dylan's hypothesis.

11 Investigate these hypotheses.
a When you double a whole number you get an even number.
b The area of a right-angled triangle with base a and height $2a$ is a^2.
c $2x \neq x^2$ for any value of x.
d The product of three consecutive whole numbers is always even.

Key point

To investigate a **hypothesis** use this method.

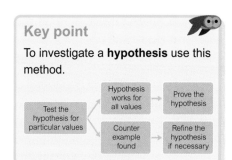
Test the hypothesis for particular values → Hypothesis works for all values → Prove the hypothesis
→ Counter example found → Refine the hypothesis if necessary

12 **Explore** What is the most famous mathematical proof?
Explore different mathematical proofs.
Why are some of them famous?
Who proved them?

13 **Reflect** You might have met the concept of 'proof' in science.
Is there any difference between a scientific proof and a mathematical proof? Explain your answer.

Explore

Reflect

Master
P225

CHECK

Strengthen
P235

Extend
P239

Test
P242

10 Check up

Log how you did on your
Student Progression Chart.

Explain, show and justify

1 Explain why 2 is the only even prime number.

2 The nth term of a sequence is $4n + 1$. Is 42 in the sequence?
  Explain.

3 Zak says, 'The mean of 100, 101, 101, 105 and 104 must be larger than
  100.' Explain how you know Zak is correct.

4 Explain why a right-angled triangle must contain two acute angles.

5 Show that $(x + 5)(x - 4) = x^2 + x - 20$.

Modelling

6 An arrow is fired from the ground into the air. It reaches a maximum
  height of 12 m. It travels a horizontal distance of 15 m before hitting
  the ground.
  a Copy the axes and sketch a graph to show the path of the arrow.

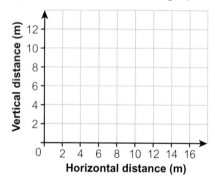

  b Estimate the horizontal distances when the arrow is 6 m above the
    ground.

7 Two garages charge different amounts for conducting an MOT.

Garage A
Fixed price £50 plus £10 per hour

Garage B
No fixed price. £20 per hour

  a Draw a graph with 'Time (hours)' on the x-axis and 'Price (£)' on the
    y-axis to compare the two garages.
  b After how many hours' work does it become cheaper to use Garage A?

Proof

8 Prove that the sum of six consecutive numbers is a multiple of 3.

9 Prove that the product of two prime numbers greater than 3 is always odd.

10 Prove that $a = 180° - b$.

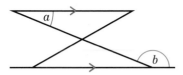

11 Either prove each statement or disprove it by giving a counter example.
  a The product of two odd numbers is even.
  b A quadrilateral containing one right angle has at least one pair of parallel sides.
  c Squaring a number always gives an answer greater than 1.

12 Karen says, 'The square of an even number is always even.' Investigate Karen's hypothesis.

13 **How sure are you of your answers? Were you mostly**
   Just guessing 😐 **Feeling doubtful** 🙂 **Confident**
  What next? Use your results to decide whether to strengthen or extend your learning.

Challenge

14 To join 4 dots to all the other dots once you need 6 lines.

  a How many lines are needed to join
    i 2 dots
    ii 3 dots
    iii 5 dots?
  b How many lines do you need to join n dots?
  c Explain your answer to part **b**. You could use words, a diagram or algebra, or a combination of these.

15 Michael designs this flowchart so he always knows the number at the end.

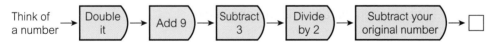

Think of a number → Double it → Add 9 → Subtract 3 → Divide by 2 → Subtract your original number → ☐

  a Show why the answer will always be 3.
  b Design your own flowchart that always gives the same number.

Reflect

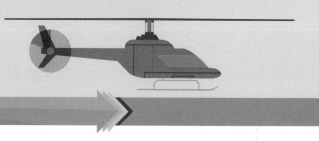

10 Strengthen

You will:

• Strengthen your understanding with practice.

Explain, show and justify

1 Anna and Rich want to show that the multiple of 4 with the fewest factors is 4 itself.

Anna answers:
4 has three factors, 1, 2 and 4.
Any multiple of 4 is divisible by at least 1, 2, 4 and itself.
Therefore the multiple of 4 with the fewest factors is 4.

Rich answers:
Factors of 4: 1, 2 and 4
Factors of 8: 1, 2, 4 and 8
Factors of 12: 1, 2, 3, 4, 6 and 12
Factors of 16: 1, 2, 4, 8 and 16
The number 4 has the fewest factors.

Who has given a mathematical explanation and who has given a demonstration?

Q1 hint

An explanation shows something is true for all values. A demonstration shows it is true for some values.

2 Barbara says, 'If you substitute any whole number into the algebraic expression $4n - 1$ you will always get an odd number.'
Choose a pair of statements to prove Barbara's claim. Choose one statement from List A. Choose one statement from list B and complete it with the word 'odd' or 'even'.

Q2 hint

Your proof should explain why Barbara's statement is true for any integer value of n.

List A
$4n$ is even when n is even
$4n$ is always even
$4n$ is even when n is odd
$4n$ is always odd

List B
An even number minus an odd number is ____
An odd number minus 1 is ____
An even number minus 1 is ____
When you subtract 1 from any number the answer is ____

3 Explain why all the numbers in the sequence with nth term $2n - 2$ are even.

4 Complete these calculations to show these statements are true.

a $(x + 3)^2 = x^2 + 6x + 9$

Left-hand side $= (x + 3)(x + 3)$
$= x^2 + 3x + 3x + 9$
$= \Box$
$=$ Right-hand side

b $(x + 1)^2 - 1 = x^2 + 2x$

Left-hand side $= (x + 1)(x + 1) - 1$

$= \square$ (Multiply out the brackets)

$= \square$ (Simplify the algebraic expression)

$=$ Right-hand side

c $(x + 3)(x - 3) = x^2 - 9$

Left-hand side $= (x + 3)(x - 3)$

$= \square$

$= \square$

$= \square$

d $x^2 - 1 = (x - 1)(x + 1)$

Right-hand side $= (x - 1)(x + 1)$

$= \square$

$= \square$

$=$ Left-hand side

5 Decide if these statements are true or false. Show working to justify your decision.

a $(x + 5)(x + 6) = x^2 + 30$

b $(x - 5)(x + 6) = x^2 + x - 30$

c $(x + 5)^2 - 25 = x^2 + 10x$

6 The heights of 3 plants are 12 cm, 16 cm and 18 cm.

a Decide which of these is the mean height, without doing any calculations.

A 5.3 cm   **B** 20.3 cm   **C** 15.3 cm

b Why is it impossible for the mean to be either of the other two answers?

> **Q6 hint**
>
> Think about what the mean represents.

Modelling

1 Modelling The table shows the fastest times for the 100 m sprint at four school sports days.

Year	Time(s)
2010	12.4
2011	12.3
2012	12.1
2013	12.05

a Copy and complete the graph and draw a line of best fit.

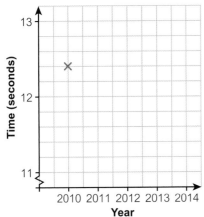

b Use the line of best fit to predict the fastest time for 2014.

2 Modelling Khalid travels 500 miles in 10 hours.
  a Draw a distance–time graph to show his journey.
  b Use your graph to work out how long it will take him to travel the first 320 miles.
  c It actually takes him 7 hours to travel the first 320 miles. Explain why your graph may not be a good model.

Q2 hint

Is Khalid's speed likely to have been the same for the whole journey?

3 A solar panel provider offers these deals.

> **Deal A**
> Each panel costs £300

> **Deal B**
> First three panels £500
> Each additional panel £200

  a For each deal work out the cost for this number of panels.
  i 3   **ii** 5   **iii** 7
  iv 9   **v** 11   **vi** 13
  b Copy these axes. Plot your answers to part **a** and draw graphs for Deal A and Deal B.
  c How many panels would you need to buy for Deal B to be cheaper?

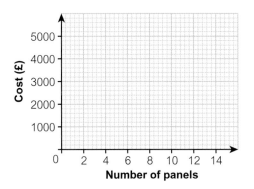

4 Two gas providers offer these deals.

> **All Glo**
> £30 a month fixed charge,
> plus 16p per kWh

> **Homegas**
> No fixed charge
> 20p per kWh

Q4 Literacy hint

A kWh (kilowatt hour) is a unit of energy.

How much energy would you use need to use for All Glo to be the cheaper deal?

Proof

1 Give a counter example to show these statements aren't true.
  a All prime numbers are odd.
  b $x^3 > 0$ for all values of x
  c An isosceles triangle must contain one angle of 45°.

Q1b hint

Try some values of x. Make sure you try positive, negative and decimal values.

2 a Work out
  i $3 + 4 + 5 + 6$ **ii** $4 + 5 + 6 + 7$ **iii** $5 + 6 + 7 + 8$
     Copy and complete this hypothesis:
     'The sum of four consecutive whole numbers is ____'
  b Test your hypothesis for several more examples.
     The first two of the four consecutive whole numbers can be written as n and $n + 1$.
  c Write an algebraic expression for the third and fourth consecutive whole numbers.
  d Find the sum of the four algebraic expressions.
  e Explain why this proves your hypothesis.

Q1c hint

A diagram can be used as a counter example.

3 Use the method from Q2 to prove that the sum of 7 consecutive whole numbers is a multiple of 7.

4 Explain why an even number larger than 2 will always have at least three factors.

5 Charlene says, 'All square numbers have an odd number of factors.' Test this hypothesis.

6 Copy and complete this working to show that $a = e$.

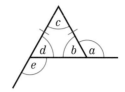

$d = b$
$b = 180 - \square$
$e = 180 - d$
   $= 180 - (\square - \square)$
   $= \square$

Q4 hint

Every number has at least two factors, 1 and itself.

Enrichment

1 Harry wants to construct triangles with sides measuring
   a 2 cm, 3 cm, 6 cm
   b 1 cm, 2 cm, 3 cm
   c 3 cm, 4 cm, 5 cm
   Which ones can he construct?
   Explain how Harry can tell which triangles are 'possible' without trying to draw them first.

2 a Think of a 2-digit number.
   b Reverse it (swap the digits).
   c Subtract the smaller of your 2-digit numbers from the larger.
   d Is your answer a multiple of 9?
   e Investigate the hypothesis that the answer will always be a multiple of 9. If you think it is true, prove it. If not, find a counter example.

Q2 hint

Break each number down into tens and units.
34 can be written as 3 × 10 + 4 × 1.
How could any 2-digit number be written?

3 Reflect The questions in this unit involved
   • explaining
   • modelling
   • proof.
   Rate the topics as easy, medium or challenging. Are there any types of question that you need more practice with?

Reflect

Master
P225

Check
P233

Strengthen
P235

EXTEND

Test
P242

10 Extend

You will:
• Extend your understanding with problem-solving.

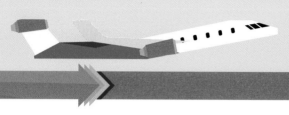

1 A right-angled isosceles triangle has one side of length 2 cm.
   Rudi says, 'The triangle must have another side with length 2 cm.'
   Do you agree with him? Explain your answer.

2 Show that these identities are true.
   a $x^2 + 3x + 2 \equiv (x + 1)(x + 2)$
   b $(x + 1)^2 + (x - 1)^2 \equiv 2x^2 + 2$
   c $(x - 1)^2 - (x + 1)^2 \equiv -4x$

3 Show that
   a $\dfrac{1}{a} + \dfrac{1}{b} = \dfrac{a + b}{ab}$
   b $\dfrac{a}{b} + \dfrac{b}{a} = \dfrac{a^2 + b^2}{ab}$
   c $\dfrac{1}{x} + \dfrac{x}{y} = \dfrac{y + x^2}{xy}$

4 **Real** The Venn diagram shows the GCSE language choices of
   students in Year 9.

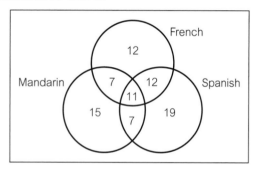

   Each class must contain no more than 30 students.
   Work out
   a how many students study more than one language.
   b how many classes there will be for
      i Mandarin   **ii** Spanish   **iii** French.

5 **Problem-solving** The prices of bread and milk at two different
   supermarkets are shown.

Quickshop
Bread £1.50 per loaf
Milk 40p per pint

Greenstores
Bread £1.30 per loaf
Milk 50p per pint

   Graham buys some bread and milk at Quickshop. Sue buys some bread
   and milk at Greenstores. They both spend the same amount of money.
   How much bread and how much milk do they each buy?

6 The nth term of a sequence is $n^2 + 1$.
   Prove that the sum of any two consecutive terms of the sequence
   is odd.

Topic links: Metric units, Trigonometry, Pythagoras' theorem, Sequences, Algebraic fractions, Expanding brackets,
Venn diagrams, Multiples, Construction, Properties of triangles and circles, Area, Bounds

7 Problem-solving Show that $a = 51°$.

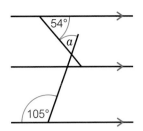

8 Nuala says, 'A triangle cannot contain more than one obtuse angle.'
Investigate her hypothesis.

9 Hassan says, 'The sum of two consecutive squares is even.'
Investigate his hypothesis.

Q9 hint
Two consecutive square numbers can be written as n^2 and $(n + 1)^2$.

10 Three numbers have mean of 20 and median of 6.
Ethan says, 'The other two numbers must be positive.'
Investigate his hypothesis.

11 Bryony says, 'The difference between any two even numbers is even.'
Investigate her hypothesis.

Q11 hint
Use $2n$ to represent one even number. How can you represent the second even number?

12 Problem-solving The graphs of $y = 2x$ and $y = 4 - 3x$ are shown.

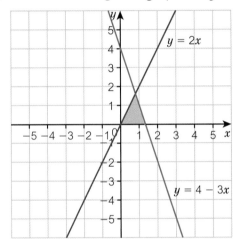

Q12 hint
The height of the triangle is the point where the two graphs cross.

Show that the shaded triangle has area $1\frac{1}{15}$.

13 Problem-solving Show that the area of this triangle is $\sqrt{3}$.

Q13 hint
Work out the height of the triangle by splitting it into two right-angled triangles.

14 The dimensions of a cuboid carton are 10 cm by 10 cm by 21 cm to the nearest cm.
Will the carton be large enough to contain 2 litres of orange juice?
Justify your answer.

15 Explain why all the terms in the sequence with nth term $2n - 5$ are odd.

16 Real The slope of a wheelchair ramp must be at an angle of no more than 4.8° with the ground.
The height of a step is 0.5 m.
What is the minimum length of ramp needed?
Show how you worked out your answer.

Q16 hint
Work out the largest angle that would be allowed. This will minimise the length of the ramp.

17 Modelling A sailor views the top of a lighthouse at an angle of 65° to the horizontal.
The top of the lighthouse is 45 m above sea level, to the nearest m. What is the maximum horizontal distance between the ship and the lighthouse?
Show how you worked out your answer.
Discussion What assumptions have you made to be able to answer this question?

18 Problem-solving / Reasoning The smallest square possible is drawn around a circle with radius r.
Show that the area of the square is $4r^2$.

19 a Draw an obtuse angle.
b Bisect the angle.
c What type of angles are created by bisecting?
d Complete this hypothesis: 'When you bisect an obtuse angle the result is ____'
e Prove the hypothesis.

20 Reasoning Explain why any multiple of 10 will always have 4 or more factors.
Discussion Why is there only one case where the multiple of 10 will have exactly 4 factors?

21 Problem-solving An equilateral triangle of side length 5 cm is contained within a circle with the vertices touching the circumference.

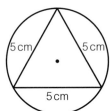

Rahim draws a perpendicular line from one side of the triangle to the centre of the circle.

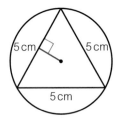

a Work out the length of the line to 1.d.p.
b Work out the radius of the circle 1.d.p.

22 Reflect Julie says, 'Mathematical reasoning is like brain gym.'
What do you think Julie means? Do you agree or disagree?

Reflect

10 Unit test

Log how you did on your Student Progression Chart.

1. Explain why adding 1 to a multiple of 10 results in an odd number.

2. Can a triangle contain more than one right angle? Explain.

3. Show that the graph of $y = 4x$ does not go through the point $(1, 5)$.

4. Show that $(x + 5)^2 - 10x = x^2 + 25$.

5. Find a counter example for each statement.
   a. Multiplying a number by an integer makes it bigger.
   b. A square number cannot also be a cube number.

6. Show that the area of the small circle is $\dfrac{\pi r^2}{4}$

7. Prove that the product of two even numbers is even.

8. Prove that the mean of three consecutive integers is equal to the middle value.

9. Prove that $a + b = 180°$.

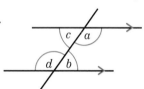

10. A car salesman claims that a car can travel between 35 and 45 miles per gallon. The car's tank holds 10 gallons, to the nearest gallon. What is the maximum distance the car could travel on a full tank? Explain.

11. Investigate the hypothesis that $x^2 \geqslant x$, when x is an integer.

12. Freya says, 'All the terms in the sequence with nth term $4n^2 + 2n + 1$ are odd.' Investigate this hypothesis.

Challenge

13. The triangular numbers are:
    1, 3, 6, 10, 15, …
    a. Take any triangular number, multiply by 8 and add 1.
    b. Repeat for other triangular numbers.
    c. What do you notice about your answers? Make a hypothesis.
    d. Can you prove your hypothesis?

    > **Q13 hint**
    > The nth term of the triangular numbers is $\dfrac{n(n + 1)}{2}$

14. **Reflect** Write down the three most important things you have learned in this unit. Include any words or phrases that you didn't understand at the start of the unit, but that you now understand.

Reflect